Some Lessons in Gaelic

This first edition
to my friend and former colleague
Kieth.

Everyone has a book in them.
This is mine

Best Wishes

McCawley Grange.

To my grandchildren, Anya, Olivia, Joel and Theo

Some Lessons in Gaelic

McCawley Grange

Delgany Publications

Copyright © McCawley Grange 2011
First published in 2011 by Delgany Publications
67 Askham Lane, Acomb, York, YO24 3HD

Distributed by Gardners Books, 1 Whittle Drive, Eastbourne,
East Sussex, BN23 6QH
Tel: +44(0)1323 521555 | Fax: +44(0)1323 521666

British Library Cataloguing in Publication Data
A catalogue record for this book is available from the British
Library.

ISBN 978-0-9567605-0-0

Typeset by Amolibros, Milverton, Somerset
www.amolibros.com
This book production has been managed by Amolibros
Printed and bound by T J International Ltd, Padstow, Cornwall, UK

About the Author

McCawley Grange was born in York in 1940. At the age of ten he emigrated with his family to County Wicklow, Eire, whereupon the family began to suffer financial hardship. Leaving school at thirteen years of age he worked in the building trade, then as a hotel worker and gardener and on his return to York in 1956, successively as a linesman, factory worker and builder.

At age seventeen, following a row with his father, he left home for London, where for a time he lived and worked with the Irish labouring fraternity. Returning to York, he joined the Fire Service in 1962 and after twenty-five years left the service with the rank of Assistant Divisional Officer. Following this, he spent two years with the Voluntary Service Overseas (VSO) organization building 'low cost' housing in Kenya.

Now retired, he lives in York with his wife, two children and four grandchildren employing much of his time playing golf and writing. *Some Lessons in Gaelic* is his first book.

PROLOGUE

I bolted out of the shack, leaving the rickety door swinging on its hinges. That girl had never spoken to me, never smiled or even acknowledged me, just laughed, joined with the others, sniggering at what Shonti Plunkett had whispered in her ear.

I kept to the trodden swathe of grass, the path which separated the beach from the refuse tip, then, leaving the tip behind, I was where the ground was hard and I could run much faster, my knees punching like pistons, propelling me upwards towards the scarp and the refuge of my den. I remembered how Donoghue had once compared my knees to a horse's hocks and how he and his brother, had laughed, sniggered, much as that girl and those others had sniggered, only minutes ago in Nolan's shack and in my head I could hear them laughing still, fuelling anger already boiling there. Now my breaths were in short, sharp gasps and, weak from my recent illness, I stopped running and crouched with my forearms resting on my knees. Sweat oozed from my forehead stinging my eyes, and sweat cleaved my clothes to my body, not healthy sweat, as I knew I still hadn't fully recovered. In the distance, Nolan's shack, a rusty tin box on a tip face and I felt I still could hear them talking, laughing. That shack was now forever closed to me, as was my heart to Nugget Nolan, that traitor whom I had thought of as a friend; I was finished with him now but the Plunketts were

1

a different matter. With this to add to what had gone before, they would not be forgotten and neither would they ever be forgiven.

Breathing heavily, I began walking steadily uphill, my mind rioting with thoughts of injustice, humiliation and revenge. Remembering that Brother Mulligan was on the hill, I stopped and looked around. A wind had sprung up and pieces of white paper fluttered and whirled about the face of the tip like seagulls with their wings outspread, and little dust clouds of sand and ash raced each other at the tip's edge to dissipate on the shoreline. The cold October sun hung low in the sky with banks of cloud, like long, dark arms, resting on the Sugarloaf Mountains. The mountains were stark and lonely and the sea looked heavy and deep with the swash writhing the seaweed in the black pools of the coastline.

I trained my eyes towards the great whale of the scarp and saw in the distance the returning figure of my teacher. I had to wait for some time before he closed on me, then, crouching behind a clump of mountain fern, I waited until he passed, passed so close that I could hear his breathing and his tread and the clinking of his rosary beads. I stayed down behind the fern until he was way past Nolan's shack, only a black dot in the distance, then I started to run again, I needed to run; running pounded at the pain inside, making it more bearable, it pounded at my tormenting thoughts and the effort gave me something else to think about. I ran until I reached the trail that meandered by the cliffs and through the rocky outcrops, all the way to the town of Bray and then I slowed to a walk.

This trail was protected in places from the steep cliffs by timber stakes, nailed with haphazard cross-pieces, as if someone, a long time ago, had made a half-hearted attempt to protect the walkers, the sightseers and the fishermen who used it. Having explored this trail many times, I knew it to be dangerously eroded and knew where and when to leave it and avoid the sudden precipitous drops to the rocks and sea below. The first time, fascinated by the huge hump of a mountain so close to where I lived, was within days of my family's arrival in the town of Greystones, and now, a year later, I reckoned that I knew this trail better than any other boy in the whole of Ireland.

It had been wet that summer and the autumn mountain was lush and green, ready to face the winter with only wind-scorched patches where the soil was thin. Thick beds of nettle, fern and thistle swept upwards from the trail to meet with dense bracken, furze and bramble thickets on the lower slopes, with higher canopies of brush and elder and stunted hawthorn bordering swathes of grassland which went on to farmland sweeping westward from the summit. Was Bray Head a hill or a mountain? I was never to know, but an eleven-year-old boy from the vale of York can make his own hills and mountains. Coolagad, rising gently behind the town was a hill, but Bray Head was a mountain as steep and savage as any in the Andes, the Himalayas even.

Leaving the trail, I began a steep ascent to find a second path, my own, one through dense scrub which I had hewn myself. Here bramble colonised the ground and wood sorrel and welted thistle grew among nettles higher than a man's head. No other foot than mine had ever trodden here and like the veranda of Calgary, our new home, it was a vantage point from which to view a hostile world. Armed with a wooden sword, I was an exiled desperado or with wooden machine gun, the G-man Lemmy Caution. Cupped in this dripping wilderness, I had wintered here. Here, and higher, in my hide where I could dream of Cora Casey, my hide, my keep, where mists would swathe the Head and angry gulls would drive me off the cliffs, where ferocious winds would blow and sullen skies would weep. I could be anyone, even the mythical Cuchulainn, there.

Climbing higher on my path I reached the wildest, most dangerous terrain on the mountainside. In this wilderness was an under cliff, with my den hidden beneath the huge finger of rock that had first attracted me. Hundreds of years ago a rock fall had formed a terrace on a narrow plateau, so many years ago that the scree-roofed terrace now grew dense with mountain flora and the plateau thick with brush and scrub. My path led to this place, this terrace and the gap between two rocks which was my hide. What a den it was, a gap between two rocks through which a boy could squeeze, a small, dark cave, bone-dry and protected from the wind, a magic place with a flat rock to sit on and a rock shelf to hold a candle. I had a candle and matches that I kept wrapped in a waterproof cloth and a rubber mat for the flat rock. It was quite the most perfect den ever to be found anywhere in the world, far too good to be shared with anybody else. If word got around about a den like this then, come summer, it would be swarming with Cuchulainns. So secret was this den that I hadn't even told my sisters.

I squeezed inside, lit the candle and sat on the rock looking out into the thin strip of afternoon light, thinking. The light was pale and grey, the sea murmured and boomed and the cave whispered in the flickering candle-light. The sweat on my body had cooled and my shirt was chill and damp on my skin and I shivered, worrying that I might get sick again. The sea booming and the candle-light flickering, this was not just a place to dream, it was also a place to nurture hate and bitter thoughts of vengeance. I was some time thinking, brooding, the betrayal, the humiliation, the lost jewels, and surely, Cora's love could not, must not be, the odious Patsy Plunkett.

At the cave entrance, leaves were murmuring; they fluttered in the light wind like the wings of a tiny bird. I got up and moved to the narrow entrance, looking out over the stirring scrub and down to the rocky foreshore and the open sea, hating the way I felt, the way I had been made to feel, that sniggering laughter and that awful torment, deep inside. Evening was approaching fast with its fingers of dying sunlight clutching weakly at the surface of a sea, ever changing shape and colour, in the shifting light, my humiliation in front of Cora Casey and her friend Nora, and in Nolan's shack, which had been a second home to me all crying now to heaven and to hell for vengeance. Everywhere I looked I could see the faces of the hated Plunkett brothers, in the underwater weed, the earnest, elfin, stupid face of Christy, those shadows on the shore line, the gangling, raw boned, fish-mouthed Patsy, a rim of flotsam, his pendulous bottom lip. And Shonti, the oldest, the biggest, the meanest of them all, touched and brushed by twilight, and his mean, green eyes squinting out of a pale, blank, bovine face, I could see, were sneering at me.

It would be dark soon and I must return home while there was still light enough to negotiate the trail. Snuffing out the candle and putting it back carefully in its wrapper, I stepped outside. The huge cone-shaped column of rock I called the stack loomed above me and suddenly I knew what could be done and my heart jolted in satisfaction. Yes, directly below, maybe a couple of hundred feet was one of the Plunketts' fishing sites. Thoughts excited me, yes it could be done, it would be done and already I felt better in my mind. With the side of my shoe, I rattled scree down the steep embankment, to hurdle over the trail to fall a further hundred feet on to the flat, bare rock of the fishing site. Little stones obeyed the law of gravity, as would this towering rock above me, this obelisk, as tall and heavy as a house, this noble turret that had first called me to this place. Rock falls were a regular feature of cowboy films, falling on Indian braves and black-hatted rustlers like confetti on a bride and groom. Cowboys, with their backs braced for leverage, did it all the time and so could I. My heart beat fast and my mouth dried as I saw the great rock falling and the devastation it would carry in its wake and I felt a dread delight.

The homeward journey was slow and careful. The cloud arms that had earlier rested on the Sugarloaves had thickened and darkened and, deep in space, a single star appeared. In the uncertain light, my foot was sure but no longer was I a desperado, a G. man or Cuchulainn, I was just a small bitter boy and would ever be so until I had revenge. I was clear now of scrubland and was running fast by the tip's edge. The light was out in Nolan's shack but I was sure I could hear sniggering laughter from inside. Could they still be in there? Sniggering and laughing in the dark?

Chapter One

Something like a huge bat with wings outstretched swooped upon the sunlit schoolyard, where I had been left waiting by my father. It hovered, but made no sound as it then led me towards the rear entrance of the school. It was a man and his fingers on my shoulder were tighter than they should have been. I had been expecting my father to return for me, but this huge bat-like figure had come instead, silent, forceful, his fingers biting deeper into the flesh of my shoulder. I looked up at him to tell him that I had been expecting my father but he looked so disagreeable that all I did was smile to let him see what a likeable young boy I was, what a pleasant young chap was this new addition to the school. But he did not smile back at me or even glance down and all that I was left with was the image of cavernous nostrils from which tufts of black bristle grew, shaggy, like deserted nests.

We entered a lobby and turned right through a set of swing doors into a long corridor before stopping at a door, inscribed in large, brass lettering P J McBride Head Brother. The huge, silent man, standing behind me, engulfing me, gave a fastidious tap on the door with gentle knuckles, then, in answer from a voice within the room, opened the door and ushered me inside. He made no other sound, but I knew that he had followed me for the door was long in closing.

The small, claustrophobic office was lined with book shelves and smelled of old dust and cigarette smoke. The Head Brother sat on a chair behind a wooden table that filled most of the available floor space with the only other piece of moveable furniture a second chair facing him across the table, on which, with a gesture of his hand, he invited me to sit.

He introduced himself as the head brother of St Luke's and continued brightly, 'Your daddy is just after leaving by the front as you yourself came in with Brother Brady at the back. I always like to have a word with a boy's daddy first, let him know that his son is going to be left in good hands. Isn't that so, Brother Brady? And your daddy is after telling me all about you and a glowing report it was too, glowing, so it was.'

His hands were white and podgy with fingers like pale, soft sausages except for the thumb and forefinger of the right hand which was stained a dark brown with cigarette smoke. A small bald head sat heavily on a small, squat body and everything about him was plump and round and soft and roly-poly except for his lips which were thin.

He looked over my shoulder to the cleric who had escorted me and, by way of introduction, addressed him formally, 'Brother Brady, Deputy Head,' then his eyes fell back to mine. 'Now your daddy is after giving me all the information that we need about you and here it is,' he said, tapping a thin green file on the table. His eyes were like dark, brown tunic buttons and above his spectacles they fastened on to mine, not unfriendly but appraising and exactly the same colour as his smoke-impregnated fingers.

Behind me, not a murmur from the second man but I could feel his presence overwhelming me, more so because he was so silent and on the flesh of my shoulder, I could still feel the bruising imprint of his fingers. From a classroom, somewhere beyond the corridor, an urgent 'Bru, Bru, Bru, Bru, Bru, Bru, Bru, Bru', unmistakeably the collective voice of children. A short silence, then, 'Bru, Bru, Bru, Bru, Bru, Bru, Bru, Bru,', again, louder, more urgent and I couldn't help but think of a motor-bike starting up on a cold winter morning.

The Head tapped the file again. 'Now your daddy has led us to believe that you are good at English, the writing of it anyway,' he paused, 'but not so much, the spelling. What do you think of that, Brother Brady? Not so much the spelling,' in the brown, button eyes, a glimpse of wry humour.

Sitting upright in my chair, I smiled broadly. 'Reading and writing, Brother, yes I was best in class, at home in England – but – spelling,' I shrugged in a gesture of self-deprecation.

'Spell fox,' was the demand, sudden and abrupt.

I spelled the word easily and the word that followed, 'beyond', uttered even more abruptly. I thought the word 'beyond' a strange word to follow 'fox'.

'Ah, he'll do, so he will,' the Head told his colleague. Then he was back to me again. 'Arithmetic, sums, your daddy reports a certain lack of interest in this subject, a certain lack of interest, dare we say laziness.' He was being a little flippant for I was sure I detected glints of humour still active in his eyes, 'Sums most important, here at St Luke's.'

'Don't like sums as much as I like English,' I answered truthfully.

'Ah, a feeble answer, do you not think that a feeble answer, Brother Brady? But not a feeble boy. Ah no, I think not. He's not a feeble boy, is he, Brother?'

The man behind me did not answer and I began to wonder if perhaps he was dumb or deaf or both, but dismissed the notion as foolish. The Deputy Head of a school could not be deaf or dumb or both. From another classroom further along the corridor and muffled by walls and distance, the motor-bike again. 'Bru, Bru, Bru, Bru, Bru, Bru, Bru, Bru.'

The Head leaned back in his chair and pushing his spectacles up the bridge of his nose peered through them for the first time. 'Forty-four divided by four?' His abruptness returned.

'Eleven, Brother.'

'Forty-four multiplied by four?'

My brain raced and I got the answer wrong. Anxiously, I got

it wrong again. My brain fused and my mind went blank. 'Sorry Brother.'

The man before me drummed his podgy fingers on the desk to give me more time, then, acknowledging my distress, said, good humouredly, 'Ah, sure, amn't I having trouble with that one myself.' Then suddenly with a smile of receptivity, his face transformed, the thin lips widened to reveal even, white teeth and the button eyes began to spark with whimsy. 'Brother Mulligan is just the man for you, just the man to be teaching you four times forty-four and you will be starting in his class, this very morning, so you will. The rest of this year and the next year, too, and you'll get on fine, I know it.' His smile faded as he nodded above my shoulder to his subordinate. 'And Brother Brady here will be with you from time to time as I will myself. All we teachers have to change around a bit or, I declare to God, we'd all go mad. Now do you think this arrangement will suit you well enough?'

I grinned at the sarcasm. 'I'm sure it will, Brother.'

He opened my file and, browsing through it, said thoughtfully, 'I see that you are called by your second name, Christian. Let us hope that you are Christian by name and Christian by nature. What do you say, Brother Brady? A boy with a name like that has a lot to live up to. Christian in Gaelic,' he mused, 'Gilla Christe will do, Servant of Christ.' He consulted the file again. 'Good at sport, I see. I have down here good at sport, what sport will this be then?'

'Just about any sport you can mention, Brother. Running, sprinting, high-jump, long-jump and, I'm a good swimmer, too.' I was relaxed and enthusiastic. 'And I can do gymnastics, cartwheels, handsprings and stuff and walking on my hands, I'm really good at walking on my hands.'

The brother raised his eyebrows, letting his spectacles slip down his nose again. 'Walking on your hands, indeed, well there's a thing now. It's something we don't have too much of here at St Luke's. And how far could you walk on your hands, would you say?'

I thought of distance and how best to measure it and, remembering the size of the schoolyard, said, 'I could walk the whole length of the schoolyard out there non-stop,' and I hoped that they would take me there for a demonstration.

The bald head tilted and thick fingers stroked his jaw. 'Dear God, but what a blessing you must be to your daddy and mammy with all that shoe leather saved, a blessing indeed.'

'Cricket and football, too,' I remembered. 'Opening bat and inside right for the school team.'

The teacher's eyes dulled a little. 'Well, we play Gaelic football here at St Luke's. You may not be familiar with this type of football, but Brother Brady will back me when I tell you that it is a most superior game to that football on the ground which for some unknown reason seems to be spreading throughout the world like a plague. And, as for cricket, well, please forgive me while I yawn. Here you will be introduced to a game called hurling, the fastest field game in the world. It is Ireland's national sport and, yes, the fastest field game in the world. More Gaelic football here than hurling, but in any case I'm sure you'll make the first team at both in no time at all.'

'Yes, Brother,' I concurred eagerly.

There was an unexpected gravity in his tone as he flicked the file in front of him and said, 'And, according to your daddy you will have no trouble here at St Luke's at holding your own.'

I did not understand. 'Holding your own?' I echoed.

He clenched his fists and made to spar with me. 'You are able to handle yourself right enough.' His closed fist touched me gently on the nose.

I laughed. So my father had mentioned fighting during the school induction of his son. I was lost for an answer, but then I thought of how my father would have joked with this man and I could see them both smiling playfully at the prospect of an English boy scrapping his way to acceptance in an Irish school. 'Well, Brother, I was best fighter in my class at home. There was this other kid and all the kids wanted to know which of us was the best

11

fighter and kept trying to get us to fight, but we kept away from one another. Then one day we just couldn't avoid each other any longer and we had a fight and I won. That made me the best fighter in the class.'

'Well, thanks be to God for that,' the cleric muttered somewhat ruefully. 'Indeed, at eleven years old I think that particular talent may well stand you in good stead.' He started chuckling. 'A good writer and a good fighter, sure he's an Irishman. A good writer and a good fighter, I declare to God, an Irishman. What do you think of that, Brother Brady?'

But Brother Brady did not think anything, or if he did, he did not say so. The look in Brother McBride's eyes was now discerning, but he seemed to smile at something in his head. He got up and put my file in a cabinet and I thought I was about to be dismissed, but he sat down again as if he wasn't finished with me yet. On top of the cabinet was a large glass ashtray littered with cigarette ends. It looked dirty and disgusting and for the first time I smelled stale nicotine on his breath. Somehow it didn't seem right for a cleric to have such a habit. It was like seeing someone holy at the cinema or dancing or drinking in a pub; a clergyman should be too pious, too holy to be prone to such petty indulgencies. 'Well, Christian, is there anything else about yourself that you think we ought to know? Anything you might be good at that you haven't happened to mention?'

I honestly could not think of anything I had missed. I wasn't particularly good at anything other than the things I'd mentioned and I didn't want to boast. 'Oh, art, Brother, I'm a good drawer, good at art-work, drawing, painting. At school there was a class prize for art and I won it every year. Don't know if my father mentioned it but no one ever taught me how to read or write or draw, I could just do it, somehow I could just do it naturally. My sister Sam, she's the same, no one taught her either, well maybe I did, just a bit when she was little but—'

'It's called genius,' the Head cut in laconically, 'must run in the family. Now do you have any questions yourself?'

I didn't. My induction had gone very well and to question him might spoil it. 'No, Brother.'

'Well, now, I think we know each other well enough. You're a young boy in a foreign land but I think you'll fit in ok. Brother Brady will take you now into class 2 where you'll get to know the lads in there and a rare bunch they are, too.' He laughed. 'Here at St Luke's you will be given opportunity plenty to do the things you're good at, opportunity for learning and improving and a good strapping, a real good leathering, if you decide not to avail yourself.'

I had risen in my chair, ready to leave, but sat down again as the brother laughed loudly at his own joke. Laughing, I joined him. 'Well, Brother, *Rich gifts wax poor when givers prove unkind*.' I had caught him so offguard. The poor man was stumped, just as I knew he would be.

He took off his spectacles and examined them thoroughly as if suspecting a hidden flaw. Behind me Brother Brady stirred and I didn't know if I was to leave or not. From his pocket, the Head took out a white handkerchief and, frowning, began to furiously polish the glass of the spectacles. They appeared so delicate amid the fast-moving sausage fingers that I feared they would snap. I sensed the man behind me moving closer and leaning over me and for the first time, I heard him speak. His voice was strange, very high-pitched and squeaky for such a huge man.

He said, 'Dear God, Brother, he tinks he's Otello.'

Chapter Two

*B*y the Christmas of 1950, following our move from the English town of Cravenvale, we had lived in our new home for a period of three months. Mid-century Greystones, in which we found ourselves, was a coastal town of a few thousand people, harbouring a small fishing industry, an even smaller summer tourist sideline and not much else. Perhaps not the best venue for my father's brick-making factory, but an idyllic place, nonetheless, lying seventeen miles to the south of Dublin, five miles to the south of Bray and overlooked by the Wicklow Mountains. Our family loved our new surroundings, so dissimilar to the flatlands we had grown accustomed to. The smell of the sea, the sea itself, like a giant, mercurial beast, easily aroused and on our very doorstep and the towering mountains were a constant source of wonder, especially, to us children, with their brooding promise of adventure.

St Luke's school, which I now attended, was a relatively new construction, my father having purchased the old school for his factory and, with a personality and wit to match any of the waggish denizens, he had been immediately accepted by the locals, this in spite of being inherently suspicious of any new arrivals from over eastern waters. Acclimatisation for my mother was not an issue. By her stoic nature and pragmatism, she could have settled just as easily in the Sahara desert or the North Pole or anywhere else my father might have chosen to redeploy his family.

For a long time I was unsure of the reason for our sudden

emigration. One day, having returned from a 'holiday' in Ireland, my father proclaimed that it was a country ready to boom. As it turned out, the 'boom' he forecast would come some forty years later and would last about as many months. Following this 'holiday', our departure was very quick and from snippets of conversation I gathered that it was motivated by two mysterious bands of people called 'creditors' and 'debtors'. I did not know much about either, 'creditors' making me think of mail-clad men with red-crossed shields, on horseback, galloping to war in foreign lands, while 'debtors' filled me with anxiety. There was a debtors' prison in the nearby city of York; had some of them escaped? Sometimes I found myself peering from the veranda of Calgary, worrying if they might leave England and follow us to Ireland.

Our new accommodation was a rented, two-storey detached house called Calgary, coloured white and sited on what was left of the North Beach Road to Bray Head. The remainder of the road, now lost to coastal erosion, was a half mile of grass, mud and gravel, petering out at the ragged extremities of the town's municipal tip with beyond, the ruins of cottages, long lost to that same erosion.

Calgary and the half-dozen surviving houses were situated so close to the sea that during stormy weather strong winds would blast sea-spray over the walls and into the front gardens. The north beach itself consisted of grey stones, a carpet of them, stretching from the pier at the south end of the beach to the rocky foreshore of the Head to the north. The stones were all flat and round in uniformity and varied in size from a penny to a discus, too big in bulk to be influenced by tides and currents and too resilient to be formed into spits by waves. They were not grey at all, but, slate-blue when wet, white and dull-gold when dry and some were unimaginably coloured when examined.

This beach was incredible, but served no purpose other than as a bulwark to the sea and to give the town its name. It was too uncomfortable to sunbathe or even sit on, difficult to swim from its tide-wracked shoreline, no sand for children to build with and donkeys would break their legs if they tried to give rides, as they did in Scarborough, the nearest seaside resort to our old home. Too shifting even to set a deck chair safely, but in spite of its limitations, our family loved the beach and during the summer to follow, albeit a wet one, we were the only ones to make use of it. How could we ignore that beach? It was at our very door. And I loved the stones themselves; all you had to do was bend down and pick up a stone, any stone, and it was perfectly shaped for feathering across the bay and, when the sea was calm within the little harbour, you couldn't count the skips. I could skim stones to the end of the storm-wrecked breakwater and my father many times had even reached the pier wall.

As our very first October day in Greystones was fading into night, I had stood at the sea's edge in awe at everything around me, the gently breaking waves so incredibly close to the house, the crazy stone beach, and most of all, the mountains. To the north, Bray Head, a whale-shaped colossus, slumped asleep in the sea, with, to the west, the two Sugarloaves, grey and gloomy in the deepening sky and directly behind the town, the gently sloping Coolagad, a mere hill to those accustomed to mountains, but a mystery to me and yet another mountain, ready to explore. There was only a flat horizon to the south where I knew Wicklow town and County Wexford were, but so far away they might as well have been at the edge of another world.

Dreamily, that late evening, I had stood on the beach for a long time and, feeling lonely let darkness settle on me like a cloak. It was my mother's voice calling from the porch of Calgary that awakened me and I began to climb the crunching, slithering stones towards the house. The house, my mother told me, was so called after a town in Canada. It was very cold, that winter of snow and ice, and the house was as cold as its Canadian namesake. Above the columned porch was the veranda with access to it from the first floor landing and soon I was spending a lot of time there, looking out to sea at the sailing boats and the fishing boats, Viking ships they were, full of warlike creditors and debtors. I would grab my wooden spear and wait for them to crunch ashore, my worst fears were realised. They had followed us to Ireland.

The veranda was special, early morning when it was great to watch the sun rise on the sea, and great, too, as night fell on this unknown land and I would wonder what each day would bring. But, best of all, was the veranda after a snow fall, where I would line up snowballs on the balustrade, ready to repel invaders, especially those tribes who might at any time step ashore and besiege the house. It was a battlement from which to practise on my sisters as they tried to reach the shelter of the porch. From that vantage point one snowy evening, Sam was kept out in the garden by my snowballs for so long that she began to cry with cold.

How sorry I was to leave that house behind, for its memories were to endure longer than any other. The vista from the veranda, the cold, airy rooms, the wide, creaking staircase, the chickens out at the back and the kitchen, warmed by the huge coal-fired range, the nub of the house, where my mother did the cooking. But above all I would recall the veranda and the snow.

The first night it snowed was soon after our first Christmas and as I watched with growing excitement the silent, lightly falling flakes gather thickly on the ground, I imagined the magic transformation of the morning and prayed that it would snow all through the night to leave drifts so high no one could leave the house. I awoke before dawn and rushed to the bedroom window, where I threw apart the curtains and almost cried with joy. I called to my sisters for them to see the pure, white fields of Coolagad and the Sugarloaves and Bray Head and the north beach and the pier, all blanketed in snow. We ran from window to window, with a different fairyland through each, fogging the glass with our squeals of delight. Not that we had never seen snow before. It had snowed, of course in Cravenvale, with snow-covered roof-tops, gardens and streets but foothills and mountains were a different thing altogether. We were dizzy with excitement. Snow, nature's most exquisite material, had created a masterpiece, as far as the eye could see, the silent snow covered garden of Ireland.

Chapter Three

*T*he lesson was religious knowledge and Brother Mulligan was uncharacteristically vague with his explanation of the feast of the Circumcision, the foremost feast day of the coming year, and boys discussed this incertitude during his short absence from the class. Considering how eloquently informed he was on the Epiphany, Corpus Christie, The Assumption and other such esoteric celebrations infusing the Catholic calendar, this was a big surprise. Why this vagueness with the feast of the Circumcision?

His return was greeted by the plump face of Rogan, asking him the question poised collectively on so many lips. 'Just what is it, Brother, this Circumcision?' The query hung in the air like a question mark, growing heavier the longer it took in answering. A glare from the cleric silenced Rogan and others of us thinking of taking up his cause. Outside the windows, older boys were assembling for Confession and soon our class would follow and I was sickened at the thought of it. The brother raised himself from his chair, averting his eyes to the boys in the yard and staring, frowning, as if something untoward had attracted his attention. No one was fooled; this was something he often did when he was perplexed or struggling with thoughts. Presently, he sat down again and addressed the class.

It turned out that the Circumcision was an old Jewish custom whereby, having attained a certain age, male children, of which Jesus was no exception, had a portion of skin removed from an appendage. Well, it was common knowledge that an appendage could be any one of a number of things; it could be a finger or a thumb, a toe perhaps, or an earlobe. Yes, in the case of Jesus, it was definitely an earlobe. Choice of appendage could vary from time to time or from village to village and could well depend on the whims of elders but usually, it was an earlobe and in the Nazareth of that year of Jesus, an earlobe it most certainly was. For quite some time following this information, as I closely scrutinised stunted male earlobes, I was astonished at the number of circumcised Jewish boys living in the small Irish town of Greystones.

Dermot Coyle, the quiet boy beside me, tore minute particles of flesh from around his fingernails with small, yellow teeth, reminding me of a rat. Taking a hand from his mouth, he examined anew fingers soft and raw, before selecting the one which had the most appetising morsel of flesh, which he then gnawed at ravenously.

Coyle was a source of American horror comics, full of scantily-clad girls being constantly pursued by mutants and monsters. At the top of a page, a girl would start off fully-clothed but by the time she reached the bottom of the page, she would have most of her clothes torn off, all except a few fragments, miraculously, the same fragments surviving in every case. The ghouls came in every colour, shape and size, all with lascivious eyes and drooling mouths, and all with one thing in mind, their intrepid pursuit of girls. These comics both excited and disturbed me and whenever I got him to lend me some, I kept them hidden behind a board in the coal-house.

Once, when I returned comics to his house, he invited me to a bedroom shared with younger siblings and I was shocked that he made no attempt to hide them, looking puzzled when I asked him what his parents had to say about such publications. Well, his parents had nothing to say, they weren't bothered, but then I thought of his care-worn mother with nine children and his father, more concerned with propping up the bar at Dan's, and I understood. I figured that it would only be in the homes of the well-to-do and in good, Catholic homes where parents would be distressed at such dubious material on display. You would never find such unsavoury stuff in a wholesome house, well, not unless you were to look behind a board in the coal-house. Always before Confession, I would agonise about whether I should confess my regard for these comics to the priest but thought it circumspect to generalise under the heading 'impure thoughts'. I reckoned them not too sinful anyway; the monsters were a real unhappy bunch and the girls did nothing else but run around half-naked and screaming. No one in those comics ever enjoyed themselves enough to be sinful.

On the day of my induction, I had left the Head's office, escorted by Brother Brady, feeling quite pleased with myself. Once again, my ears were assailed, louder than before with the cacophony of Bru, Bru, Bru, that motor-bike racket resounding down the corridor and seemingly emanating from every classroom. Increasingly intrigued, I was to learn before the day was out that the 'Bru' was simply an abbreviation of the title 'Brother' and the racket only the eager response of knowledgeable schoolboys to a question posed by their teacher, ceasing abruptly as a boy was chosen to answer.

In my new class, I had elected to sit next to Dermot Coyle and was sitting next to him still. Not that I liked sitting next to this small rat-faced boy, even though he was good to borrow comics from. I didn't like being seated right at the front of the class, either, but that first day, Brother Brady, having taken over from Brother Mulligan, was introducing me to my new class-mates, whose faces I had scanned in my heart-stopping moment of entry. A squeaky voice was telling them who I was and where I came from, disclosures greeted with something less than cordiality, from faces, which looked to me, like rows of mailed fists. Then I was standing on a small dais in front of them like some exhibit and this fearful man was explaining to the faces that when I was at school in England, I was the best fighter in the class and had especially come to Ireland hoping to find more worthy opposition.

'It might well be Christian by name but not necessarily by nature,' he quipped in his weird, high-pitched falsetto.

I cast a weak smile of intimation that such ungodliness had not travelled with me, but not one face altered its expression. My obvious discomfort and the mute receptivity of the class only encouraged the cleric further, for then, to my horror, he asked, 'Who in this class would like to be first to fight this fellow here?'

Thankfully, no one volunteered.

'Come on, now. Here's a fellow from across the water looking for a fight.' He squeezed my upper arm between an enormous finger and thumb. 'Ah yes, I'm after feeling a muscle here, but I tink it's not a big one. Come on now, there must be one o' you lot brave enough to take this fellow on. Don't disappoint him, now, isn't he all the way across the water, looking for a fight?'

Still no one volunteered.

'Young Otello here is only after telling Brother McBride and myself that not only could he beat any boy in this class but he could do it standing on his hands. That would be a grand ting to see and all we want now is someone to take him on.' No one was rising to the bait and the cleric was starting to look distinctly annoyed.

Looking up into his matted nostrils, I grinned broadly. I could see his joke and I was shaking my head in friendly disagreement, but his face was grim and unremitting. It wasn't a joke and everyone in the class knew it, including now, myself.

He lost patience: 'Ah, cowards the lot of you to disappoint a fellow wanting a fight. Can you not see him sparring on the deck of the ship, in training for what was to come, only to meet up with a lot of lily-livered motts?' Then, suddenly, to me, 'Are you a front row man or a back row man?'

Unsure of his meaning, I looked up again into the jungle of his nose, the grin still stupidly fixed across my face 'Brother?' I asked.

'Do you have your heart set on any particular row? Look now at those rows of boys in front of you and tell me which of them takes your fancy.'

21

I didn't want to sit anywhere in this class; I wanted to go home to Calgary and wished that I had never come to Ireland. The hostility about me was palpable and none more so than in the black shape hovering above me. 'Brother, I don't mind sitting anywhere,' I muttered, desperate to get out of the limelight. Then, seeing an empty seat directly in front of me, I didn't hesitate, but plonked myself down beside a small, thin boy who turned out to be Dermot Coyle.

The suddenness of my action and the corresponding shuffling of Coyle's bony bottom took the cleric by surprise; it was as if some little creature he had been tormenting had escaped and it irritated him, but with a sweep of his hand he intimated that by my own volition I had now taken my place as a *bona fide* member of the class. Then, straightening his back, he said, 'See that, you lily-livered lot, see how this boy is after making for the very front of class. A good sign that, sign of a boy with notting to hide, a boy not frightened to get into the tick o' tings, oh, how you Rooney, you Doyle, you Reardon and the rest of you who do be skulking at the back of the class, you skulkers and schemers sliding around at the back of the class, how you could do to take a leaf out of this boy's book. There's you lot tinking Brother Mulligan and myself can't see trew yous, tinking out of sight is out of mind. And now along comes young Christian, getting off to a great start, impressing myself and Brother Mc Bride with his eloquence and his walking on his hands and we knowing full well that we're about to put him in with eejits who can't string two words together and have trouble walking on their feet. Anyways, the boy here has promised Brother Mc Bride and myself that he's going to teach the lot o' you to walk on your hands and be a blessing to your parents with all the shoe leather saved.'

This affirmation was both sardonic and insinuating; with no effort to disguise the sarcasm or deflect the hostility, it was deliberately arousing. And so I found myself seated as close to the teacher's desk as was physically possible, without refuge from the hostility it might otherwise afford. This was not a good start.

Following the Catholic Sisters of Charity in Cravenvale, the Christian Brothers of St Luke's was the obvious choice for further education as I was both Catholic and of distant Irish descent, validates singularly undervalued. Calling on religious and tribal affiliations was to no avail, because, as I was already beginning to realise, not only was I irredeemably English, I was the only English boy in the school.

That first lunch hour, I ate alone, sitting on the steps of the boiler-room, a figure of interest and suspicion until a curly-headed boy called Donoghue, throwing caution to the winds, dared to strike up conversation. Sitting down beside me, he spoke in hushed tones of the big mistake I had made in sitting directly in front of the teacher's desk. 'Look at Coyle, the kid beside you, a bloody nervous wreck.' He then continued to put me right about a lot of things. Brother Mulligan was ok and the other brothers were mostly ok, including McBride, the Head, but for Brother Brady he grimaced and, rolling his eyes, slid a finger across his throat. 'Never, ever been known to smile, you think I'm coddin' but I'm not. Ask any kid in this school if he's ever seen Brady smile. An' the way he talks, as if someone's got him by the bollocks. An' Jesus if he tinks your tick you'll get toroughly trashed. An' never let him catch you in the tick o' tings, nothin' he likes better than to catch a kid in the tick o' tings.'

'But it's Brother Mulligan who is the class teacher, isn't it?'

Yes, Brother Mulligan was the class teacher but the deputy had no class of his own and was appearing in class 2 more and more. And then the boy, Donoghue, in a voice scarcely above a whisper, gravely revealed the one thing that every new boy must know as a matter of life and death. When Brother Brady got really angry, the wart on his left temple changed colour. 'Now for God's sake watch out for that wart. You can't miss it, it's a big one. When he gets angry, really angry, it turns from white to pink an' then to red an' it kind o' glows an' it won't go back to normal until some kid gets thrashed an' I mean, thrashed.'

On closer inspection, the deputy was a bulbous, meaty man

about six-feet four inches tall with a florid, dewlapped face and a cascade of pink chins. From somewhere between these chins and a large, hirsute nose came a voice more suited to an emaciated eunuch, a voice mimicked often by the boys. It was an elephant twittering like a sparrow and it made you want to laugh, except, other than behind his back, no one laughed at Brother Brady. Yes, unmistakeably, he sported a wart on his left temple, which to me, seemed to turn red the moment he entered class.

He was the most formidable man I had ever seen, clad in the bunched-up black habit of his order, with, swinging from the waistband, a thick black belt. This belt, part of the uniform, was the most important part, for it had an express purpose, the persuasion of young charges like me along the Catholic and Apostolic road to righteousness and it didn't go unused. He and Brother Mulligan appeared to swap classes and responsibility at will and oh, Donoghue, how right you were. How bitterly did I now regret my self-appointed post at the head of the class, for with my seat in front of his, no matter which boy or assortment of boys were the object of his ready rage, his salivating lips and chins were positioned directly above me causing showering virulence to fall upon my head like acid rain. And to add to my wretched position, I was soon to discover that the front row of this class was occupied in its entirety by the most despised band of boys in any school, swots. So in electing to sit where now I sat, I was automatically stigmatised as a swot, an English swot and thereby an irresistible target to a large section of the class, which seemed motivated by an irresistible and innate desire to hunt.

My unpopularity, incited by Brother Brady's introduction, seemed to increase in direct proportion to the efforts I made to redress it. All children know and fear ostracism and its inevitable consequence, bullying, a creeping monster, once on its way, nigh impossible to stop. But what was heading my way was different, it wasn't creeping, it was galloping and was to come to a head as early as the third day of the second week at school, Wednesday afternoon, history afternoon, and could I really be responsible for seven hundred years of British persecution? Apparently, yes. There, suddenly, in the front row of class 2, St Luke's, laid at my feet were all the persecuted, long dead heroes of Irish history, an emerald swathe along the blood-red road of British trespass. 'It was what the Brits were good at, trespass,' Brother Brady summarised. Weaned as I was by my father on the valiant exploits of Drake, Raleigh, Nelson, Wellington and Churchill, I had no idea that parts of the world existed where the concept of British imperial potency was looked upon with unequivocal detestation. As that first lesson on Irish history ended and, no doubt exhausted by his anti-British diatribe, Brother Brady left the classroom for a break. 'Best behaviour, best behaviour, the lot o' you,' he warned on his way out.

This absence, together with an inevitable reddening of my ears at what had just transpired, alerted the back-seated Rooney and Cronin to belated retaliation which came in the form of a missile that thwacked into the back of my head with the sting of a giant wasp. Following this initial and successful, exploratory assault and for the remainder of the week and the next week, too, whenever occasion arose, the missiles came thick and fast, taking the form of tightly-folded wet cardboard, propelled by elastic bands, entwined around the extended fingers of almost every boy on the back two rows and some sympathetic allies on the flanks.. I did not complain; I dare not. Brother Brady had warned me that should I ever be found responsible in any way for disruption in his class, then it would be met with ruthlessness such as only the very worst of my forbears could have boasted. Be it so, the situation as it was could not go on. I was becoming an archetypal victim and had national reputation and self-preservation to consider. Measures would have to be taken. They were.

It was Monday morning and, taking advantage of Brother Brady's departure on an errand for the Head, missiles came thick and fast again. But this time I didn't duck beneath my desk offering cringing smiles of subjugation. Instead, I jumped to my feet and whirled around on my tormentors with a catapult of my own.

It was one I had carefully constructed over the weekend. Meticulously, I had trimmed strips of bicycle inner tube to optimum length, thickness and precision for discharge at maximum velocity my missiles of tightly-wadded silver cigarette paper, crunched and twisted for maximum pain on impact. Surprised and cowed by my unexpected and violent retaliation, my combatants took refuge beneath their desks and, as nothing advances victory like a manifestation of defeat, I vaulted on to a desk and in the tradition of a native knight errant, shouted, *'Cry havoc and let slip the dogs of war.'*

At this the classroom door opened suddenly and instinctively I knew that Brother Brady's errand for the Head was as short-lived as was my jubilant victory. Frozen on top of the desk by an expression of outrage, I watched as a florid face paled at the effrontery confronting it and at black eyes framed by bristling brows smoking in anger. But by far the most unnerving sight was the wart; it was pulsing purple and looked ready to explode. Bowing my head contritely, I closed my hand around the catapult and made to dismount the desk. Surprisingly, the cleric extended his hand and helped me, virtually lifting me with ease, and, setting me down gently on my feet, began speaking in a tone more moderate than I could have hoped for. 'Down off of that desk now like a good lad. There now, that's better isn't it?'

'I'm sorry, Bru,' I offered, thinking, hoping that this might be the end of things, but in his next words I recognised a timbre which could never be mistaken for moderation, words in a stone-cold whisper, slowly spoken, like words of an ancient curse.

' Audaces Fortuna Juvat. Fortune favours the Brave. And well it might but not in Brother Brady's class. In Brother Brady's class such bravery is anarchy.'

'Brother, I'm sorry but you don't know what's been going on. As soon as your back is turned you don't ….'

'Cry havoc and let slip the dogs of war', is it? Oh such eloquence such theatre as I have never seen or heard in a class of mine before.' His voice then rose discordantly. 'Oh boys, what a ting

we've been privileged to witness here today, what a comfort it is to me to know that when I leave the classroom on important business, there is at least one boy willing to take over in my absence, one boy who's not afraid to get into the tick o' tings, and not a Celt but a Brit and a great example to us all. It is someting called initiative. Someting we don't see enough of here at St Luke's. Me and Brother McBride, do we not wring our hands at the lack of initiative we see around us and we're forever wondering if perhaps it's us at fault in not doing enough to encourage it. Says I to him only yesterday, Brother says I, do you tink we're doing enough to encourage initiative? "We're not, says he," 'we're not.'

At this point I dared to raise my eyes to his. Could I detect a hint of understanding in his words, even grudging praise? He should know what had been going on behind his and his colleague's back. Should know how I was being made a scapegoat for the misbehaviour of others. Know the provocation I had been forced to endure and the complete justification of retaliation. My eyes moved to the beacon on his neck. Was its colour fading? Yes, and hope revitalised. But with his next words, that pulse of hope was done for. 'Standing on a desk, armed like a Black and Tan. Fortune might well favour the brave the whole world over, but not in Brother Brady's class, ah no, not in Brother Brady's class.'

'Brother,' I began.

He ignored me and addressed the class. 'Correct me if I'm wrong here, but was it not less than two weeks ago that I paraded this Saxon warrior before you? Giving the lot of you chance to prove yourselves in honourable combat, and what happened? I'll tell you what happened. Like lily-livered motts, the lot of you cowered and not but a couple o' minutes ago I find you cowering still. The Brits, as we all well know, have a reputation on the battlefield and 'tis a noble ting so it is, to see a boy so proud of his forbears, he's prepared to demonstrate that reputation in an Irish classroom.' I looked up at him again with that little pulse of hope. Could he, after all, be championing my cause? He wasn't.

'A classroom at St Luke's, yes, but how unfortunate for young Otello here to have chosen mine.'

Then with elaborate courtesy I was guided to a dais and, as he straightened my shoulders and adjusted my school tie, he spoke directly to the class as he would during a lesson. 'A little soldier what? A little Black and Tan.' His back was to me now and, soberly, he continued. 'As you all well know, the discipline of a class of boys is a difficult ting to achieve and having managed it, a difficult ting to maintain. It's what we Christian Brothers strive to do, Indeed, Brother McBride insists on it, because he knows how all too easily it can break down. All it takes is one bad apple in a tub, one rotten egg in a basket and all our hard work has suddenly come to notting. And then, boys, what do we have? What do we have when discipline breaks down? Come now, what do we have?'

'Anarchy,' a mumble from the boys.

'Anarchy,' the cleric echoed. 'When parents send their boys to school of a morning, they are looking for polite, well-behaved young gentlemen to return of an evening. What would they not be looking for?'

'Anarchists.' Another mumble, there was no Bru, Bru, Bru, in answer to a Brother Brady question, only sullen resentment tinged with fear.

'And you all know what an anarchist is, don't you?'

Of course they knew, because, by the way he was talking and the way the boys were answering, this disquisition had been tried and tested many times. I had absolutely no idea what an anarchist was, but strongly suspected that at any moment, I was going to be held as a prime example.

I was about to speak again, but the brother swung around on me and he looked so huge and fierce that my mouth dried up at the impact of his eyes. Returning to my side, he said, 'And I wonder how many more of us have a ting hanging from our fingers like a hangman's noose. How many more of us are armed like Black and Tans?'

I looked to the class for deliverance. I could yet be saved. The cleric might yet know of the overwhelming odds that had been stacked against me. Deep down he must know what I had been going through and now, surely, the proof. 'Hold out your hands, the lot o' you', he barked.

As one, the class held forth their hands but incredibly all were pale and naked with sleeves retracted and bony wrists twisting back and forth to show that nothing was secreted. They were hands that might join together in prayer, finger rosaries or assist a priest at holy mass, but my hand which the cleric was lifting gently forward was grubby and clammy and unbelievably, had rubber bands attached.

I looked at it accusingly, unable to understand what was fastened to my fingers. Ripping at the bands, I thrust them in my pocket and held my hands out for inspection. My catapult was in my pocket, as were all the other boys' and now surely, Brother Brady could see that my hands were no different to theirs, they were pale and naked, too, and my wrists were twisting back and forth to show that nothing was secreted.

So why was I stepping down from the dais and my right hand being lifted? And why were my fingers being tenderly straightened out? I raised my eyes to the red doughy face for an answer, the trembling, doughy, sanguine cheeks. An answer maybe to be found in the chocolate eyes but there wasn't any answer and I wondered at the sudden fearful swishing that was sounding in my ears.

The belt fell mightily, noisily upon the palm of my right hand and I thought for one agonising second that my fingers had been taken off. Then the wrist of my left hand, the one that had held the catapult, was being lifted and the fingers gently opened. In some respects, Brother Brady was being surprisingly gentle. The belt exploded and I could not believe the pain. The right hand again and then the left, one after another, over and over. My eyes were squeezed shut, holding back tears of agony and injustice. 'Anarchy,' the brother panted with each stroke.

Unable to stand any more, I clasped my hands together between my knees and the brother was not being gentle any more. He was dragging at them and when he failed with one, he tried the other until he had one in his grasp and when my fingers refused to open, the belt fell like a scythe across my knuckles and the pain was so intense, I thought that I might faint.

Chins were wobbling in time to a flashing baton and dewlaps were wobbling in time to cymbal clashes across my fingers. Cheeks wobbled in time to synchronised gasps of exertion and pain and the wart, like some macabre spotlight, bore luminous witness to this microcosm of crime and punishment, until, finally, red hot tears gushed forth and brought the symphony to an excruciating close.

Breathing heavily, the cleric said, '*Audaces fortuna juvat*, maybe. But not in Brother Brady's class. Ah no.'

Chapter Four

With a toss of his head, Donoghue flicked a loop of light oak hair above his eye line and viewed me with keen-eyed estimation. Following his evaluation of Brother Brady's disposition, which had proved all too pertinent, his credibility was high and if there was a wing to be taken under, it was his. There were lots of things an English boy in Ireland ought to know and how to deal with Irish girls was one of them. Recognising my hesitation in forming positive relationships with the opposite sex, he had begun advising me on matters of approach and technique, with the air of one to whom demonstrative action was second nature. 'Don't dilly-dally with girls,' he counselled. 'Motts around here have no time for kids who dilly-dally. Like, what would you do if you wanted one to fancy you?'

I thought a while. 'Wink at her,' I answered hopefully.

'Wink at her,' he scoffed. 'Motts around here would think who does that friggin' creep think he's winkin' at? No, all you have to do is raise an eyebrow an' if you can't raise one on its own then raise 'em both. See if you can raise an eyebrow.'

I tried. I couldn't.

'You'll have to do 'em both then,' he said regretfully, one eyebrow disappearing seductively beneath the loop of light oak hair that had fallen into place again, 'an' another thing important around here, is knowin' if a girl's in love with you. You want to know if a girl's in love with you, then all you got to do is take her

31

hand an' tickle the palm of it with your finger, an' if she does it back then it means that she's in love with you. I do it all the time.'

'And do they do it back?' I asked breathlessly.

'Do they do it back,' he sniffed, exposing what looked like a crusted scab in the middle of his right hand.

I was impressed. This kid really was worth knowing.

Brother Brady had done me a big favour. My retaliation in class and the thrashing I got afforded me a grudging respect and some degree of notoriety amongst my peers. It would have been better and more deserving if I hadn't broken down but without those tears, God knows how long it would have lasted. Anyway, Rooney and Cronin were giving me a wide berth and Donoghue and Reardon, another two of the class leaders, had started overtures of friendship. This friendship couldn't have come at a better time, but proved to be a tenuous one, as, for the remainder of our schooldays we spent as much time as sworn enemies as we did as friends.

It was during this first period of friendship with the two boys, that a curious incident occurred, involving Reardon and Brother Mulligan. Reardon and I were sitting on the boiler-house steps browsing through a dictionary, when suddenly the brother was upon us. The dictionary, brought from home that morning and so big I had trouble fitting it inside my satchel, was proving to be a disappointment and we were on the point of abandoning it when Reardon said, 'Look up egg.'

Earlier we had talked of going bird nesting in the spring and I had whetted the boy's appetite by telling him of the huge wild egg collection I had been compelled to leave behind in England, its centrepiece a cuckoo's egg found in the nest of a hedge sparrow. Reardon assured me that we would find another such egg in the hedgerows of Coolagad, as that hill, every spring, was alive with the call of cuckoos. 'Rubbish book for rude words. Look up egg,' he urged again.

The Christian brothers took turns at supervising play-time and lunch breaks, but except for immediate response to violent uproar, we seldom saw them, so as I was flicking through the Es, we were surprised to see Brother Mulligan looking down on us.

'Nice to see that you are busy,' he said. The sight of the cleric's wistful, pale face and tranquil blue eyes was no cause for alarm and we returned the greeting amicably. 'And what have we here, I wonder?' he said, as his eyes rested on the huge book on my lap.

'A dictionary, Brother,' I explained proudly. 'Me and Liam thought we would improve our English during play-time.'

Crouching beside us, he allowed the bright, early December sun to settle agreeably upon his face. My mother believed that there was something spiritual about Brother Mulligan. She said he had a holy face and there was no one better than my mother for knowing who was holy in the world, and who was not. I agreed with her and liked this teacher who seemed to favour me more than the other boys. Sometimes, he would converse with me on matters unrelated to school, and he took interest in the essays I wrote and the quality of my art work. And I knew how pleased he was at how quickly I had taken to Gaelic football, saying to my father, 'Your boy forgets, while other boys are still thinking.'

Moreover, unlike Brother Brady, he didn't get angry at my abysmal progress with the Gaelic language, which their order was so eminently predisposed to teach us. He accepted that the language would never ever correlate to any aspect of my life, now or in the future, whereas Brother Brady thought it would be of immense benefit to me and belted my hands accordingly.

'I know well what you two boys are doing with that book,' Brother Mulligan said, his eyes narrowing. Reardon and I shuffled uncomfortably beneath his gaze and I snapped the book shut. Irrefutably, our quest was a sin, but surely not a mortal one. We were worried, but not unduly so. With this cleric, small wrongs were often disregarded within the more important prospectus of mutual understanding but, unquestionably, the man was unhappy with us, his eyes narrowing with distrust, while our own were shifty with guilt.

'I noticed the book was open at the letter E.'

'Yes, Brother.'

'E for education, I suppose.'

'No, Brother.' I was doing the talking and looked to Reardon for support.

'For what, then?'

'Egg,' Reardon replied readily.

'Egg!' You were looking up 'Egg', among others, no doubt.'

'Ah no, Brother, just the one, egg.'

He sat down beside us on the step and, taking the dictionary from my hand, said, 'A little word for such a big book. Why egg, may I ask?' Then, he handed back the book.

Reardon and I exchanged glances, each wanting the other to explain, my new friend taking up the initiative. 'We was talkin' o' goin' bird-nestin' in the spring. You know the way it is, Bru, collectin' eggs an' all an' he was tellin' o' goin' nestin' with his cousin in England an' findin' the egg of a cuckoo in the nest of a spuggy. An' says I to him, sure there's load's o' cuckoos on Coolagad. "We'll go an' look for them," says he to me, "in the spring." 'Says I to him, Look in that book an' see what it says about egg.'

'And what did it say?'

I took over. 'Don't know, Brother. About to find out when you came along.'

The cleric's face clouded and he seemed unhappy with the explanation and, picking the dictionary from my lap, bade Reardon remain where he was and beckoned me to follow him inside the school.

The general office, next to the Head's, was equally small and claustrophobic. Sparsely furnished in a similar manner to the Head's, it was a place where matters between teachers and pupils could be discussed which might be too delicate for the turbulence of the classroom. It was also a place where disciplinary measures, which for one reason or another could not be dealt with in the usual corporal manner could be privately enforced. Dissidents and dissenters, should they ever be found, could also be dealt with here and no doubt anarchists and I worried, as I sat down in front of him, if there was something anarchic about eggs.

The cleric took his customary time before arriving at the issue troubling him, examining his propelling pencil and fiddling with it as if it was not functioning correctly. Presently, he fixed me with thoughtful eyes and handing back the dictionary, said, 'Now find the word you were looking for and read it out to me.'

I fumbled through the pages until I found it and my mouth dried as I began to read aloud its nebulous definition. It contained words like conception and spermatozoa and other words I didn't understand, words I could hardly pronounce with a tongue swollen to twice its size. I gulped convulsively at cells produced in the bodies of humans and animals, descriptions of fertilisation and reproduction and bovine, canine and avian copulation abounded in my brain. Paradoxically, we had found the rudest word in the entire book.

With a movement of his bony hand, the cleric removed the book from mine and closed it. 'Now I'd like you to put that lot into words we can understand,' he requested soberly.

I could not and my heart thumped at the thought of being made to do so, but sensing my discomfort, the cleric inclined his head towards mine and said, gravely, 'No of course you can't and neither would I expect you to try, and neither could Reardon. But for the pair of you, a lesson to be learned.' He weighed the dictionary in his hand. 'Dear God, the size of it, the weight of it, developing your muscles with it, maybe, but otherwise, a book to be left alone for a few years yet. In this book you will find many peculiar words and see how uncomfortable you were with just a three-letter one. It is, unfortunately, the very kind of book, the devil uses to trap a young boy. The devil is forever setting traps for young minds and often in the most seemingly innocent books and words, that trap is set.' His voice was soft and serious and as his face was close to mine across the table, I could smell sweetness on his breath, mingling with sweetness of oil in his hair. His long, thin fingers tapped lightly on the cover of the dictionary as he continued. 'Now education is a fine thing and no mistake, but too much education and too quickly, can get out of hand. There are many fine books in our own school library and I know that you are one of the few boys who make use of them. Poetry, isn't it?'

'Irish poetry Brother.'

'Well, that's a great thing, so it is. How about *'The Lives of the Saints'*, now there's a book that I would urge a boy to read. St Patrick and St Frances, think of them as two young boys like yourself and Liam Reardon. Did they ever imagine as they played and went to school, that one day they would be revered around the Christian world for their great learning and holiness? And did they need a big book the likes of this one? I think not.' He paused allowing another train of thought to enter his mind. 'Do you have a prayer book?'

'There is a prayer book at home.'

'Well, of course there would be, of course,' he murmured apologetically. "But do you have one of your own?"

'No.'

He sat back in his chair, his sweet smell lingering in my nostrils. Sunlight, through the small window, fell upon the side of his face, highlighting the greying of his temple. His face looked tired and his eyes sad. Reaching to a shelf by his side, he laid a small, black book reverentially on the table before me. It was a prayer book. 'This is for you to keep for yourself, Christian, and if ever you feel that you might be slipping into spiritual danger, then, I would advise you to reach for this book. Open it at random and on any page, I know that you will find the guidance and the strength to resist temptation.'

I picked up the book and a picture fell from its folds. It was of The Sacred Heart and I looked at the sad eyes and compassionate face of Jesus, a haloed head against a curtain of stars, His right hand raised in blessing and His left hand pointing at His bleeding heart. The face of Jesus did not resemble Brother Mulligan's face, but both had that same expression of tenderness and compassion and at once I knew what my mother had meant when she said that Brother Mulligan had a holy face. 'Thank you, Brother I will open it, read it, yes.'

The weariness appeared to leave the teacher's face at once and he seemed relieved. 'Go out there now and send young Reardon in to me. That young vagabond will think he's escaped, as he usually does. Bird-nesting is it? Two cuckoos looking for the egg of another. He smiled at the thought. 'Two cuckoos looking for the egg of another, well. I suppose the two of you could be doing worse and in truth, I recollect doing much the same when I was a boy your age.'

Firmly, symbolically, he placed the prayer book on top of the dictionary as if whatever evil was in the bigger book could not now escape and do me harm and I wondered mischievously what he would have to say if he were to catch me with Coyle's comics. He stood to open the window and a wound of yellow sunlight creased jagged down his cheek, and sensing me looking at his face, he raised slender fingers and smoothed the hair above his ear. 'Go now and tell Reardon he's wanted.'

Taking the books with me, I was pleased to be out of the office and reporting to a worried Reardon that he was wanted, too. 'It's ok, we're not in trouble, but he knows what we were doing. What we were looking for.'

'Did you get a bollocking?'

'No, I got a prayer book.'

Not long after this incident, I had another unexpected encounter with Brother Mulligan. It was a Saturday morning and he was cycling along Victoria Road, towards the school, when he spotted me, got off his bicycle and asked me if I would like to accompany him to school that morning. He explained that he would like me to help him mark English compositions from class 1 and I thought he was joking, for no boy, as far as I knew, had ever been asked to help a teacher with school work. But he was serious and my heart stirred with satisfaction at this unexpected honour.

'Well, I'm not doing much this morning, Brother.'

Pushing his bicycle, we were then walking slowly, uphill towards the schoolhouse. This invitation was nothing less than an endorsement of my literacy and I felt very proud and important. Outside Pennicook's cafe, I spied Paddy Donoghue and his brother Paul and gave them an imperious wave. They looked puzzled. Earlier that week, they had laughed at my knees, saying that they looked like horse's hocks; well, they weren't laughing now. 'Helping Brother Mulligan with schoolwork,' I nonchalantly informed them.

As we walked up Jeeney Hill with the cleric stooped over the handlebars of his bicycle, he asked me how I was settling in at school and how my family were settling in, in Ireland and how did Ireland compared with England. He was most interested in the standard of Catholic teaching in the two countries and how they compared and was pleased when I told him that everyone in the family was settling well and that teaching standards were very much the same. He told me that he had a brother living in Liverpool with a good job in insurance and how he was hoping to visit him during the next summer holidays. He asked me if I had ever been to Liverpool and laughed heartily when I told him, 'Only on the day that we set sail for Ireland.'

I learned, as we walked slowly towards the school, that his family came from Sligo, where many of them still lived and how he intended to visit his mammy and daddy, if all was well, this coming Christmas. He seemed very happy at the prospect and at peace with himself and the troubled look he so often wore in class was absent from his face. His face lit up and his smile broadened as he spoke of his boyhood and the thundering Atlantic Ocean near his home and how he played hurling for his school team and was once considered for the county team at Gaelic football. I had never seen the man so happy with himself as he was that morning with his bicycle wheels squeaking beneath him and his mind far off, talking of his early days in Sligo.

In the classroom, he placed a cushion on a chair, to elevate my position beside him at his desk. The desk was stacked with English essays from Class 1 and my job, he explained, was to go through some of them, passing on to him those I thought, had merit. As I was unsure of factors eliciting merit, he selected a couple of specimen compositions, and with the same sweet breath of the office, clarified the points I should be looking for. Considering the age of the pupils, some of the stuff was passable, but I laughed out loud at most of what was written and concluded that in spelling 'fox' and 'beyond' for Brother McBride, the Head had been not so much satisfied as impressed.

There was hardly a sound in the classroom; even the turning of a page was crisp and echoing, with the only other sound, an occasional grunt from the teacher at something he had come across that either amused or displeased him and one example, a twelve-line wodge of illiteracy, he inched towards me with a groan giving me an opportunity to impress him further. 'Well, Brother, after all, *'Brevity is the soul of wit,'* I laughed.

Days passed, during which I sensed that he had cooled towards me and I was at a loss to know why this should be. I had been a help to him that morning at school and he had thanked me but how disappointed I was when he made an excuse about being in a hurry and sped off on his bicycle, for I so much wanted to be seen by Donoghue and his brother walking back to town with him.

Chapter Five

Above all, the foremost requirement for social acceptance in mid-century Greystones was something my father hadn't even thought about, a maid. But we were very soon made to understand that all the best families in the town had maids and if we wanted to be included in this category, then we had better do something about it, and quickly. 'Best families' lived on the coast road, on the Burnaby estate and in big houses and farms on the high road to Bray, with Calgary, situated on what was left of the North Beach Road, just scraping in at the bottom end of this starchy spectrum of real estate. But that depended on it having a maid, so we got one but, within a matter of months, we could no longer afford her and if class issues had been active in my home town of Cravenvale, they were paramount in this little town, so we had to hang on to her for as long as we possibly could.

'Best people' were easy to identify. They had soft voices and a genteel way of deportment and as they were confident that everything they said was important, there was never need to saddle conversation with crudity. They exuded a charm, uncluttered yet distant, attracting respect without envy. There was no room for Johnny-Come-Latelys, no high-stepping hubris, in this town. And best families had cars, sometimes two, and telephones and washing machines and it was rumoured that there were some on the Burnaby who had something called a television, hard to believe but it was something like a small cinema screen in their living room. And best people always, without fail, occupied the same rows of pews at Sunday morning Mass, those at the left of the main aisle, directly below the pulpit and, by virtue of social standing, could hear God's message more clearly than those at the other end of the social spectrum straining their unwashed ears at the back. A stranger in town, wanting to know who the best families in Greystones were, was advised to go to Sunday morning Mass and look to his left.

And position in these pews was sacrosanct. Anyone who didn't belong, no matter how busy or presumptuous they were, could possibly infiltrate this tacit zone of excellence, be it priest or pauper, it could not be tolerated. So once we had got ourselves a maid, we took up our rightful positions beneath the pulpit and best people smiled at us and slid their upholstered bottoms along the seat to let us in. And it was to our father's everlasting credit, that even when, through hard times, we no longer had a maid, we were still permitted in those pews because of an air about him that implied that although maidless at the moment, we would have maids, butlers, footmen, gardeners and chauffeurs before the next collection plate came around.

Our maid was Grandma Mary Plunkett and she was round. Everything about her was perfectly round, her mouth, her nose, her eyes, her face, her hands, her feet, her body and particularly, her bottom and was so round that my father told us to expect a cement mixer in a frock. One of her sons, the first to be employed at my father's factory, got her the job and she was appointed there and then, between a water barrel and two tons of pug lime.

From the veranda of Calgary, I watched her arrival with my three sisters. It was her first Monday morning and, dressed as she was, completely in black, Sam, the eldest of the girls, likened her to a cannon-ball rolling down the path. She was to work a six-day week, starting at seven-thirty in the morning and finishing each afternoon, subject to daily arrangements with my mother. Living-in, as maids had done in England, was not included in her contract. Her function was as a status symbol, so it was important for her to be seen coming and going as often and as conspicuously as possible.

She was a chatty, cheerful soul, thanking God endlessly for a life of drudgery through sets of ill-fitting teeth and never allowing the burden of seven children and countless grandchildren to disturb a naturally blessed and artless disposition. Having lived a well-satisfied and sheltered life of simplicity, bereft of curiosity, such souls as Grandma Plunkett should be left alone in blissful innocence for to introduce an unnecessary and disturbing factor into such a modest life is at best foolhardy and at worst, downright meddlesome. Soon after her arrival, my father bought her a wireless. 'A premature Christmas present,' he smiled as he caused untold disruption in her life.

'Dear God, will yous take a look at this,' she flustered as she undid the wrapping, 'amn't I the swank now?'

And by opening a seemly and hitherto unknown window to the world, news of it changed her life. Paranoia at the turn of a knob had the thirty-eighth parallel atop of Bray Head and hordes of Chinese and 'Korearionians' assembling en masse, ready at a moment's notice, to sweep down into Greystones and communise the Catholics. 'Darlin' people in the South but North Korearionians' don't believe in God, you know,' she told us, gravely. 'And even the divil believes in God.' Likely, then, she would make the sign of the cross and rattle her teeth in dismay.

It was from her grandson Christy that I first heard about the Irish Crown Jewels, stolen, then supposedly hidden somewhere in Greystones. During a lesson on local history, Brother Molloy had told his class about their theft from Dublin Castle and how the thief, while making his escape, had, quite probably, hidden them in our very town. Christy was helping his grandmother clean the windows in my parents' bedroom when he became fascinated by an open jewel box on my mother's dressing table. There were the usual rings, brooches, necklaces and watches, but to Christy, a veritable treasure trove, the like of which he had never seen before. He didn't touch anything but just gazed on them, enraptured and it was then, breathlessly, that he told me about these other jewels and the likelihood of them being hidden in Greystones.

'Brother Molloy says it was in 1907 when they was nicked an' was worth twenty thousan' quid then, oh jaysus, what would them things be worth now? Oh, imagine findin' 'em an' sellin' 'em. Imagine why dontcha, goin' in a shop an' sayin' I'll have one o them things an' two them things? Go to mass, all togged up in new clothes an' shoes an' all the people lookin' an' sayin, see that kid there, isn't he the one who foun' the Irish Crown Jewels?'

As with all male members of his family, Christy's jaw hung as if too heavy for his face, so that his mouth, when relaxed, was always partly open, giving him a stupid look. He and his two older brothers, Shonti and Patsy, had the same facial and physical characteristics, thin and gangly with protruding green eyes, tufted, straw-coloured hair and open-mouthed gormlessness. Christy, in two years' time would look like Patsy and Patsy, in two years' time, would look like Shonti and Shonti in twenty years' time would be the spitting image of his dad.

It was Patsy, the middle one of the brothers, whose vacuous features were the most pronounced. With a pendulous bottom lip, his jaw hung further than the others and his mouth was open wider, and, with his bulging eyes, he looked to me like a freshly-landed fish. I called him 'Pollack gob', but not to his face; he was older than me, bigger, stronger and had a reputation as a fierce schoolyard scrapper.

Brother Molloy's local history lesson had impressed Christy greatly, for he chattered with such animation as he proposed the setting up of a search party with his brothers, even hinting that I might be invited to come along. Pretending to only half-listen, I dampened his enthusiasm with lack of interest. 'Well, what a waste of time that would be,' I sneered. But as I left him still gazing in rapture at my mother's jewel box, I had already decided, that if anyone was to get their hands on that treasure, then it would be me.

I had only made two good friends during my first three months in Ireland, both adults. One was Frank Moore, the manager of The Ormonde cinema, and the other was Nugget Nolan. And it was to Nugget's cobbler's shop that I went for confirmation that these jewels really existed.

Nugget was a small, ginger man with wispy hair which fluttered aimlessly about a balding, patchy head. He also had a mousy, wispy moustache and a mousy, wispy face with skin the colour and texture of nibbled cheese and I often wondered if he ever had the need to shave. High on each cheek bone was an area of smut he called freckles, but was actually a fleshy mosaic of broken capillaries and long-established blackheads. He was loosely built, seriously round shouldered and looked, hanging over his work bench, like a scruffy, discarded marionette.

He was also Greystones' greatest exponent of the 'gimp'. The gimp was an idiosyncratic gait, employed by the local labouring fraternity to express to the world at large the sheer joy of living, especially after a few hours propped in the bar at Dan's. Feet with corresponding thumbs were splayed outwards from the body at exactly forty-five degrees and one degree, more or less, either way and it wasn't an authentic gimp. In practice, it was a bowlegged, jaunty walk, a waddle, invalidated if any obstacle in its path, however small, even a match, wasn't hurdled over with an elaborate little skip. Nugget also stank like a Billy goat.

His 'shop' was a shack, built with bits of timber, corrugated iron, asbestos sheets, carpet pieces and any other elements of construction, maximised by its proximity to the town's municipal tip. It was on the edge of it, between the tip and the shoreline, on what was left of the North Beach road to Bray Head. In this shop, shoes were repaired with a retail sideline of salvage from the tip face, hanging from nails in the woodwork. Cobblers' shops internationally might be associated with the tangy smell of freshly cut leather and shoe polish, but Nugget's shop was an exception, his shop smelled of sweaty feet and decaying refuse. Nugget himself smelled much the same, like a long-standing bag of domestic waste; he was a living, breathing extension of the heaving, dump of dross behind him.

Gentle people of the town seldom ventured inside this shack, preferring instead to negotiate transactions and purchases from a seaward, upwind concrete plinth, some distance from the door. Myself, made of sterner stuff and long since overcoming the urge to vomit, could stay for hours. I just loved resting my elbows on that work-strewn bench, watching the fluttering of that wispy moustache and listening to the most amazing stories about himself and his extended, ancestral family that filtered through it.

'Nugget, you ever heard of the Irish Crown Jewels?' I ventured. The cobbler with a line of shoe tacks between his lips, nodded in reply. I waited until his lips were free and he had stopped hammering. 'Ever hear that they could be hidden here in Greystones? Know anything about them?'

'Know anythin' about 'em!' he exclaimed. 'I on'y know an uncle o' mine was an Inspector in the Dublin Garda at the time an', on'y leadin' the investigation. Do I know anythin' about the Irish Crown Jewels? Sure on'y everythin' my Uncle tol' me. Everythin' there is to know. Exceptin' of course where they are, that is.'

'Would it be possible to speak to your uncle?'

Nugget picked up a shoe and regarded it broodingly, his top lip turned down, exuding pain and sadness. 'Dead, God rest his soul. Kilt at the very moment of his triumph, never foun' the man who kilt him either, although I have my suspicions.' With a razor-sharp knife, he pared a strip of leather, a waft of spice rising momentarily only to be swallowed in its noxious surroundings. 'Kilt in the prime of life, he was.'

'So he was he close to catching the man who stole the jewels?'

'Close! Practically feelin' his collar, so he was.' The cobbler placed a second shoe on the last and positioning a second string of tacks between his lips, spoke out of the corner of his mouth, mournfully. 'Uncle Thomas Nolan was a man at the top of his game. Inspector Thomas Nolan, a legend in his lifetime and a legend to this very day in the Dublin Garda. Very thragic, so it was.'

Tracing a finger along the chiselled edge of the bench, I said meditatively, 'so it's true then, those jewels are still hidden somewhere here in Greystones?'

'Sure they could be and they couldn't be,' he answered as he nailed a strip of leather to the second shoe. 'I recall my uncle's words at the time, reported in every newspaper in Ireland, some in England an' one or two even in America. "Chief Inspector Nolan of the Dublin Garda says investigations are proceeding but contrary to speculation are not only focused on the town of Greystones but other towns as well, but there is no cause for alarm as an arrest is imminent."'

'And that was when he was killed?'

'No sooner was them words out o' the man's mouth than he was kilt. Shot in the head, so he was, the bullet travellin' through the cortex o' the brain to embed in the corpus collosum. No one can survive with a bullet embedded in the corpus collosum, not even a man as strong an' fit as Chief Inspector Thomas Nolan. My brother Aloysius, a hospital surgeon in Dublin, tol' me that.'

I was excited. 'Nugget, please don't say anything to anybody but I'm going to look for those jewels.'

'Sure I wouldn't bother. Them things is not worth lookin' for. Why have they not been found do you think? I'll tell yer. Not worth the effort.'

'Those jewels are worth a fortune,' I contested indignantly.

'The English Crown Jewels, was it? The Russian Crown jewels, did I hear you say? The Irish Crown Jewels, for God's sake, when did the Irish last have a king? No, Chief Inspector Thomas Nolan died with a bullet in his corpus collosum for nothin', for them ones didn't have enough carats in 'em to put a sparkle on an owl one's blouse.' Finding dirt on the toe of the shoe he was mending, he spat on it, worked it into a muddy mess with his finger, then wiped it on the front of his smock to join with the encrusted grime and grease already there. 'Chief Inspector Nolan gave his life in the execution of his duty for the sake o' baubles, baubles that wouldn't put a sparkle on an owl one's blouse.' He spat on the shoe again and, after eyeing it for cleanliness, polished it with his shirt cuff.

This was not what I wanted to hear. Undeterred by the cobbler's lack of enthusiasm, but struck by his historical revelations, I silently vowed to seek further information from Christy's original source.

The day that Christy first told me about the jewels was shortly after our first Christmas in Ireland and, having made my mind up what to do about them, I returned upstairs to find him still ogling my Mother's jewel box. 'Come with me,' I told him. Time for him to view treasures he could more easily identify with, my Christmas presents.

My sisters and I have always agreed, that, as children, that Christmas of 1950 was our best ever. My father still had money and still nurtured great hopes for his brick factory. It was a magic time with the younger girls still believing in Santa and Sam, the eldest, still pretending to, while I, the 'adult' child, was under strict instructions not to disclose the true benefactor of the separate piles of presents awaiting us that morning. Christy might well have been in awe at the adornments displayed on my mother's dressing table, but they elicited in him, no more envy than would a collection of untouchable museum pieces. But what I was about to show him now was different, to these he could relate and he did so with gasps of disbelief, while I watched his eyes for signs of envy.

I let him handle mundane objects first, like books, gloves, a scarf, a pair of walnut hairbrushes and even these he turned over in his hands and viewed with rapt attention. Then, spellbound, he probed at a multi-bladed knife, boasting among other implements scissors, a bottle opener, a corkscrew and a gadget for removing stones from horse's hooves. He bounced a football about my bedroom and, stunned, he switched on a torch, the biggest he had ever seen, the beam of which, at night, could reach across the bay to illuminate the pier.

'Let you have a go with when it gets dark,' I told him loftily, all the time glancing at his eyes for that unmistakeable smoke of envy, but all that I could find there was wide-eyed, jewel–box, wonder. That was until he spied an unworn pair of leather shoes and when he picked them up, sniffed at them, caressed them, admired them, only then did I see what it was I looked for in his eyes.

'Just shoes,' I said dismissively.

'An' you got these as well?' he breathed.

'Yeah, haven't bothered to wear 'em yet.'

Feeling the thickness of the soles, he whistled softly. 'Jaysus, soles like these ones would last a boy a lifetime,' He looked at his reflection in the toe cap. 'When you gonna wear 'em?'

I shrugged nonchalantly, 'When I need to, if I need to, got plenty of shoes. What did you get?'

'What, for Christmas?'

'Yeah.'

'A toy,' he answered quickly

'A TOY?' I echoed.

He shrugged, sniffed and nodded.

'What kind of a toy?'

He shrugged and sniffed again: 'An ordinary one, a blue one.'

'And you didn't get anything else, just a blue toy?'

He also got some sweets and some nuts, an apple and an orange and as he recalled his presents, so I recalled the reason for his envy of the shoes. Christy was one of the boys I had seen kneeling in church with no soles to his shoes, he was one of the boys with a funny gait walking to Confession, Christy was barefooted in the snow and rain, yes he would be envious of shoes. 'And of course the 'toy',' I added to his meagre list.

He nodded.

'But what kind of a toy?' I demanded.

'An ordinary one I tol' you.' He was getting uncomfortable.

I was getting exasperated. 'But what? A toy car, a toy train, a toy boat?'

'One that you put aroun' your neck, an ordinary one.'

'Oh, you mean… ?' I left the question unfinished. I was not yet fully conversant with the idiosyncratic Wicklow dialect but I soon would be. After all, neck-toys were something I often wore my-self.

Chapter Six

Confession in the morning, was there ever a blessed sacrament so full of dread?

I stood at the wall of the dock blankly staring down, unhappily into nothing. The night before, low cloud had crept across the sea, sluggish and chill, to remain throughout the day slumped upon the town. By evening, the overcast had thickened and now that night had fallen the air was bitter cold and the sea and sky as black as ink. From the narrow mouth of the dock, the sound of pebbles being washed to and fro on the sandy bottom, with beyond the dock, the heavy breathing of the open sea. To the south, towards the rocky shore of Carraig Eden, fishermen made up their nets in a yellow bloom of streetlight, small vapour clouds of breath, hanging above their heads in the hazy light and I could just catch their voices, distant and complaining. Across the bay, the muffled laughter of drinkers spilling in and out of Dan's mixed with the yells and groans of adolescents, playing the penny slot machines outside the milk bar. In the pitch black, on top of the pier, someone was casting a fishing line into the open sea. I strained my eyes to where the pier should stand against the sky, but all was a shroud of black with no one to be seen but I heard again the swishing of the line.

The sacrament of Confession had not changed, neither had the doctrine of the church. It was I who had changed; I was a shameful sinner now. Across the bay, the windows of Calgary propped up the twinkling lights of town, yellow freckles, reflecting in the still, black sea of the harbour. My mother would be preparing my sisters for bed. Her son was supposed to visiting a friend but, deeply troubled he was at the dock wall, miserable and despairing. I felt that I could hear the chatter and the laughter of my sisters and I envied their innocence. How it contrasted with innocence, now lost.

Confessions tomorrow morning and I was defiled by sin. Confession is a heavenly sacrament, unless you are an eleven-year-old boy, defiled by sin and I stared again over the wall into the inky depths of the dock basin, wondering how much seawater it would take. One month ago this night I had taken a jar of seawater to the back of Calgary but threw it away, sticking my fingers down my throat instead, but it didn't work; there are only so many Wednesday nights that the symptoms of sickness or influenza can be simulated, so I would try again tonight. Anything to avoid school confession of the morning, just the right amount, briny with the added taste of oil slick, carried home to drink quickly, then to throw up noisily and repeatedly within earshot of my parents. 'No school for that boy tomorrow,' I longed to hear my father say.

Taking the jar from my pocket, I moved towards the steps and felt my way down into the dock, compacted sand beneath my feet, I made my way slowly towards the sound of lapping water, only stopping when it seeped over the welts of my shoes. I stepped back a pace. The walls of the dock loomed above me, to frame an orb of charcoal sky. A tiny wave spilled inland, suddenly to soak my feet and I leaped backwards and dropped the jar. What I was doing was a crazy thing. There must be a simpler, more convincing way to make myself sick than this stupid notion and I began to feel my way back across the sand to where I knew the steps to be.

In this pitch black well, I had a sudden premonition, a horror of time and place and a world no longer certain, a presentiment of warning equipped by primal man and refined through ages to be with us still. What was it I had thought I'd seen? I jerked my head upwards to the whisper of light in that black place, streetlight, draping over a small part of the dock wall. I had sensed rather than seen a movement in that splash of light and I froze, fixing my eyes on the spot on the wall, waiting, invisible, not daring to move or make a sound, for I knew that this was what Donoghue and Reardon had warned me of.

Still frozen, my eye fixed on the light, waiting, not daring to move. No sound at all above the muted, swelling signals of the sea. Where were the fishermen of Carraig Eden? I listened hopefully for sound of their voices. That fisherman atop the pier wall was my saviour and only fifty yards away, where was he, where had he gone, where was the reassuring swishing of his line? In this black, captive bowl of a dock, there was only silence, silent screaming in my head.

Was it a shadow or movement in the pool of light? It was movement, a tangible thing, the flapping of a bird with broken wings and there was nothing in my world but fear. My blood unfroze to murmur in terror and there was a sobbing in my breast. It had happened and it was as Donoghue and Reardon had said it would, the climax of a story from Nugget Nolan, unfolded in his shack one rain-swept afternoon and his shuddering words were seeping through my consciousness like warnings from infernal depths. With silent sobs I moved to the blackest region of the dock and pressed my back so hard against the wall, I felt at one with its weeping face. I felt I could not take a breath, for I knew that what was above me now would soon be with me in the dock and I could hear already a shuffling on the steps. No escape except to run to the mouth of the sea and swim clothed across the freezing waters of the bay. I tried to run but my legs refused to move and there was another shuffle on the steps and then there was movement close by me in the sand.

Seconds passed without another sound and I dared to breathe again. Then a minute like an hour; still no sound and the silence began to trickle and transfuse my blood with hope, advancing to my limbs, as stark terror waned. After all, I would not die, this night, in mortal sin. Swallowing hard, I took a step from the rock wall, only to shrink back again. Only yards from me, the insane mutterings of a madman the sound of dread. I was now facing what every child in Greystones feared above all else, Ooara Moara to the adults of the town, mad Rasputin to the kids.

Soon after the turn of the century, an aristocratic Russian military officer, on an assignment to Dublin, met by chance a young Irish girl and they fell deeply in love. She was eighteen years old and tender to the world and her beauty was that of a child, artless and pure. Although the Count, as he was known, spoke little English and the girl no Russian at all, they conveyed their warmth and longing for each other with smiles and glances. Then, days after seeking each other's company, their togetherness grew a little bolder, a brush to the cheek, a touch of a hand or a clasp to the girl's waist as the gallant Russian might lift her from a carriage to the ground. Very quickly, this officer and his guileless beauty became the talk of the town as he, in his uniform, and she, in the simple attire of a native girl, rode and walked unchaperoned through the streets and parks of the capital, oblivious to every-thing except the burgeoning of love. Then, all too soon, the Count had to return to his unit, involved, as it was, with his country's conflict with Japan. Tearfully, they parted at the railway station in Blackrock.

Two years passed with the girl's pitiful, loving letters unan-swered. How she pined for her lost love, reading of the war in growing certainty that he was among the dead, each night vowing, that, should he not return, then she would live her life alone or retire to a convent. Then suddenly, without prior warning, he was standing uniformed and smiling, one spring morning, at her door and as much in love with her as she with him. That day of their reunion, they swore an oath that they would never part again without being man and wife and within days, by special dispen-sation, they were married in a Dublin church.

In the few days he had left of his leave, the Count arranged a honeymoon in the nearby Wicklow Mountains, after which they would return to his family estate in Russia. They were to spend their few idyllic days and nights of marriage in a cottage near Glendalough amid the tranquil splendour of the mountains, an idyll to be blighted by subversive fate.

On their last night in Glendalough, before they were due to return to Dublin and prepare for their new life in Russia, they decided on one last walk into the hills. Earlier that day, there had been a heavy storm but, as night fell upon the mountains, the air was fresh and fragrant and the moon shone brightly in a clear sky. Holding hands, they meandered for a time, deep into the hills, laughing at silly jokes and problems with communication and the disturbing realisation that they were lost. But the Count pointed to the moon and the stars, figuring the way back home, and fancy took the girl to skip off playfully out of sight and call for him to find her. Then suddenly her playful calls had turned to shrieks of terror as she began to sink into a bog. Floundering forward, her husband reached her, entwining his fingers with hers. But he could do nothing as she began to sink slowly deeper and he began to sink himself. Clawing himself to firmer ground, he tore a branch from a tree and flopped back into the mire. Too late, he could not save her, but only watch, as shrieking insanely, she slowly sank into the suffocating peat. The body of the girl was never found.

The Count went mad with grief. He never returned to his unit or his homeland, but from that day roamed the hills and mountains of Wicklow, babbling incoherently and calling for his wife. He called whenever the moon appeared, the call, always the same, a wolf-like howl of Oooooooooaaaaaara Mooooooooaaaaaaaaaara which, to the people of the villages and hamlets, became his name. Some said the unearthly sound he made were the last screams of his wife, while others argued that he was calling her by name, for her name was Maura. And so the Count had wandered now for over forty years, railing madly at the moon, by whose light he had witnessed the unthinkable. Legend and rare sightings had him venture into towns along the coast, still wearing the long, black cloak, the tattered, mud-streaked cloak that he had worn that night as he stumbled into a village managing to relate what had happened to his wife. He never spoke to a living soul again for, it was said, that he could not forgive the moon for taking what he loved so dearly and could not forgive himself for not joining what he loved in death.

This was the story, first told by Donoghue and Reardon, then refined by Nugget Nolan in his rain-whipped shack. Nugget knew the story better than anyone, for who was it but his grandmother, living in Glendalough at the time, who, with others, had tried to comfort the crazed man, collapsed and babbling at their feet. Brother Mulligan confirmed the story, too, and my heart swooned to hear it told. This was no phantom of the mountains but a being, writhing in torment in the velvet blackness of an everlasting night.

Every boy at school had a story to tell about Rasputin, as he was later to be called. The wanderer might only appear in a town once in a year, yet somehow every boy I spoke to had had a narrow escape. Billy Wilde kept a piece of ragged, black cloth in a box, which, he claimed, was a strip of the Count's cloak, torn away as he wrestled from his grasp. Ever since I'd heard of him, I longed to see the man myself, watching for him from vantage points, like the veranda of Calgary and I frightened my sisters with tales of sightings and how I suspected he was stalking them. Often I thought of my reaction should I meet him face to face on the paths of Coolagad or Bray Head for I dearly wanted a story of my own. But never in my vilest nightmares did I envisage a meeting with him in circumstances such as these.

Nugget Nolan ended his story by telling of his own well-founded theory, corroborated by others, as to why the Count visited the town and villages. 'It is for the children,' he asserted grimly. 'He takes them back to the bogs, in a sack, and buries them alive.'

He had seen me, of that I was sure; he had watched me from the wall but I was equally sure that he could not see me now, for I could not see him, but I could hear him breathing. How long before he found me, how long before my father began a search for me? Would my father find me in the morning? Or like the poor Dublin girl, would I be buried alive, never to be found again?

A scraping in the sand and my brain caught fire. A light, high above in the pitch black void of sky, as if some lost, wandering angel had stopped to strike a match. In the shifting patch of sky, clouds were parting, widening, cleaving to a strip of moonlight and I could see a shapeless silhouette, only yards from where I stood.

It came from some infernal depths, starting as a low wail of desolation, the most forsaken sound that I had ever heard, ascending to a shrill, prolonged shriek of total despair. An anguished cry to the moon of 'Ooooooooooooaaaaaaaaara Mooooooooooooo-aaaaaaaaaaara', the cry of a tortured animal, a banished soul.

Screaming insanely, my brain an inferno, I hurtled past the baying form and slobbering curses and prayer bolted up the steps, slipping once, twice, on the mossy surface. As I reached the top, the clouds closed in again and I could sense the madman at my heels.

I never could recall the sprint across the bay or being followed by the maniac, nor did I know how or where I had lost a shoe. Later, I was told, that in my panic, I had knocked Sergeant O'Neill of the Garda off his bicycle, injuring and annoying him. All I knew was the looming white of Calgary and, wide-eyed and babbling, falling in my father's arms. I couldn't say anything about the dock or why I was down there in the black of night but I could remember dogs I thought were rabid chasing me and was astounded to find that I'd lost a shoe. My father calmed me down and took me inside. That night was sleepless and ghastly, sandwiched between the spectre of the Count and the crisis of Confession in the morning.

Chapter Seven

I knew from my avid exploration of the dictionary what adultery was and that adulterers were married persons having a sexual relationship with someone to whom they were not married and, although I didn't really understand what a 'sexual relationship' was, I could comfortably bank on Donoghue to tell me. Now I didn't find adultery special or exciting or anything, really it was no more to me than worshiping false gods or coveting a neighbour's goods. But then, after a talk to the class one day by Brother Mulligan, I was to learn that there was a lot more to adultery than I could have imagined. Who could have guessed that every impure thought, word and deed was also a grievous sin against this commandment? Now the last two I could come to terms with, language could be moderated and deeds, well, they could be controlled by abstinence and self-denial but 'thought sin' was a real worry because my mind during every wakeful hour was a veritable beehive of cogitation which I couldn't seem to do anything about, with some thoughts really sinful, absolutely awful.

Impure thought, I had to admit, was a sin to which I was definitely prone and the more I learned about adultery and its forbidden spinoffs the more compelling it became, on one hand, an irresistible vice to be nurtured, researched and pursued by an eleven-year-old boy and on the other hand, eternal damnation if you did.

How often had we been gravely told of the 100,000 souls which departed from this life each day, called to eternal judgement? And, how diligent had I once been in my daily devotion to the agonising heart of Jesus, for the grace of a happy death, in case, on any given day, I might be called to make this number up? Well, that was before I had started committing adultery day and night with one impure thought damning me for eternity.

Eternity, a word that defied imagination and filled me with an utter dread, for to die without the due and daily devotion, which hitherto had been my custom, meant an unimaginable eternity of pain and torment. Brother Mulligan, in his talk, had asked us to imagine burning at the stake. 'Imagine,' he told us, 'the blood boiling in your veins, the pain and stench of burning flesh, your own. Imagine having to endure that torment for a mere two seconds.' Here, he had paused, leaving us in awful contemplation, before continuing. 'Then think of that suffering lasting one full minute, one hour, all day long,' he paused again, conscious of the anguish in our eyes. 'Now boys, I want you to contemplate eternity, constant, intolerable suffering, forever, without a moment's relief. We often use the word 'forever' and forever to us, is simply our lifetime here on earth, but forever is something I want you to think about. Try to imagine how long it would take for our own sun to swell in size, its heat so great that our oceans would begin to boil, our very earth begin to melt and then the sun itself to die to become nothing more than a cold rock in space. Yes, watch our sun die. And then with our flesh roasting and our blood boiling watch our galaxy suffer the same, then other galaxies until our universe is nothing but a black void without a single twinkling star. And throughout this unimaginable time you are in intolerable agony, your blood is boiling, your flesh is burning and all this time you have spent screeching for forgiveness knowing how things could have been so different if only you had listened to the word of God and knowing that only one split second of eternity has passed, and the rest is yet to come. Oh boys imagine that.'

I tried to imagine; I tossed and turned in bed at night in torment, taking my adulterous soul to the nightmare edge of this abyss, to ponder in desolation the misdeeds that soiled its purity; those mortal sins indelible and indefensible and the endless pain awaiting me in this other, never ending world. And from this abyss, I could hear the wailing and the screeching of all the lost souls who had not listened, who had been given countless chances of salvation, yet had not taken them. I belonged with those who had slaughtered children in the concentration camps of the news-reels and our screaming was the same.

On nights before the morning of Confession, I would go out on the veranda, wearing only a thin shirt, wide open to expose my bare chest to the scalpel of the wind or creep from the house, across the stones to the sea, there to scoop hands full of freezing water about my shoulders and back. At the rear of Calgary there was a water trough, in which I would immerse my head and open my mouth to the stagnant, infested water and only last night, with stupid thoughts of drinking sea water, risk myself being murdered in the dock.

Where were my weaknesses, tonsillitis and bronchitis, when I needed them? Where was the phlegm, so prevalent at other times, suppurating my lungs and grating at my throat and chest? I wanted the grim face of my father as he felt my pulse and gave his diagnosis to my mother, where was he to legitimise my sickness and avoidance of confession? How often would I lift my head from the water trough or from the veranda of Calgary and look up at the stars, an ocean of stars, the sky, so full of stars it looked like a child's fantastic painting and, closing my eyes, would see each star as the sparkling, immortal soul of one who had listened, taken the chances offered and lived a good and pure life. If only I could drift my spirit up among those stars away from cold troughs and freezing winds and the awful narcotic pleasure of adultery.

But from this dilemma there was a way out, Confession. Those who go to Holy Communion on a consecutive first nine Fridays of the month are promised not to die in mortal sin without hav-ing received the 'last sacraments', for the 'Great Promise' is the divine heart of Jesus becoming a secure refuge at the last moment.

But of course, if you happen to be in a state of mortal sin before taking of Holy Communion, you have to go to Confession first and Irish Christian Brothers insisted on giving everyone that opportunity.

Now Holy Communion is a breeze, but I would do anything to avoid confession. Anything to avoid confessing shameful sins to another, anything except prevarication, once inside the confessional and kneeling down before a priest a boy must tell the truth.

It was Thursday morning and although the terror of the night before was still with me, a new terror had arisen to immerse my reason, not just confession, but the prospect of Father Duff.

By early morning as I searched unsuccessfully for my shoe, the overcast of the night before had dissipated and now, mid-morning, only a few scattered clouds remained, thin dark clouds above the mountains, tracing east to west across the winter sky. Outside the school, in the shade, the ground was still crisp with frost, the distant sea, bright and calm and on the ridges of the houses black-headed gulls ruffled their feathers and complained to one another.

Classes segregated, we marched in pairs, the older boys, the vanguard, from which example was demanded. My class was second from the rear. The brothers, each responsible for the order of a class, strode alongside us on the road, heads held high, shoulders back and arms swinging. Boys walking on the sides of their feet, alternatively bow-legged and knock-kneed were, by and large, the same boys I had observed on my first confessional walk to St Killian's. Then, I had watched these boys marching in this distorted manner, thinking they must be cripples and when I got home that evening, I remarked on the inordinate number of crippled boys at St Luke's and mimicked the way they walked. They were either crippled or had had their toes removed at Circumcision. My parents doubted me, doubted that the boys were cripples and, although raising their eyebrows, made no mention of toes or Circumcision.

It was the following month that I came to know the answer.

Some boys simply had no soles to their shoes and were trying to keep their bare feet from the freezing ground. What a shock it was to see their upturned shoes as they knelt and genuflected, with shards of cardboard hanging through the gaping holes. The skin of Christy Plunkett's feet was particularly raw and I couldn't wait to get home that day and explain the 'mystery' to my parents.

As we reached the top of Jeeney Hill, Paddy Rooney, the boy, marching beside me, jerked a thumb at a marking on the road and whispered, "This is where it happened to my mott."

I turned my head away as I had heard this story before. We were arranged in sizes for the march and, as Rooney and I were the same height and stature, we were invariably paired together. I didn't like Rooney, for as well as boring me with his oft-told tales, he called me wicked names and along with Cronin and others, picked on me. 'The truck came hurtlin' down the road from Blacklion an' hit her as she was crossin' the road with her mammy, she didn't have a chance.' He stopped talking and, glancing behind him at Brother Mulligan, considered it safe to continue. 'It went all the way down the hill with her draggin' underneath, imagine, all the way from here to The Ormonde. Imagine, why dontcha, a thrail o' blood from here to The Ormonde?' He glanced again at Brother Mulligan. 'I was at the funeral an' all the girls from St Jude's was cryin', of course her mammy an' her daddy was cryin,' too, her mammy in a right state, so she was, like she was with her when she was after gettin' hit. She was my mott, a deadly girl she was.' Brother Mulligan was beside us, glaring balefully at Rooney.

I wasn't interested in what Rooney had to say and hated his use of the word 'deadly', to Rooney everything was deadly. I was feeling anxious at the thought of confession and sick at the thought that it might be heard by Father Duff, but if I hadn't been feeling so wretched and if Brother Mulligan hadn't been so close, I could have shut Rooney up with my encounter in the dock or of being in an air raid-shelter in Cravenvale with German bombs dropping down on me. Rooney would have to come up with something better than a dead and deadly mott to beat either of those two stories. Although I wasn't interested, I did contemplate blood all the way to The Ormonde cinema, wondering whose job it was to clean it up, it couldn't just be left for the rain, it might be weeks before it rained. The next time he told that story, I would ask him who cleaned the blood up. But thinking about it, I wouldn't. Rooney would tell Cronin and others and they would run around the schoolyard calling to each other in a cadence of rounded vowels, 'I say old boy, I say, we want to know who cleaned the blood up, the blood up, the jolly bleeding blood up.'

From the dim past, a crowded air-raid shelter and a shadowy figure holding a lantern to my face, vivid, the yellow glow of lantern light. There were no bombs falling on that night but Rooney was not to know and I didn't really care who cleaned the blood up and I could never tell Rooney or anybody else about Rasputin, for fear of being asked what the hell I was doing at night, alone in the dock.

Another first Thursday of the month, another compulsory march to St Killian's, the brothers had done their bit to ensure the opportunity of eternal life, now it was up to the boy himself to attend Mass and Communion. But how awful a prospect, exciting and stimulating as they might be in private, grubby and execrable sins against the commandment 'Thou Shalt Not Commit Adultery' are shameful and embarrassing when admitted to another human being, especially to an old, grumpy, sinless one, like Gruff Duff.

I was marching up that hill, looking for forgiveness, yet not deserving that majestic sacrament of forgiveness, which all too readily I would throw in the face of God by holding my head in a water trough to avoid, and the sins themselves, awful and shameful as they were, too glib, too well-rehearsed to be forgiven in the light of my repudiation of the infinite mercy of God towards my wretched soul. Neither was I marching up that hill for justice, for if justice was to be done, then surely a truck must career into me on Jeeney Hill and carry me to The Ormonde, to die like Rooney's mott. I was marching up that hill because I didn't have a choice.

On reaching the stone bulwark of the church, overlooking the village of Blacklion and the town of Greystones, we were made to wait in line by the great doors while the brothers took up positions wherefrom they could usher us to our places. With a jerk of his pudgy, nicotine-stained thumb, Brother McBride gave the order and we began to file inside.

The church was dim and cold and smelled faintly of extinguished candles. My eyes were immediately drawn to the name plates above the two confessionals and I was overwhelmingly thankful to see that Brother Mulligan had taken sentinel beside the name McCartney. Thank God, I wasn't to kneel before the intimidating Father Duff. It was the boys of the fourth and fifth forms who would have to listen to Gruff Duff grunting in annoyance and disgust and relentlessly probing suspected denials and prevarications.

I was kneeling now with my class, my face in cupped hands, my elbows resting on the rail of the bench before me and examining my conscience as we had been trained to do. Around me, the gentle stirring of contrite boys and from the back of the church, the sound of old ladies, wheezing and coughing and clinking rosaries. Had my mother given her leave, it was likely Grandma Plunkett could be one of these. The two priests came from the sacristy and, without a glance at the waiting penitents, entered through the heavy red drapes of the confessionals.

I got up from my knees and sat back in the bench for soon it would be my turn and discounting nine of the Ten Commandments and six of the seven deadly sins, which were of no account, I began rehearsing in my mind what I would say about the only one that was.

Father McCartney dealt with penitents quickly and fairly and did not keep boys in the box an inordinately long time, which might, to those still waiting, be indicative of grievous sin. Boys rotated quickly, each genuflecting, making the sign of the cross towards the tabernacle then slipping to the back of the church to do their penance. A murmur of absolution the sound of a wooden panel sliding in wooden runners and it was my turn.

My penance of five Our Fathers and five Hail Marys was over and I was now emerging from an underground tomb into the liberation of a glorious sunlit day. Outside the church, seabirds were soaring from rooftops into the blue, frosty sky and my heart was soaring with them, its wings, words of absolution. My spirit soared with resolution to sin no more with supplication to the Virgin Mother, martyr of love and sorrow, star of the ocean, portal of the sky, the blessed Mother of Our Lord, to whom I had expressed a deep and sincere repentance. My soul, now pure again, was a spiritual vessel and I had been welcomed once again into the arms of grace, the words of Christ to his apostles, singing in my head like a choir of angels, 'Whose sins you shall forgive they are forgiven them and whose sins you shall retain they are retained.' No sins of mine shall be retained for I had confessed everything that I was guilty of and I was welcomed once again into the arms of grace and every substance of the earth and every murmur in the air was now imbued with grace.

We did not have to form lines or march back to school in pairs. That uphill, sin-laden journey was over and each boy was free to make his own way back to school. Some went in chattering groups, some in pairs and some alone. Alone, I flew in liberation like a trapped butterfly suddenly released from turgid captivity. To the east, the sea, a seat of wisdom, the sky above, the cause of joy, every tree and hedgerow adorned with mystical roses, every building on the way, a tower of ivory the school itself, a house of gold and as I alighted from my heady flight and entered through the gateway to the school, I said to myself; 'Gate of Heaven, morning star.'

Chapter Eight

*T*he April day was closing but still bold and fair in the grounds of the brick factory. Birds settled in the shawl of evening with a songbird celebrating the waning day and promise of a new one, yet still, I could not rid myself of melancholy. Everyone knew that the factory had failed and was closed for good, yet my father hung on to it in the pale hope that things would turn around. Perhaps local builders and tradesmen would pay him what they owed instead of putting an arm around his shoulder, empty promises in his head and taking him for a laugh and a few jars at Dan's. At the west side of the grounds, a small row of poplars rose stately from a thicket hedge of laurel and holly and pointed to a mackerel sky, its horizon fringed with red and pools of gold. Tomorrow would be warm and calm and I might take my first dip of the year in the sea.

The building had been the old St Luke's schoolhouse but as I unlocked the small side door and entered I could not imagine Brother McBride and the other brothers teaching there. Littered with debris and with some of the internal walls removed, it no longer resembled a school building. No echo now of the tumult of Irish education, no cultural and historical enlightenment, no overriding fear of God. All around were piles of sand and gravel, home to colonies of weed and grasses and in one corner a grotesque, heavily-crusted heap of pug lime slowly stiffened. Lime and cement dust lay thick and undisturbed on every surface and cobwebs hung like curtains from spars and broken windows. I had left the side door open, inducing draughts which scattered wrapping paper, leaves and pages of old newspapers and above, the empty roof void echoed to its skittering and to my own footfalls on the quarry tile floor.

The Austin truck, the cement mixers and brick rams had been sold and only unwanted batching boxes, broken tools and rubbish remained. A huge wooden-sided sieve lay propped against a wall, its torn wire mesh home to the bulky nest of a blackbird. The mother bird, sitting, swelled her speckled breast and eyed me warily. Not wanting to disturb her, I left the building, closing and locking the door softly behind me.

Of a workforce of seven, only Bob remained. Now, my father, with Bob as his assistant, through necessity, and in an irredeemably unworthy Ford Prefect, carried out small building works in the town and the surrounding villages. 'A temporary measure,' my father assured everyone, as he waited for the granting of a bank loan. He and my mother talked a great deal about this bank loan and how it would either resurrect the factory or finance the new ventures he was giving thought to. I sensed that the granting of this loan meant everything to him, the future of the family depended on it and I knew, through his conversations with my mother that he had made applications to a number of different banks simultaneously, working on the premise that at least one of them would find his prospects good.

Everything had happened to the family so quickly and all was strange to me. Only months had passed since we were living in a big house in Cravenvale and I was being taken to school each morning in a Mark V Jaguar Saloon. Only months since I was being given money each day to spend on damaged fruit to feed and foster an ever-growing horde of fair weather friends, mostly sons of soldiers returned from the war and domiciled in a nearby barracks. Then, all of a sudden, the Jaguar was no longer in the drive, a 'For Sale' sign there instead and seemingly overnight, I was standing in the grounds of a failed brick-making factory in Eire.

Was all this due to creditors, I wondered? No, my father's problems had been due to 'debtors'.

'Will debtors follow us to Ireland?' I asked him worriedly.

'Debtors? Very unlikely son,' he answered wryly.

Years later as I looked back, I reckoned that my father failed because, being an honest man, he told a lie. Dishonest men can lie, lies are the building blocks of their successful lives; their downfall comes with truth. My father's downfall was image, for an honest man, an only lie, but the biggest lie of all. It is in our dread we cause to happen that which we fear most. The first time failure came knocking at his door he became a Rotarian and when it wouldn't go away, a councillor; surely failure would shy away from a Cravenvale County Borough councillor. He even bought a horse, joined the local hunt and rode to hounds and fobbing off his intrepid stalker, he bought land and plant and increased his workforce, bought a bigger house, a newer Jaguar and on a visit to Ascot races won over two hundred pounds. At Cheltenham, a few months later, he won even more. And still the stranger at his door did not know it was beaten. 'Things are going wrong,' my father finally cried and in self-fulfilling prophecy they did.

Later, when talking of his success and failures, he conceded that success had come to him before he was old or wise enough to deal with it, but pragmatically he was able to start again from scratch in Ireland. He had been 'somebody' and was equally at ease being 'nobody'; but he knew, the one thing he could never be, was 'anybody'.

But failure wasn't finished with him yet. It had left him with just enough spirit and money to start again, before it demonstrated a hitherto unknown faculty; it could travel overseas. Almost as the first load of bricks were manufactured and dispatched, he saw the same thing coming and once again used image to ward it off, increased his workforce to seven and, for appearances' sake, employed a maid.

Now new words had entered my vocabulary, words like unprofitable, overdrawn, default, insolvency and business; business, the one word I mistrusted most of all. I didn't understand what these words meant, but by the way they tightened the muscles in my father's face whenever they were uttered, I knew that they were the precursors of disappointment. Everything that came through the letterbox was bad news, too, and anxiety and weariness began to crease his brow and etch his eyes with worry. As he picked up the post, his face was a barometer of the family's situation, dire, because the only thing that didn't come with the post was a bank loan.

Now it seemed that failure would finish him altogether. Before the year was out, the factory would be sold for a pittance to clear debt, Grandma Plunkett would be gone, we would have to leave Calgary, and still he would be waiting for the loan. But to his everlasting credit, he wasn't finished altogether; failure, however determined, could not compel him to remove his daughters from private school. Fingers would bleed, no, fingers would be bloody stumps before Sam, Tam and Dodo were enrolled at national school. No image here, only stark desperation. State school was tantamount to insurmountable disgrace, why; state school would mean the family having to move pews at The Church of the Holy Rosary. Even rampant failure has its limitations.

Closing the double gates to the factory compound, I set off walking wearily. The sun had dipped behind the mountains and the sky was claret with promise as shifty dusk began to trespass into town. In Church Road, a noiseless shower came from nowhere to damp and black the ground. I looked up; behind the spire of the Protestant church a cloud was gathering her dark skirts and scuttling westward, towards Delgany intending to wet the village there.

On reaching the North Beach, the spring tide was far out, so far out, that the wrecked breakwater was accessible. After filling my pockets with skimming stones, I climbed out on to the slippery concrete slabs and carefully made my way out to sea. On the last and largest of the slabs, I stood, skimming stones towards the pier's edge, watching, with some satisfaction, the sequence of small, foaming explosions. When the stones were gone, I sat on a dry patch and looked about me. Darkness was falling swiftly, too late now to feed the roosting chickens at the back of Calgary and skimming stones had not lifted my melancholy. In the water, at my feet, was seaweed, crinkled fronds of oarweed, swirling, drifting. Just beneath the surface, a forest of feelers, mingling with giant thongweed and I imagined terrible things lurking there, waiting to pull me under and devour me. I longed for my first swim in the Irish Sea, maybe it would be tomorrow but I would keep well away from seaweed.

To the north, the finger of rock I called the stack, my stack and I thought of the secret path I had made to reach it. It was caught in a noose of dying sunlight, a white exclamation mark against the dark backdrop of Bray Head. Brother Mulligan had told me, 'You can't have a stack halfway up a mountainside; a rock stack is created by the erosion of the sea.'

'But it looks like a stack,' I told him dryly.

I had not returned to the cave, my den beneath the stack, since my terror in the dock as I feared to be alone, but I must face my fear and return soon for I was happy there on that mountain side. On the coastline beneath were ruined cottages, with little left but foundations, a few stalwart, stone-built external walls and chimney breasts with fire openings, remarkably intact. How long since people had lived in those cottages? And I always had a vision of an old woman in a shawl rising from her hearth and going to the window, worrying that the sea was so much nearer her door than it was the year before. I had been thinking about these cottages a great deal lately. Thinking about the cottages and worrying about my father and the family's decline. It was almost dark now and I was drifting into hopelessness. I thought about Christy Plunkett and the Irish Crown Jewels and the cottages and the bank loan. Finding those jewels would be the answer to a lot of problems.

I started watching waves but watching waves was lonesome so I started counting clouds.

Chapter Nine

I was waiting in the school yard for Brother Molloy to finish talking with Brother Ryan when Donoghue started advising me again. We were good friends just now and I was learning a lot from him, really adventurous, sexual stuff that some day I would put into practice. 'Got a mott yet?' he began.

'Don't want one,' I lied. I was totally infatuated with a girl called Cora Casey, completely besotted, but I didn't want Donoghue to know, didn't want anyone to know, certainly not Cora.

'Girls are quare creatures,' he declared knowingly, 'an you gotta know how to handle 'em. Is there any St Jude girls you fancy?'

There was a St Jude girl that I would readily die for. 'Naw, some of 'em are ok, I suppose, but nothing worth getting excited about.' The boy was about to tell me something and he was going to have his way. Lately, Donoghue was telling me all sorts of juicy stuff.

'Well ok, but imagine if there was. ok, there's this girl you fancy and you find yerself sittin', next to her in The Ormonde. Might be an accident or you might o' kind o' planned it. Doesn't matter, you're there an' you're after sittin; next to her. What do you do next?'

'Buy her some sweets,' I tried.

'Buy her some sweets,' the boy echoed mockingly. 'Buy her some sweets! Jesus, she'll think who does this friggin' creep think he is, tryin' to buy me sweets? Know what she'll do? She'll move to another seat, leavin' you feelin' like a twat.'

I was about to suggest ice cream, but thought better of it. Ice cream was likely to invite even more contempt than sweets. 'What, then?'

'Ok, listen. Start a fight over the arm rest. Start by shovin' her arm off. Do it quite deliberately. Just shove it off, that arm rest's yours. Know what she'll do? She'll do it right back. So shove her arm off again, then, let her shove yours off. Keep doin' it to each other until you both start laughin'. You will. I promise, you'll both start laughin'. Now, here's the secret, make sure that in the end, it's you what's given way. Make sure that she finishes with the arm rest all on her own. She'll feel good about it, she's won a little battle. Not a word spoken, no sweets or mush like that. She's won a friggin' arm rest, you've won a mott.'

The psychology was sound. I could see it working. The trouble was, Cora's arm rest was up in the gallery, while mine was in the front row four-pennies. I couldn't afford the gallery, while Cora wouldn't be seen dead fighting over an arm rest in the front row four-pennies.

'Works every time,' Donoghue added smugly.

Brother Molloy was free. 'I'll give that a try,' I promised as I ran across the yard to get to the brother before anybody else did.

Brother Molloy was a muscular young man who retained a spark of childhood that would never die. He looked more like one of the pupils than a teacher, and was much admired by the boys for his prowess as a sportsman. He was also good-humoured and approachable. 'Some boy in your class, Brother, was telling me about the Irish Crown Jewels, about them being stolen. Is—'

He stopped in his tracks, put his hand to his brow and said in open-mouthed wonder, 'Dear God, boy, don't tell me you're after finding them, where, where?'

I laughed at his antics, as I was expected to. 'No, seriously, Brother, is it true that they were stolen? Is it true that they could be hidden somewhere here in Greystones?' I was beside him as we walked towards the schoolhouse. He paused, then turned and began making his way towards the playing field. I was eager to learn and he sensed it. Brother Molloy always had time for boys who wanted to learn.

'Well, that was the story at the time and I've never heard anything since to the contrary.'

'What is the story, Brother?'

It was lunch break and as we walked slowly around the perimeter of the school playing-field, he gave me a brief history. The jewels were stolen from Dublin Castle in 1907 and rumour had it that the thief, (he believed that there was only one) made his escape south, through Bray and hid them in Greystones or on the way to Greystones. The jewels had been presented to the state, the Irish state, that is, by King William 1V and were to be worn on state occasions 'Should have been called the Irish "State" Jewels,' he added thoughtfully.

'What kind of jewels were they, Brother?'

He mused a while before answering. They consisted of gold collars (he didn't know how many), a jewel box containing diamonds and a Brazilian, eight-pointed diamond star.

'Is that all there was, Brother?'

'All there "is". They're still out there somewhere. Tell you what if you find them I'll give you a fiver for the lot.'

I laughed. 'Nugget Nolan said that they wasn't up to much, worth nothing much at all.'

'Ah well, Nugget would know, wouldn't he? What Nugget doesn't know isn't worth knowing, a fortune, and no mistake, an absolute fortune.' He had other bits of information too, but, not relevant in terms of a search and confessed ruefully to having absolutely no idea where they might be hidden, but allowed that Greystones was as good a place as any.

'But worth a fortune?' I enthused when I had drained him of information and was relishing the prospect of a search. 'Not that I'm thinking of looking for them, Brother, but if I happen to find them, you're in for a share.' I had heard what I had wanted to hear and was happy. When the whistle blew for assembly I thanked him and ran back to the school yard to join my class.

My strategy was simple; come next Saturday, swear my sisters to secrecy and get them to help me in the search. A most encouraging factor was my not having heard further mention of the jewels from Christy or from anybody else. I found it amazing that such a goodly treasure was likely hidden in the town for such a long time without anyone making a concerted effort to find it. I loved the irony, the Irish Crown Jewels discovered by an English boy, and I looked forward to untold wealth and fame.

With motivations of promise, threat and bribery, I had secured in my sisters a readiness for the search which was unexpectedly laced with enthusiasm and the four of us were delighted to find that the Saturday morning had turned out bright and fair. In the kitchen, Tam was preparing a large flask of sweet tea, while Sam helped my mother with a picnic box. The girls had been indoctrinated by my strongly-held conviction that the jewels were hidden in the sea-eroded ruins beneath Bray Head, where we would go, that morning.

'A known fact,' I had told them. 'The thief comes south keeping away from the roads, he passes through Bray, heading for Greystones; the police are waiting for him, so what does he do? He hides them. Where? In those ruined buildings, where else?'

'Of course,' Dodo agreed, as she laced her walking boots.

'It's not a great treasure chest or anything,' I reminded them, 'just jewels wrapped up and stuffed in a cleft in the stonework. When we find them, the family's troubles are over.'

The front door slammed and Grandma Plunkett bowled into the kitchen, her face puckered in consternation and her face effusing from within the confines of a tight black bonnet. Unequivocally, the end of the world was nigh. Without a pause for breath, the international situation was deteriorating rapidly, Korearionians had launched another offensive beyond the 38th parallel and Communists were demonstrating in the streets of Paris which was practically next door and oh, she had brought a nice slab of home-made toffee for the childun.

We were ready and about to leave on our mission, when, following a timorous knock on the kitchen door, her grandson, Christy, entered.

'What do you want?' I demanded ill-humouredly.

'Jus' come to help Gran,' he replied meekly.

Sam snapped shut the picnic box and turned her back on the boy as he smiled at her. His attempts to ingratiate himself and his slavish desire to be included in our daily routines irritated me. He was undoubtedly in love with Sam and the way he hung on her every word I found pathetic, but, when necessary, a wonderful tool to goad her with. Not this morning though, no calling her 'Mrs Plunkett' this morning, no making wedding plans today. In preparing for today's event it was important to keep Sam in a compliant frame of mind, so no word on Christy's overtures. She was so sensitive to his unwanted attentions and my ridicule, that one word out of place and the venture would be finished before it got started.

Grandma Plunkett began dusting ledges but, to my disgust, Christy made no attempt to assist her, which was unusual. Instead, he hung about us, watching our every move and, I suspected, waiting to be asked to join us. As we made towards the door, he could not contain himself any longer. 'Where as yous goin'?' he blurted.

'Out,' I told him curtly.

'They are going up the north beach to have a picnic and look for crabs,' my mother, who was not party to our real intentions, answered kindly. I recognised invitation in her voice and did not like it.

'Can I go with them?' he asked her.

'NO,' I cut in quickly, before she could reply.

Sam looked at Christy for the first time. 'A family outing,' she explained reasonably.

'He could be a help,' Dodo suggested innocently, 'he might…'

My glare silenced her.

'But he could be a help,' Tam agreed.

I glared tacitly, this second glare, more meaningful, more silencing, than the first, it told of secrets and pledges made. I had also tried indoctrinating the younger girls into dislike of Christy, but had been unsuccessful. The young girls had no reason to dislike him and had not yet reached the age to relish or reject the cruelty that comes with petty power. The boy could not accompany us under any circumstances, and Sam, mortified by the boy's attention and the future prospect of my inflaming mockery, could be relied upon, to side with me. 'Help, help with what? Who needs help to walk up a beach? Who needs help to look for crabs? Who needs help to eat a picnic?' I demanded my irritation obvious to all.

Christy's eyes clouded with disappointment, 'What do yous need a crowbar for?' he asked, his mouth open, his lower lip loose and stupid, his tongue actually resting on his bottom set of teeth.

'Crowbar,' I echoed, scarcely believing that I held it in my hand. 'For the crabs, of course,' I answered quickly, looking long at the slim black implement 'To lever rocks up.'

'So yous are not goin' lookin' for the Irish crown jewels then?' he asked his eyes again focusing on the crowbar.

My jaw dropped. Physically, I felt it drop. I looked incredulously at my three sisters, but their jaws had also dropped and they were looking at each other, in turn, with mute, wide-eyed disbelief. There had been a leak. In spite of my insistence on absolute secrecy, there had somehow, been a leak. 'WHAT?' I gasped, inwardly seething at this breakdown in security and at Christy Plunkett's silly little face, disappointed but still thrusting hopefully above the table top.

'I jus' thought if yous was goin...'

I interrupted hurriedly. 'What made you think of a stupid thing like that? Crown jewels, they're not 'crown' jewels anyway. I thought when you told me, how can they be 'crown' jewels when the Irish haven't got a king? Only 'great' countries have kings. It was the Irish STATE Jewels what got stolen, bits of rubbish, not worth a bean. And no one knows what you're talking about. The tide's out and we are going looking for crabs and no, you can't come with us. Help your gran, that's what you're here for. Give him a mop and bucket someone."

'He could come,' Tam suggested innocently. 'Why can't he come?'

'Because he can't.' I winked at her knowingly.

'He'd be a help, he's not frightened of spiders,' Dodo reminded me.

I winked again. 'Well, I'm not frightened of spiders.'

'I was just thinking about those holes in the stones...' Dodo began before my withering look silenced her. Winks were not working with my youngest sisters and if withering looks failed, they would have to be cuffed about their ears. The idea of Christy Plunkett having a share in the jewels or the subsequent glory was inconceivable.

'Take him with you,' my mother ordered, softly but firmly.

'But... '

'No buts. Don't be petty, let him come with you.'

'Mum, you don't understand,' I protested. Then I appealed to Sam. 'He can't come, can he, Sam?' I knew my eldest sister didn't want the boy with us but she didn't want to clash with her mother either. Sam gestured helplessly.

'There's only enough picnic for four,' I reasoned, 'and the flask is only big enough for four.'

'Five, I think,' my mother corrected. A shadow on her face hardened and settled in two lines between her eyebrows as she handed Christy a paper cup.

Responding angrily to her unreasonable demand, I took the paper cup from Christy's hand and, placing it before me on the table, crushed it with my fist. 'Don't bother, I'll do without.'

My mother smiled at Grandma Plunkett. 'Charitable children are such a blessing.'

'Come on, we're off,' I called truculently to my sisters as I made for the door, trying to pretend that the boy's company was of little consequence but inwardly infuriated at my mother's interference. Things were going badly wrong already and we hadn't even reached the front gate. Letting the younger children out before me, I slammed the door harder than was needed.

Outside on the road, leaving Christy shuffling uncomfortably behind, I muttered to Sam, 'Ignore him completely. Don't speak to him, don't even look at him.'

'But Mum said… '

'Mum knows now what we're really doing. Ignore him completely and he'll get fed up and turn back.

'But… '

'Completely,' but my intentions were already being thwarted by Tam and Dodo before we had reached full stride. They had fallen back to question Christy about his digging for lug worms.

'Ooo, in the mud!' I heard Dodo squeal. 'Oooo, thick mud.'

'Well, kinda muddy sand, when the tide's out,' Christy responded enthusiastically.

Then, as we left Calgary behind us, he was telling how lug worms left little whirls on the surface sand and how you could only catch them if you dug down quick and deep beside the whirl. Then, to oooohs and aaaahs from the girls, he was telling how the worms still had enough life left in them to wiggle, even when impaled on hooks. "Fish love lug worms, especially cod an' pollock,' he added sagely.

Gritting my teeth, I increased pace, wracking my brain, thinking how we might get rid of him without incurring my mother's wrath, but found an answer impossible with my brainless younger sisters hanging on his every word. Now, the imbecile, emboldened by the attention he was getting, was loping backwards, hopping from one leg to another, enacting the difficulty he experienced when trying to retrieve his shoes from thick mud. 'Come up owadat,' he kept shouting at each foot in turn, 'Come up owadat,' a banality, which for reasons that escaped me, the girls found absolutely hilarious.

'I'm going to hit him with this crowbar in a minute,' I confided in Sam, as aloof and disdainfully we lengthened our distance between him.

On reaching Nugget Nolan's shack, I couldn't stand the boy's antics any longer.' Nugget wants you, Christy' I shouted, Nugget's form just visible through the dirt-streaked window.

Reaching us, the boy cast an eye to the window, unhappy at being interrupted. 'Nugget wants me?" he questioned painfully. Tam and Dodo stopped laughing and followed Christy's eyes distastefully towards the shack.

'Wants you to visit him,' I urged.

'What for?'

'How do I know? Think he wants you to dig for lug worms.'

'Dig for lug worms. Where?' Christy asked uncomprehendingly.

'You could try his vest,' Sam suggested kindly.

Bray Head loomed, the cliffs glimmering white in the sunlight, seabirds, in their thousands, hovering and sailing on the thermals. Not far to the ruins and I tightened my grip on the crowbar. But first there had to be a way of getting rid of Christy. The only way now was to pick a row with him and send him packing. Then, Nugget, even more filthily clad than usual, came rolling out of his doorway, gimping, as if aboard a ship in a tossing sea. I hailed him courteously.

'Yous lot goin ' lookin' for the Irish crown jewels, then?' he called, although I thought my ears might be deceiving me.

'Half of County Wicklow knows,' Sam remarked laconically as she dropped the flask.

When something is dropped, even something fragile, there is always hope that little or no damage has been done. But this is not the case with flasks; universally dropped flasks break with sickening certainty, especially when they are full of tea. This flask was no exception. We viewed in disbelief a steaming pool forming beneath the stricken vessel.

'I'm awful thirsty,' Dodo lamented as she gazed raptly at the expanding pool.

I was still trying to come to terms with Nugget Nolan's thunderbolt and now this. Sam picked up the flask and shook it, tea streaming from its base and glass rattling inside. I think it might be damaged,' she observed thoughtfully.

Sinking my teeth into my bottom lip, I looked to the cobbler for an explanation, but he was horn-piping back inside his shack. My instinct was to immediately berate the stupid girl but Sam was not one to manifest either guilt or contrition so I kept my teeth embedded in my bottom lip. If we couldn't get rid of Christy, then the mission would have to be abandoned, but it was still important to keep my sisters in a positive and acquiescent frame of mind. The mission would be restarted at a later date.

'It could happen to anyone, Sam,' I managed, without having to release my bottom lip.

'I'm awful thirsty, too,' Tam confided in her younger sister.

'The picnic,' Dodo remembered plaintively, taking the knapsack from her shoulder. 'What about the picnic?'

'Picnic,' I snorted. 'We've only just left home and we're in the middle of a bloody tip.' Pulling Sam to one side, I whispered fiercely in her ear, 'What's with Nugget Nolan? How comes he knows what we're up to? Who's been opening their great big gaping gob?'

The girl shook her head vigorously. 'No one has said a word, I swear it. Christy knew, Nugget knew, half of Wicklow knows.'

'Well someone must have told them. We might as well have set off this morning with a bloody great placard, "Join in the Treasure hunt".' Christy, mouth drooping, was stirring the tea pool with his finger, his tongue again resting on his bottom teeth. Dodo was at Sam's side pulling at her dress.

'I'm awful thirsty, Sam.'

Tam, voice lowered, said, 'Let's go home. I mean, we haven't found them yet.'

'We haven't found "what" yet?' I hissed angrily.

Tam winked. 'You know...the things.'

My temper was still under control, but only just. 'Listen, stupid,' I snarled quietly, 'those "things" have been missing for forty years. Did you expect to find them in the first five minutes? Did you expect to walk past Nolan's shop and say, "Oooo, look, there they are on that windowsill." We're looking for something that hasn't been seen for forty years, over forty years and worth a bloody fortune, we're not looking for a snotty handkerchief we're not looking for an old sock. Anyway it's abandoned, it's finished for today. It's over and we're going home.'

'Because of Christy?' Tam asked uncertainly.

'Because of Christy, because we can't get rid of him,' I answered fiercely, jerking my thumb in his direction as he squatted by the tea pool, making faces in the ooze.

'My throat's awful dry,' Dodo croaked.

'So is mine,' moaned Tam. 'I said to bring some lemonade as well. Even a bottle of water,' she added bleakly.

'We will in future,' Sam pledged, nursing the flask as if she harboured hopes for its revival.

'Well, I'm going to have to get a drink from somewhere or I'll just die,' Dodo bleated. 'I've never been so thirsty in my life.'

'Nugget's shop,' I suggested maliciously. 'Ask him if you can borrow his cup.'

'And poison me?' she spluttered indignantly.

'Well, shut up then, the pair of you. Shut up, we're going home.' But they would not shut up and my temper was reaching boiling point. Still carrying the crowbar, I was fearful I would hit someone with it. With the breaking of the flask the younger girls had been afflicted by a thirst of biblical proportions. A thirst never equalled in the annals of human deprivation, not by lost souls in arid deserts or baking wretches adrift in torrid seas. No tongues had ever been more swollen, lips more parched or bodies more ravaged by dehydration than those of my little sisters that Saturday morning, as their lives ebbed away beside a pool of tea, which Christy Plunkett, mouth ever open, mindlessly prodded with a stick. And I knew I couldn't stand it any longer.

'For Christ's sake, shut up, the pair of you. And Plunkett get away from that tea before I mop it up with your face. I'm warning you, get away from it.'

'It's just that we need a drink,' wailed Tam.

It was then, I lost it. 'There's NOTHING to drink,' I yelled in her face, so close our noses touched. 'Do you understand that? NOTHING. There's nothing to drink cos Mrs Plunkett here dropped the bloody flask.'

Immediately, I regretted what I'd said, but it was too late, Sam's face seized and she smashed the flask on a rock, then started stalking homeward, the quest for the jewels over before it had begun. I called after her in my most conciliatory tone, 'Sammy, I'm sorry,' but the call went unheeded.

The younger girls appeared at either side of me, a pincer of reproach. 'What did you want to upset Sam for?' Tam demanded. 'Me and Dodo, we're with her.' A seagull landed on the roof of Nolan's shack and viewed the acrimony quizzically, then, sensing no threat, screeched a message to its fellows, before swooping over our heads to join them at the sea's edge.

Breaking into trot, I reached Sam before the others and, negotiating her bristling, ribboned braids, I placed a delicate but firm hand on her shoulder and tried to slow her down. Twisting her shoulder quickly, my hand fell away. Dropping the crowbar to release both hands, I stopped her and swung her around to face me. 'Sam, I'm really sorry. Nothing has worked out right today and I lost my temper. First of all, Mammy interfering, bloody Plunkett tagging on, everybody knowing what we were up to, honestly Sam I'm really pissed me off. Then the flask and those two wittering on about being thirsty, I just lost my temper.'

Her face rigid, she levelled her eyes. 'Yeah, and you just lost any chance of us helping you.'

'Oh, don't be like that. Think how happy we would all be if we found them. They're there, Sam, I know it. I never felt anything so strong. Those jewels are hidden in them ruins and it's up to us to find them. What do you say?'

Her face melted just a little and I was hopeful. 'I have got something to say, yes. Christy,' she called loudly.

The boy scampered to her side.

'I've something to say, Christy. You were right we were going looking for the Irish crown jewels. My brother is convinced that they're hidden in those ruins. If I were you, I'd get your brothers and go and look for them.'

Speechless with anger, I watched Tam and Dodo overtake us and run ahead.

Sam wasn't finished. 'Oh and another thing, Christy, if you and your brothers want some help in looking for them, me and my sisters will help you, promise.'

'You treacherous bitch,' I spluttered as Sam and Christy, close enough to be a courting couple, began walking briskly following the girls. Sulking, I sidestepped down the beach and began skimming stones. 'Mrs Plunkett' had stung her badly, but already she had more than got her own back, she had exacted due revenge, but, knowing Sam there would be more to come. There was. From the corner of my eye I saw heads together. Sam never talked to Christy unless she had to; now suddenly, they were veritable lovebirds, their cheeks touching and Sam whispering conspiratorially. Now she showed him something rummaged from the pocket of her dress. My other two sisters were well ahead of them, turning their heads now and again to make sure they were still in touch.

Wiping grit from my hands, I returned to the path but kept my distance. I could hardly contain my rage but knew that anything said or done now would only exacerbate matters. I could nurse rage for ages and I promised myself that I would. It had been a thoroughly miserable failure of a morning which had started by promising so much. Lengthening my stride, I closed the gap.

What was it my sister, smiling secretly, was showing to Christy Plunkett? The boy was smiling too and scratching his head at whatever she was showing in her hand. He turned and looked at me, then turned back and scratched his head again, an abstract motion of his fingers, reflecting a mind absorbed with something yet untold. Intrigued, I moved closer still. Then Sam jerked her head in my direction and, momentarily, our eyes met and there was a glint in her eye I had seen many times before, but this time

I didn't understand what was behind it. Then she was back whispering again, leaving me wondering uneasily at the look she had given me, almost one of triumph.

Walking faster, I was now close enough to see that she was directing the boy's attention to words written on a card and they were both laughing loudly. And now I knew what they were laughing at. Bolting forward, I parted them roughly, Christy falling to his knees. Holding the card behind her back, she dodged behind the boy, her eyes flaring with defiance.

'Give it back to me. I'm warning you, give it back to me,' I hissed.

Braids erect, red ribbons in them, flaying, eyes sparking like hot coals she skipped to one side and avoided my sudden lunge. 'Tell your brothers, Christy, don't forget. Tell everyone at school,' she ordered the boy frantically as he regained his feet, then, I had her in my grasp and she fell and I fell on top of her.

'Give it back, give it back, you thief.'

Tam and Dodo returned and, taking each side of our writhing bodies, implored us to stop. I had reached under Sam's body, grabbing the hand that held the card, a hand like iron, fingers unyielding. Her breath rasping, she whimpered with stress, tears of temper welling in her eyes. I grunted in triumph as her fingers yielded enough for me to get a purchase on the card.

'You must have planned this, you must have done,' I breathed hotly in her ear.

She stopped struggling a moment and said, 'Yes I planned it. I picked it up the minute I knew Christy was coming with us because I knew you'd have a go at me, you just can't help it.' She was struggling and with her free hand, grabbed my hair and hung on, only releasing it when I turned her over on her front and twisted her arm behind her back. Still she wasn't finished, her lithe body wriggling beneath me like a snake. Tam and Dodo, with futile attempts to pull us apart, exhorted us to stop and, through a film of sweat, I could see Christy's little head bobbing about like a cork in a stream. Wresting the card from her fingers, I folded it and managed to get it in my back pocket while still holding her down.

'Tell your brothers…' she managed before I smothered her lips with my hand. She had lost a ribbon and I could see her dress was dirty and there would be trouble when we got home, but to steal that card from my bedroom was indefensible.

'Please let Sam up,' Tam implored as I released my hand from her mouth and made to stand up. Then a pair of arms flailed around my neck. They were thin and impotent and for a second I thought that one of my little sisters had taken leave of her senses. Snorting at the indignity, I was astonished to find that it was Christy swinging from my neck. The boy was trying to pull me from my sister. I got to my feet, humoured that he was still hanging there, then, with little more than a shrug, I sent him sprawling to the ground. He was up again immediately and, with a face puckered with rage, was coming at me, arms flailing. I sneered at his inept attempts to fight with me; this could never be a contest and I held him off with just one hand.

Sam, chin quivering, was now standing, examining her dress and being comforted by her sisters. Pushing the boy aside, I faced her. 'And you needn't be telling your mammy it was me, it was just as much… '

The blow that landed on the side of my jaw jolted me and stung badly and I blinked to see Christy coming at me once again. I punched him hard, once. I must have hit him on the forehead because my knuckles hurt. The boy's eyes blanked, his knees buckled and he fell to the ground and lay still. Time I went back for my crowbar, time I visited my den, a little solitude in order to prepare my defence. 'I'm going up the mountain,' I told my sisters nonchalantly.

'What about poor Christy?' Tam cried in alarm.

'What about him?'

'Look at him. He's all quiet and still.'

Christy was prostrate, the side of his face pressed to the ground. 'Ssshhhh, I think he's listening for lug worms,' I said quietly.

Chapter Ten

Jennifer Boyle was a delight. With a face full of freckles, she was nicknamed Poppy, was a little younger than Sam and a little older than Tam and the first girl I ever wanted as a friend, well, more than a friend really. She was different, so, of course, she was talked about, a life force, a girl who simply couldn't be ignored. Adults called her precocious, cheeky, foul-mouthed, insolent and terribly disrespectful and the way she chewed bubble-gum and blew bubbles in the face of the establishment was worse than disrespectful, it was confrontational. But everyone agreed upon one thing about Poppy; having made her, someone lost the mould.

She came to the attention of our family soon after our arrival in the town and my sisters' admittance to St Jude's. One morning, the two youngest had been walking across the deserted school yard, when an older girl they knew only as Mary confronted them. 'Where do yous two think yer goin'?' she demanded.

'We've been sent by Sister Angela with a message for the cook,' Tam explained reasonably.

'She said, "It takes two o' yous for one message, does it?" and then she pushed us both over,' Dodo complained, displaying a blood-spotted scrape to her knee.

'This Mary is just huge,' Tam continued. 'Looming over us, she was. We only know her as Mary, Big Mary.' She looked to Sam for identification.

Their older sister tightened her brow. 'That'll be Mary Clooney.

She's in the class above me. Always rolls her stockings down the minute she out of school She's a bully. Her name is Mary Clooney.'

Dodo said, '"Get home owadat," she told us. "Get home owadat to England where yous come from. You're not wanted here." We were frightened to death.'

'We were in a heap on the ground,' Tam went on. 'This Mary had her fists clenched as if she would give us a belt the minute we tried to get up and there was no one about, no one. The middle of a schoolyard and there was no one about.'

'Then a really funny thing happened,' Dodo said in turn. 'A girl appeared out of nowhere, a little girl, not much bigger than us. She's in your class, Sam, her name is Jennifer. I've heard her name at roll call. It's… '

Sam cut in. 'Poppy Boyle, Poppy, cos of her freckles.'

'That's her, Poppy Boyle,' Dodo confirmed. 'She suddenly appeared out of nowhere like an angel and saved our lives.'

It was Tam's turn; she addressed her mother. 'Mum, this little girl, Poppy, is tiny and this other girl, Mary, is huge. And Poppy didn't say a word but tapped the big girl on the shoulder and pointed up to the school clock. It was twelve and, as the clock began to strike, Poppy pulled this big girl down on her knees in the schoolyard and the two of them made the sign of the cross. Dodo and me, we were going to run but we daren't, so we got down on our knees as well although we didn't know why, then suddenly there's the four of us, saying "The Angelus".'

' "The Angelus", Mum,' Dodo continued, 'you know, "The angel of the Lord declared unto Mary and she conceived of the Holy Spirit". There's the four of us on our knees praying 'The Angelus' because it was mid-day with little Poppy winking at us behind this big girl's back. Then on the last stroke of twelve we all got up and we were about to go to the dining room to see the cook, like we'd been told, when big Mary is in front of us again. "It takes two of yous for one message does it?" she says again. Then this Poppy just flew at her, saying the most awful things to her real swear words, awful, but it looked so funny, this little mite waving her fist in the nose of this big Mary and big Mary's frightened and runs off. Poppy just winked at us and she was off, too.'

'Saved our lives,' Tam finished sombrely.

So Poppy Boyle became a family favourite. Well, that was until her uninhibited and ribald use of invective became more than our mother could tolerate and she was banned from the house.

'But, Mum, it's just her,' I argued. 'You can't dislike Poppy, you just can't.' It was the same as disliking a baby yawning or a kitten sneezing and if there were those who said they hated Poppy, they had something missing in their lives.

'She's cheeky and her language is awful for a young girl,' my mother said.

Parents couldn't see the girl the way their children could. She wasn't bad, she was colourful and so was her language. She wasn't even a show-off she was too natural; a show-off is an opportunist introvert, forever seeking chances to impress. Poppy didn't seek attention because she didn't have to. She sparkled like a diamond or a star, without knowing. Gregarious and sociable, she chattered non-stop with a candour that made other children laugh without resenting being made dull by comparison. I had never met anyone quite like her and found it hard to put a finger on what it was she had that others didn't. When I thought about her, which was often, I figured that what made her 'special' was her wanting to be party to everything going on around her, but not wanting anything too much. She seemed to have absolutely no fear of rejection; indeed her attitude and language was such, she seemed to court it.

'She can be insolent without saying a word. She uses bubble gum,' my mother reminded us.

I laughed. Poppy's chewing and her infamous bubbles were a statement. She couldn't chew at school, even Poppy daren't do that. But out of school, her wads of gum were quite her own affair and grown-ups, especially Sisters of Mercy, girdling wrath and rebuking Poppy in her own space was an infringement of her liberty and might well be met with a bubble, starting slowly and expanding in proportion to the tempo of reproof until all that was left to admonish was a blank, pink balloon, ready to pop at the girl's volition. The slow expansion of the bubble was a subliminal statement of intent and the pop it made, a puncture of pomposity. Of course she was 'insolent' with her bubble gum. It left adults speechless with annoyance but unsure exactly what it was about her that had upset them so.

Sam defended her. 'That's what's so funny about her, Mum, she just doesn't care. She's the cheekiest girl in the school by far. There's even been talk of her getting herself expelled. But she's kind, Mum, she's kind to everyone except 'some' adults, Sisters of Mercy and Mary Clooney.'

My father was ambivalent. He enjoyed the girl and her personality and had often joked with her, but he wouldn't take our side against our mother. He could be rude himself and often was, but blasphemy and profanity, never.

I was stirred by Poppy Boyle, but not in the way I was stirred by Cora Casey. There was a bond with Poppy that certainly wasn't there with Cora. I could identify with Poppy's world but Cora's world was one of wealth, aloofness and the snobbishness of the Burnaby estate where she lived. There were lots of other girls with looks and personality who might arouse me but didn't. No other girl had the alluring witchery of Poppy Boyle or Cora Casey, sorcery so different in origin, their breathtaking attraction to me was incomprehensible. Poppy made my heart lift, whereas Cora made it sink, yet it was the latter that kept me awake at night.

One example of Poppy's capacity for bewitchment had occurred one afternoon in the midsummer of that year. I had taken my parents' Kodak camera to the pier, hoping to catch on film a phenomenon I'd unexpectedly witnessed the day before and without knowing it, all I caught that day was Poppy.

A huge shoal of mackerel had entered the harbour. It was awesome. Suddenly the swimmers were yelling with fear and excitement as they thrashed frantically towards land, swimming through a boiling crust of silver-blue. The water of the harbour had exploded with millions of fish. "A very rare occurrence," a fisherman told me, which may not happen for another twenty years and yet could happen the very next day. It was with this in mind that I took the Kodak camera. The mackerel didn't turn up, but Poppy did.

Some weeks later, the developed film exemplified the strange enchantment of this girl. Head tilting, eyes glancing, tongue poking, Poppy had captivated the entire reel. When had she embraced a shaggy dog on the pier steps? How could I have missed her, upside down on the dock wall, her face peeping impishly through the folds of her dress? I remembered her pirouetting, laughing, frowning and blowing bubbles, but I didn't know I'd filmed the ubiquitous, freckled star. Flicking through the snaps with bristling displeasure, my mother deemed them a waste of money while I cringed with embarrassment. Attraction to the opposite sex was something I was not yet ready to admit to.

'Someone must have borrowed the camera,' I told my mother lamely.

Another afternoon that summer there was a second incident with Poppy that enraptured Sam and me, bemused Tam and Dodo and re-enforced my mother's strong objection to the girl. It was a blazing afternoon during that otherwise dismal summer. The sun was high in a cloudless sky, slumping heat on the coast like a suffocating blanket. We children lay sunbathing on a rug stretched on the stony beach outside Calgary with, a few feet away, our mother reclining precariously on a deck chair and through dark glasses was buried in an Agatha Christie novel. And as usual, we were the only family inhabiting this singularly uncomfortable stretch of coastline.

Eyes closed, I listened to voices drifting in the still air from the pier and faintly, the sluggish movement of traffic back and forth along Victoria Road. The heat stunned; even the sand flies could scarcely bother dodging the half-hearted swipes of our limping hands.

Coming out of the heat, a cheery voice, instantly recognisable, 'Hello, everybody.'

Raising ourselves from the rug, Sam and I welcomed her readily, with Tam and Dodo pleased to see her, too, but knowing our mother's antipathy towards the girl, checking immediately for a reaction. It was the one thing cold that boiling afternoon. Poppy knew that she was barred from our house and knew why, but she genuinely didn't seem to care.

'Hello, Jennifer,' my mother acknowledged grudgingly.

'Phew, isn't it bloody hot?' Poppy remarked as she sat down beside us. She was not permitted to cross the threshold of Calgary but no one could stop her sitting outside the gate. As there was no room on the rug, she wriggled her bottom into the stones for comfort and said, 'Jesus, these stones crucify my arse.'

Stifling laughter, Sam and I found it impossible to look at the girl or at each other as she continued wriggling in the stones, oblivious to the shock she had inflicted on our mother. We turned on our stomachs, burying our faces in the rug, but one sideways glance to each other and we were wracked and trembling with suppressed hysterics. Poppy Boyle was, without exception, the most outrageous and uninhibited creature we had ever come across. Trying to straighten my face, I sat up again, stealing a look at my mother, who appeared to be in a state of shock. The book on her knee had fallen shut without its bookmark in place, her sun glasses were askew and her face was stricken while Poppy still wriggled in the stones, blissfully unaware of the contrasting merriment and rile that she was causing around her.

'These bloody stones wedge right up into the crack of your bum,' she discerned astutely, nudging Sam's prostrate, heaving body for affirmation.

My sister, face down, was convulsing on the rug and could not bring herself to answer as simultaneously, the wide-eyed younger girls put their hands, symbolically to their mouths and looked to their mother for reaction. Without a word or glance at anyone, our mother stood up from the deck chair and, with a jerk of her head towards the house, summoned us to follow. Tam and Dodo obeyed immediately, hurrying to keep up with her and, turning their heads to Sam and me, expressed bewilderment at our refusal to comply.

Poppy frowned at their departure as if, inexplicably, she could have been, in some way responsible.

As I regained my breath and wiped tears from my cheeks, I told her as soberly as I could, 'In our house we're not allowed to swear.'

Copper lashes fluttered above blue, astonished eyes. 'Who was swearing?'

'Well, you was Poppy.'

She looked aghast at Sam, who had now disengaged her tear-stained face from the rug. 'Who was swearing? Sam?'

'Well, you.'

'What, *me*?' she exclaimed incredulously.

'You were, Poppy.' Sam had started laughing uncontrollably again.

' "Jesus" and "arse" are absolutely forbidden,' I wheezed, 'especially in the same sentence.'

'I didn't say Jesus and arse,' Poppy contested emphatically.

Sam regained some composure. 'We can say bum,' she advised, conciliatory, 'as long as we don't say it too often in the same conversation, but "Jesus", "arse" and "bloody", no way can we say anything like that.'

Poppy's eyes were as big as saucers as it dawned on her that she alone was responsible for our mother's and the younger girls' unscheduled departure. 'When did I say that?' she demanded.

'When you sat down,' Sam said. ' You said that it was "bloody hot" and "Jesus these stones crucify my arse".'

The girl's eyes registered remembrance.

Sam was face down on the rug again. 'Then you said about the bloody stones wedging into the crack of your bum.' Sam could not go on. Her shoulders shook with laughter.

For a moment I saw Poppy's jaw tighten, then a light skimmed across her eyes and she began wriggling again until we could hear clearly the stones grinding beneath her. 'Oh, but they do, Misses, they do,' she called towards the door of Calgary. 'They do.'

My sides were splitting. 'Do what, Poppy?' I prompted.

'Wedge into the crack of your bum,' the girl called out loudly.

'Do what, Poppy?' choked Sam.

'Crucify your arse.' And Sam and I had vaulted off the rug and were sitting beside her in a synchronised buttock-crunching extravaganza among the stones, hysterical with laughter.

'Jesus, one's just got stuck,' howled Poppy.

'Where?' Sam gasped.

'You know where,' wept Poppy.

'Not the crack of your bum,' I hooted. 'Well mine too,' as through misty eyes I saw my mother, arms folded, grimly listening at the gate.

It was at that moment that Jennifer Boyle became my soul mate, my personal introduction to that alien species, girls, not sisters, girls, and as I immersed myself in friendship with Poppy and dreams of Cora, the two girls so intrinsically different in nature had one thing eminently in common; without knowing, they had evoked in my helpless heart that most ardent of emotions, love.

Chapter Eleven

Donoghue and Reardon were annoying me, hinting that they knew something really secret and were whispering the word 'periods' to each other, periods of what? But no matter how I badgered them, they refused to be drawn. The dictionary told me that a period was a length of time, could be long, or could be short, what was secretive about that? What had a period of time to do with girls? One day, I might lure those boys to my den, one at a time and refuse to let them out until they told me all they knew.

'If you've got something to tell me then tell me.'

'Can't jus' now, gotta check it out first,' Reardon replied mysteriously

'Oh forget it.' Grumbling, I walked towards the outbuilding where the brothers kept their bicycles. Behind the outbuilding, laughter with voices raised. Boys from the lower class were trying to walk on their hands and I was pleased to see how self-conscious they looked at my sudden arrival. I was the only boy in the school who could successfully walk on his hands; were they attempting to emulate my virtuosity? Of course they were. One boy was still on his hands, one foot supported on the outbuilding wall, the other foot waving as he tried to keep his balance. He collapsed in a heap as I approached him.

'Try again,' I advised graciously. 'What you've got to do is get up on your hands, then lean your legs over to the point where you're going to topple backwards, then walk your hands along the ground to keep up with your legs.' I addressed them all. 'Want me to show you?'

The boy sprawled on the ground got up and joined the others, all silent, eyes blank.

'First thing is you gotta be enthusiastic, you gotta want to learn, you gotta keep trying, practice makes perfect. That's what I did, started when I was about five and by the time I was six, I could walk fifty yards at least. If you want to learn, I'll show you.' Springing on my hands, I set off in a wide circle, aware of shuffling as they made way for me. When I had completed the circle, my arms gave way and I collapsed on the ground with a self-deprecating laugh. Yes, in spite of my proficiency, I was one of them, I could fail too. But, to my disgust they were all moving to another section of the yard. 'Please yerselves,' I yelled. 'Most of you lot can't even walk on your feet, never mind your hands.'

Angrily, I caught the boy I had found on his hands. 'Stand there,' I ordered brusquely. 'I'm gonna show you. How can you learn anything if you don't listen, don't watch?' I was on my hands again, aiming for a boundary fence, some thirty yards away. I reached it.

A voice, Rooney's voice, 'Oh yes, Oliver, we know you're good.'

I was on my feet shaking my head to clear it and exchanging insults. I looked around. My pupil was nowhere to be seen, only Rooney, surprisingly alone.

Following my violent retaliation in class, both, he, Cronin and their followers had avoided me. They were still using catapults, but thankfully I was no longer their target. But lately they had regrouped and Paddy Rooney and Billy Cronin, that spring, were my main adversaries. These boys were a mystery to me, their qualities of leadership, although undeniable, were indefinable and therefore impossible to imitate, a concept that confounded me. Neither could fight too well, nor was rhetoric an answer because they couldn't string a sentence between them. They were not sportsmen either, couldn't handspring, cartwheel or walk on their hands, couldn't swim and were not in the Gaelic football team or the hurling team either, although when I got them on their own, I had to admit, they could run. Yet with consummate ease, they could get other boys to follow them, many with blind obedience, whereas I, with all my talent, couldn't even captain my younger sisters.

But I was spending far too much of my time fighting. Not only at school but on my way home from school and evenings and weekends as well, setting out full of anger, purposefully to settle scores, avenge wrongs. Most of the fights were not full-blown brawls, but a trip, a single blow or a hefty push, skirmishes, threats and warnings, but all so stressful and wearisome. But some were bloody and others humiliating. A kid might make a snide remark, usually about my being an English dog and I would react, then likely, within seconds, reinforcements would arrive, baying cronies who had lain in wait and with, odds against me, I would have to back off, this hurting more than any blows that might have followed. Yes, I was surprised to find Rooney alone.

Rooney, even more than Cronin, was the problem. The only time he was civil towards me was when he wanted me to listen to the tale of his dead and deadly mott, otherwise he was galvanising foot-soldiers against anything and everything British and anything and everything British at St Luke's was me.

He must have decided to confront me because we were squaring up, then we were manoeuvring side by side, exchanging further insults and flaring at each other like squabbling blackbirds. Fists were flying now and I had wrestled him to the ground and suddenly I could smell nicotine and the meaty hands of Brother McBride were hauling us to our feet. 'What's all this nonsense about?' the brother growled.

'No gang with him, Bru,' I spluttered. 'Rooney's no good without Cronin, and neither of them is any good without a gang.'

The cleric's baleful scowl swung Rooney's way, looking for response. The boy was breathing heavily. 'No one's ganging up on him, Bru. Where's Cronin now? Where's a gang? We jus' don't like him. No one's gangin' up on him, we jus' don't like him.'

'Only cos I'm English,' I retorted bitterly.

'Sure it's nothin' to do with English,' Rooney scoffed. 'He could be Chinese, Irish even, we still wouldn't like him. Any trouble at school and look to see who's in the middle of it, it's allus him what's after causin' trouble, showin' off, walkin' on his hands an' all and talkin' stuff what no one understands. High follutin' stuff like poems what no one understands. An' insultin' stuff like sayin' Ireland's called Ireland cos that's all it is, a rubbish little island, but Britain's called Great Britain. He said even America isn't called great, on'y Britain, an' know why, cos it is.'

'So what's after causin' the trouble today?' the cleric rasped.

Rooney was breathing steadily now and had managed to shake himself free of the brother's grip. 'On'y walkin' on his hands, showin' off.'

I protested quickly. 'I wasn't showing off, I was teaching some younger boys how to do it.'

'No law in this country or this school against a boy walking on his hands,' the brother said.

'Calling me names, as usual, he… '

Rooney interrupted; 'All I said was, "Ok Christian, we all know you're good," an' he said, really clever like, '"Yeah, but do you know how good?"'

The cleric's scowl swung my way. 'That true?'

I got in quickly. 'True enough, but it's Christian now, Christian now cos you're here.' I looked up, hoping to find that understanding had replaced the grimace behind the spectacles. No understanding yet. I continued, 'But it wasn't Christian when I was walking on my hands. It was Oliver. And the minute you're gone it will be Oliver again, or worse.'

The glaze of the spectacles rounded on Rooney. 'What's this Oliver business?'

The boy had dropped his head sheepishly and I cut in before he had time to think up an answer. 'Oliver Cromwell, Brother, or later on today, it might be English dog and not just Rooney either; he'll have his mate with him, Cronin and maybe half a dozen others.'

The Head straightened his back and, grasping Rooney by the collar of his jacket, spoke in an even, passionless tone. 'Oliver Cromwell, is it, boy, English dog?'

Rooney was squirming. 'He calls us names too Bru, Bit o' name callin' on the way home from school sometimes. Bit o' fun really an' no harm meant.'

I saw the cleric's hand leave Rooney's collar and fingers position themselves at the back of his neck. 'Ah a bit o' fun, well now, that's all right so it is, as long as it's only a bit o' fun.' With his other hand, he used a finger under the chin to thrust the boy's head back. He then spoke directly into his face. 'A bit o' fun for who I wonder? No harm meant to whom?'

'Sure doesn't he be pickin' on us,' Rooney whined.

I liked the look in the cleric's smouldering eyes; brown coals, ready to flame, they were flaring on Rooney. 'Brother, they pick on me, not the other way round. I'm always outnumbered.' His hand on my arm was relaxing and there was an encouraging change in his posture, more inclined towards me, more distant from Rooney, the boy, further helping my cause by failing to meet the cleric's eye and trying to wriggle from his grasp.

Brother McBride shifted his grip from the boy's neck to his ear and gave it a tug.

Rooney winced, then suddenly came to life, his blazing eyes arcing between the two of us. 'He gets picked on cos he asks for it, Brother, showin' off, airs an' graces, talkin' stupid stuff.' His eyes pooled with venom and his lips quivered; his words a panting fury: 'Lookit me, why dontcha, amn't I the great one just? Lookit me walkin' on me hands. Amn't I the bees knees, just?' He blinked and twin tears spilled down his suffused cheeks. 'An someone will do somethin' or say somethin' that he doesn't like an' he'll be pretendin' he isn't bothered but all the time he is. Then a week later some kid what did somethin' or said somethin' will get such a smack for himself. I swear Bru, this kid might be on a message for his mammy or on the way home from Mass even an' he'll get a smack in the face, an' he'll wonder what's after hittin' him, an' it'll be for somethin' he did so long ago he's forgotten all about it. I'm tellin' the truth, Bru, cos it's happened to me.'

The cleric's big white head dropped towards me, a big white globe with a face on it, like a child might draw on a moon, neither friendly or unfriendly, it was balancing a scale of justice, a heap of damning data, weighted either side. 'What's the truth in this, then?' he demanded of me.

'Sure it's true, Brother,' I admitted readily. 'There's nearly always a gang and just me, so I wait and I try to get them one by one.'

'And it's Oliver is it?' he asked.

'Or English dog. I get other names as well.'

The cleric shook his head and said softly, 'I don't think I like the sound of this, not at all.'

'English pig as well,' I added helpfully.

The brother's face was really fierce as he addressed Rooney. 'Dog and Pig is it?'

'And worse, Bru.' It was my place to help the cleric all I could.

Rooney did not commit himself and the cleric did not pursue further any question of veracity; it seemed his mind was already made. Releasing us, he steered us together so that we were both facing him. His fierce expression still remained and we were both fearful. I felt that he had favoured my defence above Rooney's but I was still not sure upon whose head his wrath would fall. It fell heavily on Rooney's.

'Oliver Cromwell, is it, Rooney? A man not deserving of a name, Slaughterer maybe, that's a better name for him, a man responsible for the murder of countless Irish men, women and children. Use the name Cromwell in Wexford, boy, and you'll be lynched, a name to fill any honest Irishman with loathing, a curse on his name and a curse on you, Rooney, for using it. Call someone 'Cromwell' in Drogheda, boy, and see what you get.'

Rooney had begun by nodding vigorously in agreement of the brother's indictment, but when the stricture included him, he averted his eyes and hung limp. Then the Head's gaze swung my way, his face still fierce, and for a moment I thought that I was in for much the same. 'And you, boy, let me tell you something too. And I'll tell you in front of this oaf so that he can tell Cronin and then the pair o' them can share it with their gang. If ever this boy or any of his cronies ever call you Oliver Cromwell or English dog, or anything else for that matter, you have my full permission to give them a smack in the mouth, any time you like, whether it's immediate, a day later, a week later or ten. And I'll tell you what; give them a smack next year if you like or the year after that, and I'll tell you something else, give 'em one for me, too.'

I had won the judgement and I laughed in Rooney's face. Rooney was looking at the cleric in disbelief and was about to say something when the brother gave him a light push to the chest, light but unexpected, causing the boy to stagger backwards. And as he slunk away I felt really grand and vindicated and I wanted to kiss the brother's shiny head.

'Sure, try not to let them bother you,' Brother McBride said kindly. 'We know that it is hard for you just now, we know that things are not as they should be with the boys, but I'm sure they don't mean the half of it, a lot of bluster, sure it is. Perhaps you might provoke people unintentionally, the other boys especially, but they don't mean the half of it.'

I laughed. 'They don't bother me at all, Brother, "*They are idiots, full of sound and fury, signifying nothing.*"' He then dismissed me and I walked away from the encounter feeling very pleased with myself.

Ok, I was not popular but, being English, that was to be expected but I felt that with my first phase in the country, in the school, being over, at least I had won Brother Mc Bride to my side.

Summer would be my second phase and the holiday could not come soon enough. After the 'Rasputin' incident in the dock, I had overcome my fear of being alone and longed to detach myself from the turbulence of school-life for my cave-den on the Head. There, there would be peace; my life, more as I felt it should be. A more concerted search for the missing jewels would be launched and in the cave a log would be kept, a daily record of my progress. Having failed to regain the good will of my sisters for the enterprise, I had lost interest in them, pledging to rope in Poppy Boyle, the only person I could trust. I imagined the two of us being interviewed on the wireless and I chuckled at the thought of Poppy turning Irish airways blue.

Chapter Twelve

The seat beside Donoghue was empty. I slid along beside him. 'Now Paddy, what's all this about periods?'

Donoghue shook his head. 'Me an' Reardon are still investigatin', we got to make some more enquiries. This is really weird stuff.'

'Well, just tell me what you know. Is it do with girls?'

'Leave it, can't say jus' now, it's somethin' me an' Reardon are investigatin'. It's kind o' unbelievable, somethin' to do with cycles. Listen, you got a mott yet?'

'I don't want one,' I lied. 'I just want to know what periods are.'

'Leave it for now. Listen ok, some day you will want one, a mott an' I'm goin' to tell you what to do to get one.'

Periods could wait. If I was going to learn how to get a mott, then maybe I could get one, ask her and find out for myself.

'Like I'll tell you what really drives 'em mad, makes 'em go all wide-eyed an' weak-kneed.' Periods forgotten, this boy already had one hundred per cent of my attention. 'Snuggle up her neck, you know, as if you're gonna whisper somethin', then stick your tongue in her ear, right in, don't mess about, right in her ear. Jesus, it drives 'em mad, makes 'em kind o' faint into your arms.'

'What about tickling palms?'

Grinning his eyes alight with lascivious mischief, he said, 'Sure it's palms to begin with, then ears, It's what's expected nowadays.

Irish girls anyway, don't know what turns 'em on where you come from.'

'But what if it's waxy?' I queried uncertainly.

'Jesus, you're not goin' to pick a waxy one, are you?' He paused, thinking, his grin fading. 'Well, if you're not too sure, it might be better to check first.'

'Check what?'

'Check her friggin' lug-hole first before you stick your tongue inside.'

'Yeah, course,' I answered, feeling a little foolish. From the corridor, the sound of Brother Mulligan returning, I leapt back in my own seat with something to think about for the rest of the afternoon. I sat up attentively, pleased to see that he had his tuning fork with him.

The attitude of he and Brother McBride confounded me. Following the issue yesterday with Rooney, I thought I had it made with the Head, but I hadn't. Only this morning, he had cuffed me quite hard for some triviality in the cloak-room and the look he gave me was full of irritation. And Brother Mulligan seemed exasperated with me for some reason and was treating me most unfairly. I tried hard to think what I might have done to annoy him. He had been pleased with me that day I had helped him with the compositions, so what had happened since? As it turned out, this day I would upset him more than ever and it would be quite deliberate.

Most days Brother Mulligan managed the class in a spirit of weary melancholy, watching the clock as restively as any fidgeting boy in front of him, but odd days, and it looked as if this day might be one of them, he shook off this melancholy as if it were a mild disorder and conducted the lesson with heightened enthusiasm, a visitation most evident when holding a tuning fork which he waved about and twanged with all the vitality of a manic impresario.

He began by singing the first two lines of "The West's Awake" before inviting us to join him. 'Ah the class is in great voice today,' he told us gladly when the song was over. 'Except for

Flanagan and Sullivan, out of tune as usual, with them two it's more a duel than a duet.' He smiled to himself, then, raising his eyes to the class, said with an impassioned voice, 'Oh boys, last night on Radio Erin of all places I heard something that made my blood boil. Some eejit was referring to "Danny Boy" as "The Londonderry Air". Not "Danny Boy", not "The Derry Air" but "The Londonderry Air". Oh how angry it made me to hear that beautiful, sad song called after the capital city of England. Oh, but to hear it, does it not make you think of Billingsgate, the very heart of Hackney, sad and sentimental Cricklewood maybe. We cannot have the Brits steal everything we've got, please leave us with our songs.' His face had become uncharacteristically mobile during his lively declamation but now it settled quickly back over its angular bony support and following a twang of his tuning fork, we all began to sing "The Derry Air".

As the song died on our lips with its melody hanging sadly in the air of the classroom, there was a stirring of wellbeing, none more so than in myself, and I hadn't the heart to tell him that the song was written by an Englishman! Having never taken an interest in English ballads, I had become enchanted by the traditional songs and poetry of my adopted country, imbued as they were with national consciousness, the image of a nation in bondage, a dream of unity which stirred me to my roots. I felt that it was I, above all, who could hear the cries of those descendants of Cuchulann, those long dead, imprisoned heroes and patriots of Ireland, those who would leave a legacy in Irish Catholic schools until the end of days. Only a few months in the country and it was none other than 'Oliver Cromwell' who was the most avid exponent of rebel songs and poetry in the school. Oh, how that man must be turning in his grave.

Soon, those of us who could sing and others who thought they could were squabbling for attention. 'Bru Bru Bru Bru Bru Bru Bru.' The rumbling stopped, "Down by the Glenside" was the song and McGuire was the chosen boy. He stood up, cheeks reddening at the prospect, his tongue flicking dryly, then after a deep breath he began to sing but the words were like limpets on his lips and defeated he slumped down in his seat. But he had done enough to ensure the cleric's good humour and the class applauded. Salmon then volunteered to take over, managing two verses with more fervour than finesse. His effort was receive generously and the cleric, still in a heightened state of gusto, began again to view the raised hands, noticeably avoiding mine. Then a sudden thought appeared to have entered his head for, narrowing his gaze, he said quizzically, 'Any boy know who it was composed that song?'

No one knew of course and I waited. His gaze rested on O'Farrell but the boy shook his head and still I waited. I waited until the cleric was about to tell the class himself, then, without bothering to raise my hand, I said quietly, 'It was Peader Kearney, Brother.' Sitting as close to the front of the class as I was, I was able to perceive even the smallest alteration in a teacher's expression and I watched closely. Maybe an eyebrow would lift in mute admiration but what I got was, unmistakably, a tightening of the mouth.

Ok, if that was what he wanted. 'He also wrote the Irish National Anthem,' I announced with an equal detachment.

In the cleric's eyes as they slid across my face was disgust, but surely disgust at the ethnic ignorance I was exposing. I was deserving of felicitation but, satisfying myself with self-congratulation, I did without. In a few short months this new nation's lyricism had become a wellspring of my life, words, whether sung or spoken, had a kind of grace for me and this land's very own had awakened in me a dormant consciousness, more potent than eloquence, far deeper than sentiment, an ancient legacy, a hunger perhaps needing the work of Irish ballads and poetry to appease it.

The teacher grunted and for a moment I feared that my scholarship might have blighted the favourable milieu of the afternoon, but I was reassured when he twanged his tuning fork and asked for another volunteer. Many hands were raised but fell to their sides with an audible gasp, heralding the raising of a most unexpected hand. Snot Nose Flanagan, the inimitable class clown, had never before volunteered for anything in his life.

The clown's raised hand reciprocating between a frayed cuff and the ceiling caused a titter around the class, escalating into full scale merriment as Brother Mulligan gathering his garments and his brows, feigned a full-scale heart attack. 'Dear God, but do my eyes deceive me? Or is that Flanagan with his hand up in the air?' This boy had never been known willingly to sing a single note, not even when oscillations were diluted by the imposition of thirty other voices, acute and permanent nasal congestion prevented it. 'Is it the lavatory you do be wanting, Flan?'

'Ah no, Bru, It's not a song, but a poem.'

At this news the cleric crossed his eyes and staggering across the floor had a second heart attack beside the blackboard and, clinging to the blackboard, convulsing, had the class roaring with laughter, none more so than Flanagan himself. 'A poem, Flan, a poem you say?' he gurgled in his death throes. 'What poem might this be then?'

'"Hup the Hairy Mountain," Bru.'

'Would you believe my very favourite, 'the cleric chortled. 'Oh Flan, the floor is yours.'

The boy stood with his back as rigid as a washboard, his eyes fixed straight ahead and his nostrils bubbling like twin bowls of broth.

' "Hup the hairy mountain, down the rushy glen,
We daren't go a huntin' for fear o' little men".'

Then he sniffed frothily and sat down.

'Continue, Flan,' the brother urged.

'That's it, Bru.'

'That's what?'

'That's all I know.'

The cleric put a hand to his brow and, with the wistful, aesthetic pose of a troubadour, complained painfully, 'Oh pity

Mangan, Moore and Tynan, now rolling over in your graves.' The class began to laugh heartily. 'Goldsmith, Swift and Yeats, are yous after hearing Flanagan? Seamus Flanagan's the name, a wordsmith to out-do the lot o' yous. "Up the Airy Mountain" the inspiration of generations but Flanagan's "Hup the Hairy Mountain" will inspire generations more.'

We were all now laughing uproariously, conducted by Flanagan, with the brother, in stitches, allowing the mirth to fade naturally, without interruption. When the laughter died away, the brother shook his head and said ruefully, 'Well I've heard everything now so I have, but nonetheless I think the boy deserves a good round of applause.'

The class agreed and, with Flanagan on his feet again, bowing graciously to the four walls in turn, he acknowledged with aplomb far greater appreciation than had hitherto been bestowed on any of the preceding performers.

Singing forgotten, hands were now being thrust at the ceiling in support of Flanagan's poetic innovation. Surely I could no longer be denied? Be it recited or composed I was the best poet in the class and I began to juggle favourites in my mind.

At the behest of the cleric, Murphy ruined "The Rising of the Moon", as did Sullivan "The Memory of the Dead" and, as evocation of the '98 rebellion stuttered to muted applause Brother Mulligan chose O'Farrell's hand instead of mine. But the real wound was his choice of poem. '"The Wayfarer", Brother,' my poem, my first choice and my heart sank at the loss.

'Do you know it from start to finish?' the brother asked.

Of course he did. Was not O'Farrell the all-round cleverest boy in the class? A quiet, studious boy, who spoke softly, never got into fights and was earmarked for the priesthood. This boy did not join with others in crude, childish banter neither did he ever badger me with ethnic insults. I wanted O'Farrell as a friend but he kept himself to himself. Being conscious of his vocation, he avoided those who might despoil it.

Listening to O Farrell's soft, lilting voice, I saw that faraway look in Brother Mulligan's eye, the same look that he had that morning when he talked of his boyhood in Sligo and I understood well the nostalgia evoked by the condemned patriot's epitaph to a world he was soon to leave. Often as I read or quoted Pearse's last written words, I would be with him in his cell, watching through walls, those 'rabbits in a field at evening,' 'or some green hill, where shadows drifted by'. I liked to think that the green hill he saw was Bray Head, as he would view it from Killiney or from Dalkey Island in the north, as I would, now, years later, view that same hill from the south.

There was no denying it, O'Farrell had made a good job of the poem, but I declined to join in with the applause, not jealous, but annoyed with Brother Mulligan for choosing O'Farrell. With "Dark Rosaleen" poised upon my lips, I raised my hand again but the brother chose Keogh's.

'"Dark Rosaleen", Bru.'

I groaned as my hand plunged downwards with my soul. Keogh's "Dark Rosaleen" would be an affront to the man who wrote it and to a nation's culture and in desperation I raised my hand again. It was ignored again; I was being marginalised and deliberately so.

'Can you recite the whole of it?' the brother asked.

'Ah no, two or three verses maybe.'

'Two or three verses maybe,' I mimicked under my breath. I was being deliberately ignored, the same way whining beggars and small yapping dogs were ignored, the same way I ignored Christy Plunkett. I did not deserve this treatment, it was so unfair.

Faltering, Keogh began his recitation, his lips sticking and stumbling over stanzas, far too emotive for one as crass as he. It was so unfair; Brother Mulligan knew that I could give an infinitely better rendition than this coarse boy and not only did I know every word of every verse, I also knew who wrote it. James Clarence Mangan wrote it, what was more Mangan was born in 1803 and was bald by his thirties. Did Keogh know that "Dark Rosaleen" was a representation of Ireland in the image of a woman in bondage? Of course he didn't. Kathleen Ni Houlihan was another, did Keogh know that? Oh, how that beautiful ballad was wasted on Keogh. Was she a vinegar-faced crone squatting in a Dublin slum? Well, Keogh made her sound as if she was. He didn't even know words of my favourite verse.

> "To think of you my Queen,
> My life, of life, my saint of saints,
> My dark Rosaleen! my own Rosaleen!
> To hear your sweet and sad complaints,
> My life, my love, my saint of saints,
> My Dark Rosaleen!"

Oh, but Brother Mulligan was enchanted, or at least he chose to be, heaping praise on Keogh's puerile enunciation. 'Such feeling, such flair,' he gushed.

'James Clarence Mangan,' I called without being asked. What followed was a blatant and quite deliberate snub, which hurt and angered me. What was wrong with the man? What had I done to deserve such treatment? He no longer even called me by my name; it was Gilla Christe now, another name I didn't like. Gilla Christe, Gaelic for Servant of Christ or Christian if you like, first conjured by Brother Mc Bride at my induction, as if I didn't have enough to put up with. I could just about survive being English and unpopular but 'Servant of Christ' was a cross as hard to bear as that of my namesake, two thousand years earlier.

No one was more pleased than I to see our teacher in such good humour and who, more than I, was rectitude in trying to sustain the spirit of the afternoon? Who was the class's best poet? I was. Why had my avid eye and eager hand been overlooked in favour of the poetic dross of Keogh? Why, only last week, Brother Mulligan had been happy to have me sing 'The Wearing of the Green' and had been greatly impressed when I told him that it was written by Dion Boucicault. That was the Dion Boucicault that had lived in Lower Gardner Street, Dublin, just in case he wasn't sure which Dion Boucicault I was referring to.

Anyway, I was finished for the day. He could have his Murphy, Sullivan, and Keogh, if that was who he wanted. I was sulking now, my mind more on periods, tongues and motts' ears. More on what Donoghue had told me and was yet to tell me. This lesson was supposed to be, music, singing, the brother had let the class take over too readily and I resented it.

'Bru, Bru, Bru, Bru, Bru, Bru, Bru.' The class was eager to tell the teacher something, but in my sulky frame of mind, I had missed what it was.

Yet he was addressing me. 'Gilla Christe, you no longer have your hand up. You were right about James Clarence Mangan.'

'Yes, Brother, I know I was.'

'And you no longer have your hand up.'

'All the best poems are gone,' I answered truculently.

'But surely you have English poetry in your repertoire?' the tone of the question, not unfriendly.

'I prefer Irish poetry,' I answered truthfully.

'But you must know English poems.'

I thought hard for a moment and was surprised to find that I didn't. I knew a few opening lines of "The Charge of the Light Brigade" by Tennyson and some of "Hiawatha" but that was American, I really had had no interest in poetry before I stepped ashore this lyric land.

'You have many English quotations I'll grant you that, but no English poetry.' The brother sounded irritated.

Through a window, sunlight spotlighted the teacher's angular face, skeletal bones of the skull through pale, stretched skin. In the sunlight, his eyes shone like bright, blue stars until they jerked into shade where they clouded at me suspiciously.

I sensed that the class behind me wanted to hear an English poem, too. But what was an English poem? An Irish poem was about ancient freedom, struggle and terrible failure. What was the essence of an English poem? Was "Rule Britannia, Britannia rules the waves", the essence of an English poem? Was "Hearts of Oak are our Ships"? "Onward into the Valley of Death"? 'Honest to God, Brother, I just don't know one, I'm surprised that I don't know one, but I don't. I've only been interested in poetry since I came to Ireland.'

The cleric was pulling at his nose. 'Try to learn an English poem for next time,' he suggested moodily.

A thought, a sudden comic impulse made me laugh out loud. Yes, I did know an English poem, one verse of one anyway. One that would put Brother Mulligan in his place for the way he had been treating me and was guaranteed to bring the house down at the same time. I was excited, I was about to cause a bigger laugh than Flanagan. His "Hup the Hairy Mountain" had nothing on this poem. 'Yes, Brother, I do know an English poem, one verse of it only, though'

The brother seemed relieved, good humour returning to his face in an instant and he smiled as he gave me a nod on commencement. I stepped out of my seat so that I could stand up, tall, gave an exaggerated cough and recited obliquely, over his shoulder.

'"Twas brillig, and the slithy toves
Did gyre and gimble in the wabe;
All mimsy were the borogroves,
And the mome raths outgrabe."'

I finished, expecting a huge roar of laughter from behind, indeed, I was prepared to bow to the four walls as Flanagan had done. What I had not expected was stunned silence. Brother Mulligan's pale face had turned white and he seemed to be trembling with anger. 'Lewis Carroll,' I apologised lamely.

The teacher replied through gritted teeth. 'Charles Ludgwig Dodgson, I think.'

No more was said, but festivities were over for the afternoon, replaced by maths and the atmosphere in the class room was subdued. Unquestionably, I was to blame and I awaited insults and asides of accusation, but nothing came my way. I think it was because no one could quite put a finger on the strange chemistry of blight engendered by my verse, which I now knew to be ill-judged, although I did not know why.

I was sure I would be called to account and be required to stay behind when school was over for the day and I lingered with my books until I was the last boy in the room but Brother Mulligan didn't even look up from his desk or answer me when I bade him goodbye.

It was the last day of term before I heard anything more about that afternoon. School had finished early in readiness for the summer holiday when the teacher stopped me in the corridor. 'Gilla Christe, a moment now.' his voice was low as excited boys stumbled past us to open air and freedom. His expression was friendly, the first time in an age, but as he kept me standing in the corridor, I knew that this exchange was not destined to take long. Stragglers still passed us by, happy, their faces glowing in anticipation.

'How do you think that you are doing, Gilla Christe, here at St Luke's?' he asked.

'I think I'm doing ok, Brother, really fine.'

'Do you know of any Scottish poets?'

I thought the question strange. 'I don't know any Scottish poets.'

'Ever hear of a poet called Rabbie Burns?'

'I've never heard of him, Brother.'

'An excellent Scottish writer of excellent Scottish poems, "Ode to a Louse" is one of them.'

'"Ode to a Louse",' I laughed, suspecting he was making fun of me.

'You might do well to read it. A couple of lines you might find appropriate.' His tone now was light-hearted, but his next words were as unintelligible to me as the words of 'Jabberwocky' were to Flanagan and to everybody else; '"A wad some power the giftie gie us. To see oursils as ithers see us".'

I was mystified as he bade me to leave. 'Have a good holiday, Gilla Christe.' As I was leaving by the main door, trying to make sense of what he had just said, he called to me. 'Rabbie Burns, died 1796, you know,' he said with a meaningful wink that I didn't understand.

Brother Mulligan was acting really odd. Maybe he was tired. I had absolutely no idea what he was talking, about. He must need a holiday as much as his pupils did, and I was pleased to be rid of him and everyone else for the next nine weeks.

Chapter Thirteen

Although bewildered by the cleric's peculiar attitude towards me, nothing could dim the rosy glow in my heart at the prospect of my first, long summer holiday in this new country. I was wrong; that rosy glow was extinguished even before I had reached the school gates.

At the gates a gang was waiting. As I had often to run the gauntlet of school gangs, I was not particularly afraid because they often amounted to little more than bravado and name-calling but there was something about this gang that was different. There was menace in the air and Pollack Gob was detaching himself from the throng and striding purposefully towards me, his pendulous bottom lip stapled grimly and uncharacteristically to its upper and an air of hostility about him, like a swarm of wasps.

I glanced back, hoping that the focus of his intent was behind me, but on turning again I received a savage smack on the nose, my worst fears realised; the focus of his intent was unquestionably me.

Shocked and sprawled on the ground, I tasted blood, warm and sticky on my lips and my nose felt as if it ought to belong to someone else. Through a mist of pain and outrage, Rooney and others were forming a ring in a preordained arena, on the pavement, outside the gates. As I was dragged inside it, I watched with hopelessness, the ring thickening with bloodlust, much as a gazelle with a lion at its throat must watch a gathering of vultures. A huge, pink dinghy of a bottom lip had been released from moorings on its upper and was quivering with raucous snorts of satisfaction. 'What was that for, Patsy?' I spluttered.

'You know well enough,' he sneered, his pale green eyes awash with venom.

As I lay on the ground, my head only inches from Patsy's stinking feet, I could hear the word 'foyt' rippling around the ever-growing circle of boys with brute anticipation. This boy hovering above me was older and bigger and I didn't want to fight as I was no match for him but, above all else, I feared to be seen a coward. 'Patsy, I don't know "well enough",' I pleaded, spitting a gob of fresh blood at his feet.

'Well, ok, you're goin' to get beaten up an' you won't have a clue what it's all about.'

Leering Rooney was bending over me. 'Jesus, that's not right at all, a fella gettin' a hidin' for somethin' he knows nothin' about. I say, I say, awful, what?'

I had to play for time. Under normal circumstances, the dropping of a toffee paper anywhere within a hundred yards of the school gates was guaranteed to bring any one of its black garbed harbingers of didactic propriety shrieking to the scene, so where was one now, now that a pupil's life was in the balance? Casting wounded eyes up into the face of my attacker, I appealed, 'Come on, Patsy, you can give a man a chance.'

Leering Rooney was bending over me again. 'Maybe he'll give you the same chance as you give to others.'

'Ok, Rooney, gloat, make the most of it.' He was enjoying himself. Still smarting at the Head Brother taking my side, it would not surprise me, if it was he who had put Plunkett up to this.

'Getupouadath, an' fight like a man,' Patsy ordered.

Cringing submission wasn't working. 'Listen, Patsy, I don't know what the hell I'm supposed to have done to you. I'm not getting up until you tell me what this is all about.' This was a demand, tempered with aggression, but hopefully not enough aggression, to provoke him further.

Rooney's greasy black curls framed brown eyes, murky with spite, 'Doesn't like being called Oliver Cromwell. Well, shouldn't carry on like Oliver Cromwell, then. Jesus, Oliver, you might be gettin' smacked for somethin' you did weeks ago, months ago even. Jesus, you might even be gettin' smacked for somethin' you've forgot about.' Rooney turned to his cronies, laughing. 'I say, I say, what an awful thing to happen to a chap. A damned disgrace, what! I say, Mr Plunkett why don't you give this posh English gent another so that he might remember.'

'He knows well enough, so he does,' Patsy said, his clenched fist hovering inches from my bleeding nose. 'Sure this kid's been askin' for a smackin' ever since he arrived here an' now he's goin' to get one. That's what I've been waitin' for. Start the summer holidays with somethin' for the lads to talk about.'

'Hit him again,' Rooney urged. 'I like to hear the yelpin' of an English dog.'

Patsy swelled his chest triumphantly. 'Get up on yer feet owadath, you English mott, an' get another smack for yerself.'

The rippling murmur of approval was not encouraging. Blood streamed from my nose, bridging my lips and transfixing my horrified eyes on crimson spots on a white shirt, telling of unprovoked assault and barbarism. Whatever I got from Pollock Gob this day, Rooney was going to get the same, with interest, and he would wait until it was all 'forgotten'. But what had I done to upset the fish-faced bastard standing with him? It was weeks, months, since I had felled his little brother on the north beach and ungrudgingly, the little sprog, that same day, had turned up at Calgary, ostensibly to help his Gran, but in reality, to sustain his improved relations with Sam. Even so, distrustful of his forbearance and fearing retribution, I had tried pre-empting what was happening to me now with unreserved apologies and the gift of an unwanted Christmas present. Moreover, I had met with his two older brothers many times since, without sign of antipathy towards me. What the hell was it all about? Surely Patsy hadn't waited this long.

'Ok Patsy, I'm getting up.' Blood in my throat tasted rich and thick and I spluttered as I spoke. Urged on by Rooney, two of his cronies tried to drag me to my feet, but I resisted with a dead weight they couldn't handle. When I got up it would be of my own volition. Patsy's eyes were still gleaming with hostility and now only the sudden appearance of a Christian Brother could save me.

Rooney was squatted down beside me again. 'Honest, Oliver, this is awful what's happenin' to you, but it's happened to me, loads of times. Maybe now you know how it feels.'

'And it's going to happen to you again,' I promised calmly and unequivocally.

'Well, jus' tell Patsy what you done an' it might be all over,' he suggested malevolently as I spat another gob of blood on the ground and, with watchful distrust, began to scramble to my feet. Fearing another blow, I kept my hands, passively by my side, disappointing the encircling crowd, who were demanding blood and drama.

Without defence, it was easy for Patsy to answer their call and this blow was even harder than the first. It exploded on my cheek-bone, electrifying, with a thousand bright stars, the black, empty dimensions of my brain. Falling to a crouch, I watched in disbelief as the skin of my knee folded back on itself as I raised it from the concrete kerbstone. 'Jesus, I wasn't expecting that.'

'Well, you shudda bin. You shudda bin.' That was Rooney.

Tears stung my eyes but, grimacing fiercely, I kept them at bay. I could arise from defeat and could be even stronger for it, but a flood of unmanly tears would expose a backbone, weak and con-temptible to see and as Patsy had promised, start the summer holidays with something for the lads to talk about, the tears of Oliver Cromwell.

'Who'd o' thought he was the best fighter in his class, in England?' Rooney said in wonderment.

'It was a school for girls though, school for soppy motts,' Cronin laughed.

The theme in favour of retaliation was gathering pace. 'I wouldn't stan' for that, would you?' one boy asked of another.

Things were getting desperate. I was going to have to fight.

Patsy slapped me hard over the ear with his open hand, stinging greatly.

'Give up Patsy, I 'aven't done nowt,' my Yorkshire vernacular surfacing in the fear and tension of the moment. I rubbed at my smarting ear. 'By eck, Patsy, is there any need for this?'

'You've scrambled his friggin' brain,' Rooney observed derisively.

A sudden though occurred to me. 'Is it your granny getting the sack?'

'You're talkin out o' your arse,' my assailant fulminated as he slapped my face again.

But was I? Had I hit the nail right on the head? Grandma Plunkett's position at Calgary had been terminated by mutual consent, but was her dim-witted, fish-faced grandson to know that?

Spring was edging into summer and Grandma Plunkett's anxiety at the state of world had been exacerbated by news that the 'eejit' Truman was 'after sackin' the only two men capable of saving it, two sound God-fearing Irishmen, Senator Joe McCarthy and General Doug MacArthur. 'Sacked, the pair o' them,' she lamented, wringing her hands and rattling her teeth.

This talk of sacking had eased the door my mother had been long in waiting to open, the inevitable displacement of the old lady herself. My mother had been waiting to talk to her for some time but had found it too difficult. The old lady was a treasure to the family, but the sad truth was we couldn't afford her any more.

Plump, round hands had gripped my mother's wrists as kind, understanding eyes greeted the tentative but irrevocable proposal with pragmatic assent. Apparently, the vagaries of our financial circumstances had long been known to the woman, who told my mother, it wasn't her place, but she 'could o' tol' the Mister about them skivers and chancers aroun' these parts, masqueradin' as builders and speculators without one of 'em having two pence pieces to rub together of a morning. 'Sure I seen 'em whit me own two eyes, gidin' your poor husband across the road to Dan's for a bit o' business, whit one hand aroun' his shoulder an' the other in his pocket. But please don't worry yerself one bit about Mary Plunkett for she'll manage well enough, so she will, as she's managed all her life.' And as she released my mother's wrists, her soft, round face beamed with grace and comfort.

A final severance, yet undetermined, would be deferred as long as possible, hopefully, until the schools broke for the summer holiday and would be conducted with the heavy hearts of mutual regret. A glowing reference would be provided along with whatever remunerative generosity my father would be able to muster. The conversation that day between my mother and Patsy's grandmother had ended without acrimony of any kind, and could, in the next few minutes, save me from the biggest hiding of my life.

'Thing is, Patsy, my dad gave your grandma a job when she needed one, and your uncle, too, but times are hard just now. There's not much work about and I know my dad's struggling. We didn't want her to go, we think a lot about your grandma, we're all still the best of friends.'

Askance, Patsy looked about him for reason. Among a sea of faces, Rooney shook his head despairingly. 'What the hell's me granny got to do with it?' Patsy demanded.

Now among the vultures, an air of frustration, of anti-climax, was a budding conflict, holding so much promise, about to abate to nothing more than discussion on the affordable merits of domestic employment?

Grumbling, two boys detached themselves at the fringe of the circle and I heard the word 'coward' muttered as they walked away. I was a bull in a bull-ring who wouldn't fight a wounded fox that couldn't run and all about me all that was small and mean and vicious in the human species. Playing for more time, I plucked at bits of grit adhering to the raw flesh of my open knee. My head throbbed with a leaden ache and I prayed for the emergence of a Christian Brother and the instant dispersal that would follow. Should one suddenly appear, I could redeem myself with one good blow, one savage blow to that cod-like head, without the fear of his retaliation, the cleric would see to that. What a relief it would be to be able to go our separate ways under the restraining eye of a watchful Brother.

'Tell him what it's about, then hit him Patsy, get it started.' Rooney's voice radiated urgency.

Patsy lowered his head until his great, pink, fleshy, horseshoe lip hung just above my bleeding nose. 'You smacked my little brother, knocked him out. Christ, he's only ten.'

'Ey up Patsy, that was summat 'appened months ago.' My Yorkshire singularity rising once again in fearful anticipation of what was coming next.

'Oh dear, months ago,' Rooney crooned, 'The good Lord save us but whatever next?'

'Christy jumped me, Patsy, it was him what hit me first,' I appealed. 'Me and my sister Sam, was having a bit of a row on the north beach and the next thing I know, is Christy laying into me. I hit him just the once, he fell.'

I was being hoisted to my feet and the circle was widening. Cronin delegated Coyle to watch the schoolhouse, ready with a warning and the two boys walking away, sensing a change in dynamics, returned. There was no escape. In the circle, insidious smiles were being exchanged, the mirthless smiles of circus clowns. With my handkerchief, I mopped first at my nose and then at my knee, the hand at my knee fisted but still holding the handkerchief as a distraction, in prime position now for a full swing upwards into Patsy's face, but the boy was still on guard. 'I thought I'd squared things up with your brother. Apologised, even gave him a gift.' I had dropped the handkerchief and when the time was right, I was going to hit him, hard.

'Well' you haven't squared things up with me. A gift, what gift?'

'A pair of hairbrushes.'

'A pair o'wha'?' Patsy snorted.

'Hairbrushes, polished walnut hairbrushes.'

'Polished arseholes.'

'I got them for Christmas, last.'

'Enough lice an' nits in our house without spreadin 'em with polished walnut friggin' hairbrushes,' he laughed and for the first time relaxed his guard. 'Know wha' he was rowin' with his sister about on the north beach? Listen to this, he got a Valentine from Cora Casey, a lovey dovey Valentine in verse from Cora, 'cept he'd sent it to hiself, wrote it an' sent it to hiself. His sister showed it to Christy, tol' Christy what he'd done.'

There was much laughter at what was oozing from a crescent-shaped slobbering canoe of a gob as a clenched fist came whistling upwards from the ground and split it open like a ripe tomato. What a lovely squelching sound it made.

Patsy staggered backwards and was only stopped from falling by the weight of boys behind him and now he was tottering forward, propelled by those who had saved him and my left fist hit him flush, where it couldn't miss, on a bottom lip already twice the size it was. He was stumbling, trying to clear his senses, his eyes wild, like a stricken animal, his face ashen with shock and pain and rage. One more good crack to that cod-like head and he was finished, but in my eagerness, I swung and missed and with momentum, fell into his arms.

Tangled together, we fell and now I could only lose. If only it could be stopped now, with honour even, no, honour weighted on my side, how happy I would be to survive with only a throbbing nose, a shrieking cheekbone and a ravaged knee but this hard bony boy was bigger and stronger than me and in a towering rage. Any chance I had was gone. We wrestled to the ground, trying to get each other in a head lock, low, guttural noises of encouragement radiating from the circle, mostly in support of Patsy, but surprisingly, one or two supporting me, but then I was the underdog, and finally putting on a show.

I was about to get beaten, crushed. The only issue now was, how severely? But at least I had redeemed myself, no more calls of coward, now. We had separated and were on our feet, lashing wildly with our fists, the ring of boys pulsing backwards and forwards, making room for us to swing. The faces whirling around us had tense jaws and bright, wide eyes and the rumble was want of a victor and a vanquished. We clinched and Patsy's strength prevailed. He had the upper hand of a headlock and I was desperately trying to free myself, because once he fell on top of me, I was finished. I couldn't breathe and, as his grip tightened further, he began punching at my face with his fist. We fell and his crooked arm was like a steel cable around my neck and I could hear his grunts of exertion in my ear and smell his hot, rancid breath. I couldn't even gasp for mercy, I was passing out then, suddenly everything released. It was if steel cables enfolding me had snapped and I was clear of him and upright.

Breathing deeply to clear my fuddled brain, I blinked with incredulity at the source of my salvation, a red-clad, dwarf-like creature, strangely familiar, astride of Patsy's back, clawing at his face. The gathering of boys was dumbstruck, gawping open-mouthed at a skinny thing digging into the gangly, raw-boned neck of Patsy Plunkett. Roaring like a mad bull, Patsy threw off his tiny tormentor and was on his feet, swinging wildly with his fists at anything and everything until he focused, once again, on me. He lurched towards me and I hit him hard between the eyes, stopping him in his tracks. He swayed, then fell heavily on the pavement, his head making an awful cracking sound as it hit the kerb. He lay very still as boys began to gather about his prostrate form and a girl was walking away down Jeeney Hill. Not running, walking, and not looking to right or left or at what she had left behind her, what a special girl she was, my saviour, Poppy Boyle.

Duggan was slapping Patsy's face, trying to bring him round. 'Holy Mother o' God, but you're after killin' him.'

Rooney, pale and sickly, lifted Patsy's head from the kerb and looked up at me with genuine concern. 'I think he's dead.'

Grim-faced and panicking, I knelt by the stricken form, limp and with a small pool of blood expanding slowly over the pavement beneath his head. 'But he started it,' I appealed to those who still remained around me. 'He fell and banged his head. It wasn't my fault. Oh Patsy, you ok?' I pleaded, cradling his bloody head in my hands. 'Patsy, Patsy, please wake up, please wake up.' Then to the ever diminishing band of onlookers: "Look, you all saw what happened. All I was doing was defending myself, this isn't my fault.'

'He ain't breathing.' There was a quiver in Rooney's voice

'Of course he's breathin'.' There was a deeper quiver in mine.

'Go get a Christian Brother.' Cronin was looking for Coyle but the boy was long gone.

'Jesus, Mary an' Joseph, but you're after killin' Patsy Plunkett.' Rooney was not accusing me but making a terrifying statement of fact.

'Wake up, Patsy, please,' I beseeched, shaking the boy's shoulders, in horror at the ramifications, should the boy be really dead.

'Get a priest,' Maguire said.

'Get a friggin' undertaker,' someone else advised. Not wanted to be involved, all boys had peeled away except for me and three others. 'A friggin' undertaker,' the same boy insisted from afar.

A miracle, Patsy Plunkett, groaned, stirred and opened one eye and a wave of relief washed me to my feet. I stood above him, legs apart, triumphant and, as he began to regain consciousness fully, I said, 'Well, Patsy, I hope you've learned your lesson, first Christy and now you. When are you Plunketts going to learn not to mess with me?'

Patsy had raised his weight on to an elbow and moaning softly was feeling at his head.

'Well, we'll be able to start the summer holidays with something for the lads to talk about, won't we?' I taunted.

'Oh Jesus, look at his head,' Cronin gasped, Patsy's head swelling as he spoke.

'Last time I saw a head like that it was in the bottom of a boat with a fish hook in its gob,' I remarked as casually as I could.

Only Rooney, Cronin and Maguire now remained, ministering to the injured boy and at the bottom of Jeeney Hill a small, red form grew smaller in the distance. Patsy had been hoisted by his attendants into a sitting position and, head in hands, was still moaning. Blood streamed down the side of his misshapen face and gathered in the skin folds of his neck. What was done was done and there was no need for me to say another word. Like Poppy, I would walk away, not looking to right or left or at what I was leaving behind me. Adrenaline was surging through my veins and the pain in my face and knee was the garland pain of victory that does not hurt. I had more than redeemed myself; I had won. Since my arrival at St Luke's, I had fought many battles, but this had been the big one and against all expectations, including my own, I had won.

By the bog, I called out for Poppy, hoping that she had waited for me, then I called again by the railway bridge. I was disappointed, but another time I would recall with her today's injustice, her timely intervention and my own great victory.

Still buzzing with the exhilaration of it all, I headed for home. My mother would complain bitterly at the state I was in, but my father would be proud of me, he would say very little, if anything, but I knew he would be proud. Yes, the summer holidays would start with something for the lads to talk about, but I would not be with them. I would be at my retreat on the mountain, re-living again and again this triumph in the quiet darkness of my feral den.

Chapter Fourteen

My brother Tommy is home on holiday from London,' Coyle marvelled, the word 'London' lovingly guarded, as if Tommy had lent it to him for the afternoon. 'An' this mornin' he's after tellin' me about a filum he seen in London, I can't remember what it's called, but there's Billy the Kid in it, an' Doc Holliday, an' Pat Garratt. You know who Pat Garratt was?'

'Yeah, he shot Billy the Kid.'

'Tommy says that if this filum ever comes to The Ormonde, then I gotta see it.' Coyle put a ravaged pink finger to his mouth and scraped chip crud from his teeth. 'Wanna know why?'

I didn't respond and adjusted my eyes to show that I wasn't really interested.

The boy, piqued by my indifference, replaced his finger with a fat, hot chip and, talking around it, said, 'All three of 'ems after the same mott, one with the biggest tits that Tommy says he's ever saw. Tits that can on'y be seen in London.'

'Is it coming to 'The Ormonde?' I enquired casually, not even bothering to look at him. Coyle must know that he was talking to someone unlikely to get overly excited at the notion of bosoms, whatever their proportion.

We were eating from bags of chips and drinking lemonade at a window table in Pennicooks, the cafe overlooking a large front lawn with Victoria Road beyond. From the kitchen at the back came the appetising aroma of fresh frying, adding to the wholesale miasma of pies and bread, baked that morning and displayed in trays behind the glass-fronted counter.

'Is it comin' to The Ormonde?' he replied gloomily. 'Tits as big as them ones would never be allowed to be shown at The Ormonde. Well, maybe in comedies, you know, like Laurel an' Hardy, you know, big, fat, owl ones with 'em wobblin' all over the place. These tits wouldn't be allowed cos these are proper ones.'

'Bare ones are they?'

'Bare ones,' Coyle echoed. 'No, but they might as well be. Tommy says the mott has a dress on all the time but it's hangin' low and there's tit-ends stickin' through it like bottle corks.'

'And it was showing in London?'

'London,' he sighed protectively. It was still his brother's London, still on loan to him.

'Well, who is she then, this mott?'

Gingerly, the boy chose three fat chips from his bag and popped them in his mouth without cooling them, allowing me to observe them at close quarters being shifted about his maw by a squeamish tongue. 'Jesus Christ, these are friggin' hot,' he managed when they had cooled enough for him to speak. 'That's jus' it, I can't remember, I can't remember the title o' the filum or the name o' the filum star. Tommy tol' me but I can't remember.'

'Why don't you put some vinegar on those chips or blow on them before you put them in your mouth?' I suggested, not bothering to disguise my disgust.

'She's famous though, cos I seen her in filums before an' in picture books. She's got long, black, curly hair, big wet lips an' big…'

'Tits,' I finished.

The boy laughed, open-mouthed a masticated coating on his tongue and teeth and in disgust I averted my gaze through the window, to see a family coming up the path. Taking a single chip from my bag, I blew on it gently before chewing delicately in the hope that the ignoramus, sitting with me, might learn something of the etiquette employed. Still with a half-smile on his lips and his blue-grey eyes unchanged, he took a sip of lemonade from his glass, leaving droplets of congealed fat on the surface. Nauseated, I took a sip of my own lemonade and pushed the remainder of my chips aside, I couldn't face food any longer. The family seated themselves at an adjacent table.

'You don't want 'em, I'll have 'em,' Coyle volunteered. I nodded and, turning my face to the window, saw Donoghue arriving at the entrance to the path. 'Bottle corks, friggin' bottle corks.' He was leaning over the table, his words whispered. 'A low-cut dress an' bottle corks,'

Donoghue entered, exuding that air of confidence I so grudgingly admired. Ordering a squash, he began talking agreeably to the woman behind the counter. Coyle watched him, and as he finished his own chips and began eating what was left of mine, he beckoned the new arrival to come and sit with us.

Pulling a chair between us, Donoghue started to suck at his squash through a straw. Straight from the bag, Coyle emptied the last of the chips into his mouth and, with words filtering through them, said, 'A cowboy filum, Paddy, Billy the Kid, Doc Holliday an' Pat Garratt all after the same…'

Donoghue didn't have to think or even take the straw from his mouth: '*The Outlaw.*'

Coyle whooped, spluttering sludge into the air and on to the table in front of him, which he then thumped triumphantly. 'That's the one, be Jaysus. What's the woman in it called?'

'Calamity Jane.'

'Calamity Jane?' Coyle puzzled, then, a light of understanding ignited in his eye. 'No Paddy, the filum star what played her?'

'Jane Russell.' Donoghue was bored already. He took the straw from his squash bottle and began turning it through his fingers. Coyle thumped the table again and the light in his eye became a flame. Conscious of the adjacent family, he closed on Donoghue's ear. 'Been tellin' Christian here, about the way Jane Russell is in *The Outlaw*. Then he started describing the star's great attributes and drooling, lovingly cradled thoughts of them.

Donoghue yawned, finished his drink, ironed out the straw on the table and looked ready to go.

'Found out about them periods?' I asked.

'Yeah, nothin' much, it's to do with cycles an' they makes women grumpy,' he replied, sounding disappointed. 'Listen, you doin' anythin' this evenin'?'

'Not particularly.'

'Got a date an' she's got a friend. Want to come along?'

Much as I would have loved to join my adventurous chronicler, my courage wasn't up to it.

'Gonna try somethin' new, tonight,' he muttered quietly, mysteriously.

I had not yet come to terms with tickling palms and tongues in ears and 'something new' sounded dangerously experimental. 'No, wait, just remembered, got loads to do for my dad tonight,' I excused myself, loathing myself for cowardice.

Coyle had Donoghue's attention again. 'You know our Tommy, well, he lives in London now. He's home on holiday an' he's after tellin' me about seein' that filum in London. On'y place in the world where a filum like that can be seen is London.' No longer so protective of the city, he seemed happy for the first time to share it. 'One day I'm goin' there to live whit Tommy. You can visit us, Paddy an' then we can see filums the likes o' *The Outlaw*, any time we want.'

Donoghue yawned again. 'That filum was made years ago I saw it at The Ormonde when I was a kid, "U" cert.'

Crestfallen, Coyle wiped grease from his lips with his sleeve, desperately thinking of words sufficiently vituperative to express his outrage. 'Jesus Paddy, what an eejit thing to say. Tommy lives in London, for Christ's sake. You think Tommy doesn't know wha' he's talkin' about?'

'Don't care about London or Tommy. *The Outlaw* is U Cert, kid's stuff.'

'Can't be,' Coyle grumbled into his lemonade, his gorge of indignation harder to swallow than his chips, this classification completely destroying any illusion of forbidden fruit.

I smiled to myself, Coyle's breathtaking revelations an irrelevance, when compared with the stuff that Donoghue had to tell. What could Dermot and Tommy Coyle tell Donoghue about motts, big-titted or otherwise? Dermot had his comics, all Tommy had was risqué London cinemas, while Donoghue was accustomed to the real thing. Why, only a week ago, the boy had shown me a red mark on his neck, something called a 'love bite'. Apparently a girl had sucked on his neck so hard that blood had risen to the surface of the skin. 'Had to stop her, like a bloody vampire, she was,' he had complained.

Coyle was quiet, disconsolate. Poor Tommy was going to have his work cut out restoring London's reputation after this; it was going to take a lot more than bottle corks.

Donoghue had twisted his straw into a figure of eight and had an air about him of someone who had just won an argument without really trying. Ironing out the straw, he threw it like a dart into a waste paper bin.

'Can't be,' Donnelly murmured disagreeably.

Donoghue had tired of Coyle and, standing up suddenly, made it look as if he was tired of me also, something he might have to pay for. Without excusing himself, he hooked his thumbs in his trouser pockets and swaggered to the door then, turning suddenly as if about to draw, the look he gave us was like a bullet from a Colt 45, then smiling mysteriously, he left.

At the table beside us, the father remonstrated with his small son over some misdemeanour and the mother, a tired-looking woman, smiled at us self-consciously.

Coyle was back to nibbling on his nails and sulking. 'That Paddy Donoghue thinks he knows everythin'. Tommy lives in London for Christ's sake, where does Donoghue live? On the bloody road to Delgany.' Studiously consulting the fingers of his left hand, which looked as if they had just been freshly boiled, he began gnawing at the stunted nail of the index. Donoghue had crushed him and he was sulking. 'That Paddy Donoghue thinks he knows everythin', so he does. Tommy says there's cinemas in

London showin' filums whit wimmin whit no clothes on at all. Tommy says there's special cinemas in a place called Soho. Absolutely naked so they are.' He now appeared disgruntled with *The Outlaw's* notoriety and was looking, once again, to establish London on the Rabelaisian map. Taking his finger from his mouth and checking that he could not be overheard, he continued, a little more brightly, 'When I leave school I'm off to London to live whit Tommy. He lives in Brixton in London's stockbroker belt. Tommy's got a job deliverin' laundry. He knows every street in London, an' I tell you wha', London's even bigger than Dublin 'Soho an' naked wimmin for me as soon as I get to London.' His chin jutted out and he gave a yellow-toothed smile of expectation. 'Another thing Tommy tol' me, in this Soho place, you can get magazines whit naked wimmin, imagine that, why dontcha? Not much chance o' that in Greystones,' he finished mournfully.

Coming up the path was Seamus Flanagan, waving cheerfully. I turned away, pretending I hadn't seen him. Rat-faced Coyle with his yellow teeth and disgusting eating habits was bad enough, but to be caught sitting with Snot Nose as well could ruin altogether the credibility I had gained from my victory over Patsy Plunkett. What if Cora Casey and friends should decide on an afternoon in Pennicooks? I would never live it down.

'Here comes Flan,' Coyle announced happily.

I groaned. Yes, here comes Flan, loping through the door, grinning inanely and wearing clothes to fit a boy only half his size. Tall, gangly, bony and disjointed, he looked as if he had been carelessly constructed with knotted pipe cleaners as a cruel joke. 'Hia Flan,' I greeted him.

'Donoghue tol' me you was here,' he grinned, pulling up a chair between us.

'We jus' had a bag o' chips, an' I might get another,' Coyle told him.

'You're not going to get another?' I groaned painfully.

The boy rattled coins in his pocket. 'My da gave me a sixpence, he had a winner.'

Flanagan shook his head. 'I got no money jus' come in to see yous two.'

Oh, if only Flanagan would carry a handkerchief, lavatory paper even, for already viscid, curd-like emissions were gathering and plugging up his nostrils. I didn't have any money left or I would have treated him to chips and excused myself. 'Can't help you there, Flan, I'm skint,' I told him.

Voice lowered again, Coyle was telling Flanagan about the lewd books, risqué films and the wonderful licentious life to be had in brother Tommy's London The newcomer's nostrils bubbled with excitement and his eyes seemed to grown in size. His hair stood on end like tufted straw and pubescent, organ stimulating hormones could be seen, trying to escape from beneath the over-tight fabric of his trousers. 'No clothes at all,' he moaned.

I was bored. 'You two ever read a book with Lemmy Caution in it?' Too engrossed in carnal imagery, the boys ignored me. A question wasted anyway. Lemmy Caution came from a bookcase beside my mother's bed. In it were books I was not allowed to read until I was much older and in that bookcase there was an interesting exercise book that my Mother wrote a lot of stuff in which I would read and remember. My mother was far cleverer than anyone would think. It was a world of prohibition. She would be horrified to know that I knew where the key was hidden.

I tried again. 'You two ever see Humphrey Bogart in *The Treasure of the Sierra Madre*?. I was ignored again. Coyle was waxing on about *The Outlaw* and Donoghue's presumptive ignorance, while Flanagan, hanging on his every word, shuffled uncomfortably in his chair and eased himself inside his trousers by stretching out his legs. Emissions now threatened on his septum and were edging towards his lips, now singular, now twinned, nauseating, but grossly fascinating to watch, their progress halted by a tongue tip before a huge sniff sent them hurtling back upwards, whence they came. This company could not be tolerated for much longer, and not at all, should Coyle decide on more hot chips or Flanagan's nose issue worsen.

'Jaysus, but we'll have to get to London, Flan,' Coyle avowed, slapping the table with the palm of his hand. 'We'll live whit our Tommy, lookin' at mucky books an' watchin' mucky filums every night.'

'Every night,' Flanagan rejoiced, his long bony fingers attached to long bony wrists, reptilian-like, clasping and unclasping in agitated anticipation.

'Tommy's got a top job at a laundry in London's stockbroker belt collectin' mucky laundry but, for us Flan, we'll be collectin' mucky mags an' mucky films.' Coyle sniggered. The thought pleased him and he burst out laughing. He now disregarded the proximity of the family, who, preoccupied with their son's subdued behaviour, were paying no attention to his outbursts.

Flanagan cooed with delight. As the family got up to leave, the mother smiled at me again, the father shook the boy, who started crying and as they left, the mother turned her smile apologetically to the lady behind the counter.

Coyle was now elaborating on the juicy delights of Soho causing Flanagan's trousers to strain unreasonably. Truth was, London and Soho in particular, sounded very desirable to me but not Tommy's Coyle's London. I could only see dirty laundry in Tommy's London. 'Let me tell you about this guy Lemmy Caution,' I interrupted, 'He's a Yank, an FBI agent, wears a slouchy trilby and a trench coat. Know why he wears a trench coat? No, it's cos he's got a machine gun hidden under it.'

'Completely naked,' Flanagan groaned.

'No mags like that in Ireland,' Coyle lamented.

The company of these boys was becoming more aggravating by the minute. 'Draw some,' I snapped a spontaneous suggestion which would cause me months of untold misery and regret.

The boys stopped talking and stared at me, open-mouthed. 'Draw some,' they echoed simultaneously, as if I had just suggested something too outrageous to even contemplate.

'If you're desperate for naked women, then get some sheets of paper and draw some for yourselves.'

'Draw naked wimin?' Coyle was aghast at the suggestion as Flanagan unloosed the belt of his trousers and moaned ecstatically. 'Can you draw naked women?'

'Sure,' I beamed breezily. 'I can draw anything.' Representation of the naked female form had never before occurred to me and I was struck at how such a brilliant idea had hitherto escaped me. I found the thought of it intriguing and exciting and the faces of the two boys, both lustful and sceptical, amused me and gladdened my heart but oh, how I would, in the near future, pay for this little test flight of vanity.

'Naked wimmin,' Flanagan breathed as green-tinged mucus became a real threat to his top lip. He eased his chair to allow another family to take up the table recently vacated.

I had to lower my voice again. 'Can I draw a naked dog, a naked horse, a naked man? Of course I can.'

'Would you draw some for us?' Coyle enquired slyly.

'Maybe,' I replied demurely.

'Do some for us then,' Flanagan urged.

'Shhhhhhhhh,' Coyle advised, in deference to the new family whose small boy was far more boisterous than the last.

Flanagan lowered his head, lowered his voice 'Like bent over.'

'Shhhhhhhhh,' Coyle advised again as the small boy knocked over a sugar basin.

Flanagan lowered his voice even further and, squirming on his seat, tried to adjust himself more comfortably. 'Like grown-up motts, they gotta be grown-up?'

In celebration Coyle was on his feet for another back of chips and was rummaging in his pocket for money. Flanagan was in serious trouble with his trousers, repellent snot had finally breached his lips and, as the small boy began sweeping sugar off the table on to the floor with his hand, I stood up to go. The state of affairs had become far more irksome than I could tolerate.

Chapter Fifteen

*F*or some time after this meeting in Pennicooks, I was avidly pursued by the two boys, feigning a want for companionship easily seen through. Drawing the kind of pictures they had their hearts set upon was easy for me, but this was the summer holiday and such a prospect offered no incentive; their transparent overtures were wasted. Anyway, I didn't want either of them as friends and the actuality, that I had no others of the same age couldn't even add to their appeal. What had Coyle to tempt me with? Red-raw ravaged finger-ends and disgusting eating habits, his comics, maybe, but by now I must have seen them all. And Flanagan well, apart from being able to lasso himself with his own snot, what other talents did he possess? I didn't trouble myself to think.

I didn't really count Donoghue as a friend just now, for although he furnished me with lusty and alarming snippets of his amorous encounters, which I couldn't get enough of, I couldn't help but feel that he was getting more out of these disclosures than I was. Of late, I was befriending Reardon, as we had great fun borrowing skiffs from Charlie Hemp and racing each other out to sea. Anyway, this was the summer holidays and at home things were looking up. Having tendered for two big construction jobs in Bray, my father had been promised both of them. The really good thing about these jobs was that they would be carried out on the basis of time and materials, my father's time at three shillings per hour with materials paid for by the clients themselves. No need for any initial financial outlay and with four to five months work ahead it would be enough to get the family on its feet again. Moreover, I could have as much work as I wanted during the holidays and I would get paid. My father was lighter on his feet of late, the cloud had lifted from his eyes and I had even heard my mother talk of Grandma Plunkett coming back.

Not that I didn't have friends, I had some very good friends, but being highly selective in my choice of them, they were few, my tendency being towards quality rather than quantity. Not for me a collection of clumsy, pre-pubescent duffers like Coyle and Flanagan, but rather friends I had chosen for myself, adult, intelligent and versed in the ways of the world, as befitting a boy such as I, talented and athletic, not to mention, of superior national heritage. My friends were Nugget Nolan, Old Mr Malone and The Ormonde acolyte, Frank Moore. Friends, who, in the fullness of time would be of benefit to me and I thought of them as an investment in my future. Nugget Nolan, the eccentric raconteur, beautifully balanced by Mr Malone, delightfully taciturn and guaranteed to hang upon my every word and Frank, an inexhaustible source of cinematic fantasy. One, the talker, one, the listener and one, the purveyor, my chosen friends, the kind that I deserved, what need had I for the numbskulls at school?

Summer days would likely start with my feeding of a neighbour's chickens, the extent of their feed dependent on the availability of waste foodstuffs. The owner of the chickens was a crusty old man called McCarron, who spent most of his time pottering about wasteland at the back of Calgary, which he claimed as his garden. The old man didn't like me, but then, he didn't seem to like anybody, never speaking to anyone, unless it was about trespass in his 'garden'. He was suspicious of me at first, waving his fist and cussing when he saw me, but when he realised that I wasn't about his coops to steal eggs he left me alone to feed his chickens, at will. Sometimes they would only get a scattering of food, but other times, as when the waste collection cart was late, they would get a feast, hands full of food from a bucket, scattered far and wide so that all would get a share. It made me feel happy to feed chickens early on a morning, and sometimes the happiness would last all through the day. That was when I first learned that giving and happiness were synonymous.

Later, after feeding the chickens, the day would likely find me in my mountain den re-living my spat with Patsy Plunkett, or on the cliffs, leading armies or saving maidens who all happened to look like Cora Casey. Or I might be Cuchulainn with sword and spear, or Lemmy Caution with a machine gun, fighting off marauding creditors and debtors, I had never really found out which was which, so banded together I could be equally suspicious of them both. The intended quest for the crown jewels had not materialised as I had hoped. Two lone forays into the ruins had proved boring and as fruitless as they were half-hearted. The search was not abandoned, just postponed, awaiting some tangible clue as to their whereabouts, an old map or a cryptic letter or someone appearing on the scene with a long-held secret to impart. The only thing absolutely guaranteed to re-kindle interest and galvanise me into action was word that the Plunkett brothers were on the move again.

The Plunketts didn't know it, but I often watched them from my mountain lair. Sloping steeply, the rock strata fell away to a low spur of tableland, extending out to sea which they used as one of their fishing sites and from this secluded height, I had the voyeuristic pleasure of seeing without been seen. I loved being on the mountain when the Plunketts were below. But on really hot days, Poppy Boyle's visit to the North beach being one of them, I would not go to the mountain but spend hours on the beaches or swimming from the pier or rowing in the harbour with Reardon, but lack of sunshine didn't really concern me too much.

Fair or foul, the weather, each day, had its own unique singularity, an exhilarating wonder, disparate in a town cupped between the mountains and the sea. Best of all was when it thundered and lightened and the clouds boiled like tar and a coast towered white with foam against a fetch as black as ink. Best too, when the wind would cackle on the broken stones as if the crags were in black humour and a small creature such as I, the object of their unbridled whims. To my den then and safe behind curtains of rain at its narrow entrance the lady Cora would be waiting breathlessly inside.

Clouds would clear and a new world awaited me and with ready sword, I was on the steaming Head again with Black and Tans coming at me fast. How they resented an Englishman choosing to fight for Dark Rosaleen against the noble soldiers of an English king.

Each day as I made my way to the mountain, I would pass Nugget Nolan's shack and when I found him in good story-telling form, which was often, I would stay a while, sometimes, the whole of the morning, for he was the most entertaining man I had ever known.

Often I would meet with him on his way to work, gimping along with a sly smile on his face and his feet and thumbs outstretched, skipping as if negotiating a ship's deck in a storm and often, in infectious imitation, I would find myself rolling along beside him. He was always at his best when gossiping about locals or telling of his early days as a professional billiard player in the halls of Dublin and the number of hundred breaks he'd made or of his time as a regular in the Irish Free State army. Oh, what stories that man had to tell of himself, his extended family and his illustrious lineage. How enthralling for a young boy to hear of Nugget's great-grandfather, gold prospecting in Montana and witnessing the entire Little Bighorn encounter from behind a rock. What a man and what a family; only a great uncle on his mother's side being the radio operator on a ship called *The Carpathian*, and receiving, in 1912, a distress signal of some significance. And closer to home, who would believe that the very pen with which Michael Collins signed the Irish Free State Treaty, had been borrowed from Nugget himself. 'I'm after signin' me own death warrant, Nugget,' Collins correctly forecast as he handed back the pen. 'Jesus, we was a pair if ever there was one,' Nugget attested proudly.

But I couldn't help but have one niggling doubt about the man; he could be so different when there were others with him in the shack. A couple of cronies from Dan's or an audience of schoolboys and often he would make me feel like an outsider, a veritable fall-guy. Nugget the parodist, the jester, making everybody laugh, but why at my expense? There is a huge difference between a boy who can take a joke and a boy who is expected to take all of them. But I didn't complain because I knew he meant no harm, it was just the way Nugget was, he needed a platform and a foil to bring out all the best in him and really deep down I was pleased that he had chosen me. Anyway, the answer was in my own hands; I could avoid the shack if others were inside, or leave if others joined us, a small price to pay for hours of entertainment and a man's sincere friendship.

Or I might pay a visit to my second-best friend, Frank Moore, The Ormonde dynamo. How I admired and respected this guy, cinema controller and servant to every department. Shop sales, ticket sales, cleaner, usher, projectionist, Frank was your man, and if you wanted sweets or popcorn during the matinee, who could be relied upon to be seen standing in the aisle with a huge confectionery box around his shoulders but Frank. And any matters appertaining to movies, ask Frank the oracle. Did Mr McGrath, the owner of The Ormonde, know how lucky he was? He did not, or if he did, he never showed it, complaining about Frank constantly and blaming him for every little thing that went wrong.

Virtually unaided, this man ran that cinema as if he were the captain of a ship forever in danger of foundering on rocks. Conscientious and ubiquitous, it was said that he had never had a day off sick in the ten years he had been there. Everything he did, he did with a fevered passion, his wiry frame, clad in blue overalls, moving at double speed, like an old Mack Sennett cop-chase, yet, in the same hour, the same man could be seen in a dark suit and dickey bow, selling tickets in the kiosk. One day I would tell Mr McGrath what I thought of Frank and what I thought of him for the way that man was treated. But my unbounded admiration was reserved for his encyclopaedic knowledge of films and Hollywood and what he knew of producers, directors and stars was a well to which everyone was welcome. Why, Frank Moore could tell you who produced and directed *The Treasure of the Sierra Madre* with the same unassuming candour as he would tell you the time of day. And he was modest, too, his information never extravagantly volunteered; you would have to get it out of him but I was good at that, well, providing I could get hold of him in the first place. A hard man to pin down, sometimes I would call at his house but he always seemed to have just left and I was unlucky when I called to see him at the cinema, for I invariably found the door was locked.

But most of all I respected Frank for the way he had stopped the children of well-to-do families from tossing coins from the gallery into the four-penny front-row stalls. Cora Casey was one of those doing the tossing, but although I belonged in the four-pennies, I was the only boy never to be seen scrambling on the floor for a coin.

Then there was Mr Malone. Really, to call Mr Malone 'a friend' was a misnomer, but to someone (by choice of course) as short of friends as I was, this enhancement could well be excused.

In reality, he was a broken-winded, pipe-smoking septuagenarian, at least, who qualified as 'a friend', by being a great butt to a boy whose loquacity had been restrained by a day of isolation on a mountainside, but how pleased I would be to find him, on descent.

With my rhetoric aimed between a pulled-down trilby and the turned-up collar of a great coat, what looked like a brown, gnarled platter for a pair of leaking poached-egg eyes might not be everyone's idea of a friend, but it was mine. If a friend is someone who will, unselfishly, give you what you want, then Mr Malone was just the man for me. I wanted a ready ear, available for what I had to tell, preferably without interruption and with the right audience for I always had a lot to tell. Mr Malone was the right audience, he never interrupted.

Anyway, I loved the way he stroked his raspy jaw, nodded his head and muttered, 'Aye, indeed aye,' at intervals of one to twenty minutes, when bouts of coughing and the lighting of his pipe allowed. But I never looked for him, just happened on him from time to time, except for one occasion that summer, when, after conversation with Nugget Nolan, I had found myself rushing out of the shack in the hope of finding him.

It was this old man who had got me thinking rationally about Rasputin. Were they not about the same age? Ever since that terrifying night in the dock basin, I had kept a watchful eye out for the lunatic, particularly after nightfall and especially when the moon was shining, but I had never discussed that encounter with anyone, not even my sisters.

'What were you doing in the dock at that time of night?' they would ask, and, 'collecting sea water, to drink and make myself sick' would require far more explanation than I was prepared to give. But I had made discreet enquiries and it emerged that O'Toole, snaring rabbits on the golf course had seen something lurking in the gorse that night which spooked him enough to abandon his snares and run for the safety of the road. Carmody, the green-keeper, corroborated this story with an earlier report of seeing something black and scary crossing the seventeenth fairway at dusk. No one else, as far as I could gather, had seen anything untoward that night, but for me it would always remain one of the most frightful nights of my life.

I was not afraid when alone on the daylight trails of Bray Head unless I allowed my imagination to run riot; then, I felt I saw him behind every rock and bush and could only relax when I reached the sanctuary of the North Beach road. And yet I longed to see him again, but this time from a place of safety, much as one would observe a pack of savage wolves from the safety of a truck.

But now, with Mr Malone in mind, I was much more rational in my concept of the wandering Russian. Yes, they were about the same age, Rasputin possibly up to ten years older. How could I be so scared of a man in his late seventies? Surely too old and

139

feeble to run and catch a healthy child, especially one who would soon be twelve years old and as fit and hearty as I was. I could certainly out-run, out-jump and out-swim old Malone, so what had I to fear from another equally decrepit? And how weak and undernourished he must surely be; no one had ever reported seeing him eating food. No, what if I had leaped out at him that night, which of us would have been the more afraid?

Out on the Head, I imagined all kinds of scenarios, the most oft-repeated was his capture of Cora Casey, my leaping to her rescue and her submissive undying gratitude.

And it was this issue of comparison that I had raised with Nugget Nolan that day and he agreed with much of what I had to say, but cautioned that a derelict he may be, but one with a mission, the mission being to catch children, bury them alive and so avenge his wife and what in the world is more scary than someone with a mission?

From Nugget Nolan I learned little new about Rasputin but what he had to tell that day about Mr Malone would shake me to the core.

'Wanted on both sides o' the border,' Nugget confided with a conspiratorial tap to the side of his encrusted nose. 'Of course, you can't get a word out o' him he's scared he gives himself away.' Nugget, after filling his cheeks with air, exhaled slowly. 'Dodger Malone' is a man with a dark past, so he is. You didn't know they called him 'Dodger', did you? An' there's an awful lot more that you don't know about him as well. Did you know that in his heyday Dodger Malone dodged more bullets than Tom Mix. Only ever hit the once, so the story goes. On the run when a bullet shot by a Black an' Tan entered his latissimus dorsi an' embedded itself in his placenta to remain embedded there to this very day; tried to dig it out with a rusty screwdriver while on the run, so he did. That's how he got his name, dodging bullets. And sure who gave him that name? None other than my uncle, Chief Superintendent Thomas Nolan, long gone now with a bullet in his corpus callosum, shot by who I wonder.' He tapped his nose again. 'Now don't be breathin' a word o' this to anyone else 'n' certainly not to the man himself. Old Malone was an IRA man an' he's still wanted on both sides of the border. Be careful what you say, too much from you an' you'll scare him off.'

This really was incredible news and I was shaken. 'You would never, ever think so,' I marvelled. 'So that's why he hardly ever says a word, I've always wondered.'

'Still lookin' for them crown jewels?' Nugget's switch from Mr Malone's dark past was quite casual.

'Not interested any longer.' My answer was of equal detachment.

'Not botherin' no more about them ruins then?' This question was more pertinent, one ginger eyebrow raised quizzically above the other.

'Ruins! What ruins?'

The lofty eyebrow lowered to the level of its twin and the cobbler began glancing about the shack as if fearing an eavesdropper. His mouth tightened. 'I gotta be very careful here an' I gotta be able to trust you, them jewels, somethin' might o' come up.'

Suddenly I was very interested and not pretending to be otherwise. 'Nugget, you could trust me with your life.' Was this what I had been waiting for?

'It was you what got me thinkin',' he continued, his voice scarcely above a whisper. 'Thinkin' about them jewels an' the thragic death of me poor Uncle Thomas, an' then I remembered somethin'.' Moving from the bench, he stealthily checked that there was no one listening at the door. A large fly buzzed crazily against the window glass. 'Somethin' from a long time ago.' He tapped at the side of his nose; two blackheads among many shone bright purple in a shaft of sunlight. The buzzing fly touched its wings on a strand of spider web but its panic was strong enough for it to free itself.

Nugget looked around the shack and listened at the door again, before saying, 'Dodger Malone is the somethin' that's come up. That's why I've been tellin' you the truth about him, why he doesn't talk any, and why some people who don't know him think he's slow.' The fly launched itself against the window glass again and Nugget searched beneath his slimy smock and scratched himself intimately.

'Mr Malone?' I queried, trying not to sound excited.

'Himself. I remembered an owl suitcase me Uncle Thomas gave to me just before he copped it. "Keep this Nugget and guard it with your life," says he to me. What's in it? says I to him. "A matter o' life an' death," says he to me an' I've allus wondered if it was his own death that he was after meanin' for when Uncle Thomas spoke that day to me he had a faraway look in his eye as if he was about to go some place an' was never comin' back. Sure couldn't he see what was comin', God rest his soul, cos it was jus' before he copped it from that bullet in his corpus callosum.'

'Oh Nugget,' I breathed. 'You found something in the suitcase?'

'May the good Lord strike me down if I ever tol' a lie, but I never so much as took a peep inside that suitcase until the other night when you had got me thinkin',' then, putting his hand on his heart to steady it, he said, 'I got it down from the loft where it has been all these years an' I started goin' through it.' Ginger eyebrows met in the middle as his face screwed in consternation at thought of what that suitcase had revealed. The fly flew headlong into the trap and in a mullion corner a spider moved cautiously along a strand of web.

The cobbler closed his eyes as if memory of the suitcase pained him. 'May God protect me from what I foun' in there,' he said as he crossed himself reverentially. 'Things that mortal man could on'y expect to see in nightmares, things that could not be showed to another mortal man without bringin' the wrath o God down on him from Heaven.' After ferreting beneath his smock and withdrawing a crumpled piece of paper, he added, 'Except for this, the on'y thing that can be shown in top secret to an interested party, an' the interested party in this case, is none other than yerself. Sure you're on'y a boy, so you are, an' may God forgive me for what I'm about to do now.'

Almost overwhelmed with honour, I craned my neck forward for a better view of the piece of paper which he was straightening out on the workbench. The spider moved quickly and felicitously to the centre of its web and began inspecting the mortal remains of the fly. Pulling a box towards me with the toe of my shoe, I perched on it for a closer look. Smudged words in pencil, the word 'jewels', unmistakably scrawled on top of the paper, with what looked like a list of names, crossed out beneath. At the bottom of the list, one name only remained, 'Malone' and a question mark.

'Dodger Malone,' I breathed, trying to keep euphoria from my voice.

The cobbler was quiet now, introspective, as if regretting what he'd done. Suddenly he darted to the door and threw it open, as if expecting to catch someone listening outside. There was nothing, only wind and the sound of the sea. He tilted his head at me. 'What's done is done now, and be it on my head if anything goes wrong.'

'Oh Nugget, do you think I could look inside your uncle's suitcase?'

A dark horror crossed the man's face. 'My God, but the contents of that suitcase could never be seen by a chislur. Ten years in Mountjoy jail, should I ever lift the lid. Remember my Uncle Thomas was a Chief Superintendent and privy to the very worst of humankind. And that's what's in that suitcase, yes the very worst of humankind. God forgive me, but I've said enough an' the hairs on the back o'me neck is standin' on end at thought of what I'm after doin'. Enough is enough, this piece o' paper is goin' back an' may I be struck down by a bolt o' lightnin' if that case is ever opened up again an' I'm thinkin' now I've made a big mistake in mentioning it all.'

'Nugget, I'm glad you did, I'm glad you did,' I said excitedly.

'Maybe this piece o' paper is nothing,' but then again maybe it's somethin',' Nugget said and, shaking his head ruefully, he folded the paper and secreted it once again beneath his smock.

'But I was thinkin' it might be just what you've been lookin' for an' with us bein' friends an' all.'

'It is what I've been looking for, it is. You would never think it of Mr Malone, would you? An IRA man, the suitcase and his name on that piece of paper, your uncle getting killed and all, Nugget I'm on the trail again and I must start with Dodger Malone. I'm a big friend of his you know.'

The cobbler's face clouded. 'So you are, I've heard, but remember what I told you, don't question him. If he's goin' to tell you anything,' let him do it hisself. It's my belief that Uncle Thomas copped it because he asked too many questions. No, now forget I said that for I've said too much already. Maybe you should folley him, folley him an' report back to me anythin' suspicious. Then when I give you the nod, take him to them ruins an' make him show you where they are. It's called surveillance. Folley him an' report back to me, you know, us bein' friends an' all. Start immediately, if not sooner.'

And that was when I found myself rushing out of the shack in the hope of finding the old man.

I had no idea in which direction I should go but by chance I chose the south road by the sea and after only a few minutes quickly walking, was confounded to see my quarry in the distance, surely an omen, a presentiment of wonders to come and my heart was thumping madly as I neared him.

The sun was pale in the early afternoon, the clouds high and the smell of sea and seaweed astringent on the wind. As I closed on the man, I saw that he was nursing his pipe in cupped hands and staring out to sea. He had not noticed my approach and was startled when I touched the collar of his greatcoat. He swung around on me, but his eyes were light and pleasing when he saw that it was I. Immediately, I began talking of the windy weather and the prospect of rain later in the day with my mind feverishly busy with need for dialogue more fruitful to my purpose.

As he listened to me, he took out a handkerchief and wiped his rheumy eyes, then began pulling heavily on the stem of his pipe until the bowl was glowing. Through black smoke, I continued talking about the weather, wondering how long it would be before the hawking started, wondering why he didn't save himself such distress by simply throwing his pipe over the wall into the sea. When it came, it came from his boots, that awful, bronchial expectoration, distressing to observe but giving me the chance to change the subject from the weather.

A recall of Irish history and his involvement in it might loosen his tongue, so with dramatic expression and theatrical flourishing of hands and arms, I evoked the crying of the hound of Finn and the swelling of the harp of Tara. Could my audience, an erstwhile, fighting man, be impervious to the image of the raven in Cuchulainn's dying eyes? Could he not see, as I could, clearly, on the tossing horses of the waves, the ghosts of his nation's past, of which he would ever be a part? He must feel my passion, yet I, not just a mere chronicler but of the same nation as the soldier who shot a bullet into him, embedded in his placenta to this very day.

I stole a look. Nothing I had said had impacted on the man, was he wise to me? He just fussed with his pipe, lightly tapping the bowl on top of the wall to watch loose ash be taken quickly on the wind. With liver-spotted hands he filled the bowl again from a tattered leather pouch, compacting tobacco with a calloused thumb. I was quiet now, waiting. Presently, he looked at me keenly, as if perplexed by eloquence from one so young as I, keenly, the way a critic might look at an obscure piece of art, impressed but unsure of its merit. Then, after what seemed like an age, he said, 'Aye, indeed aye,' and puffing at his pipe, turned his gaze again back over the sea wall to the tossing waves.

He was not wise to me but I was annoyed with myself for not having found a way of bringing the Irish Crown Jewels into my nationalistic and passionate rhetoric.

Chapter Sixteen

We were halfway through the summer holiday when back word came from the two construction jobs in Bray. How relentless is failure once it gets a grip. This was a bitter blow for my father and for me, not one hour's work, not one shilling's pay. And, aggravating adversity, he was owed money. When work is successfully completed why can't people pay? A builder lays out his own money for materials and his time in execution of his skills only to be disappointed and frustrated by the hauteur and sheer deceit of the shameless users who have employed him.

Among others, two widows were in debt to him for a total of thirty-five pounds and I could expect to be rewarded if I was successful in collecting it. Mrs Keogh of Delgany owed him twenty pounds and Mrs Darling of the Burnaby owed him fifteen. 'Get to old Mrs Keogh before the pubs open,' my father had advised.

Mrs Keogh was wonderfully ugly, the kind of ugliness that really ugly people revel in. With a weathered face, scattered with dark blotches, she reminded me of a potato fallen from a sack and forgotten for a year, her whiskered chin its sprouting roots. The widely held belief among the children of the village that she was a witch was a reputation she endorsed by refusing to trim these whiskers and waving a stick at every child she came in contact with. 'Don't be frightened if she waves her stick at you, it's all show,' my father assured me when I expressed my reservations.

But Mrs Darling of the Burnaby was quite a different person. A tall, austere woman who sat in the bench in front of us at Mass and had a most haughty manner but was undeniably handsome in spite of my father's contention that she applied her make-up with a fish-slice. She held her stern head high compelling her to look down her nose at everything she saw and was famous for wearing a different suit each day, with matching hat and frown. But she smelled nice, so nice that I would always try to manoeuvre myself directly behind her in church, where I could close my eyes and breathe her perfume in; the lovely way she smelled would make me think of her at night.

The uphill walk to Delgany would take an hour or so, plenty of time to stop at The Ormonde and have a chat to Frank.

Frank always spent Sunday morning cleaning, in preparation for the afternoon matinee. No cinema today for me, though; I wasn't spending pocket money on an invisible rabbit called Harvey, especially on a lovely day like this.

As I approached the forecourt, I could see him working in the foyer and I waved to him. I think he saw me although he didn't wave back, fiddling as he was with the bolts on the big glass doors that were always hard to open. He disappeared into the auditorium as I approached and, trying the doors, I was surprised to find them still locked. The emergency door at the side of the building was also locked too, so he couldn't have seen me after all. It didn't matter. I would be passing the cinema on the way back I would have a word with him, then.

A heavy rain storm had broken at daybreak and the road to Delgany was black and shining, the trees and hedgerows still laden with rainfall, raindrops glistening in horizontal shafts of morning light. At each side of the road, a thin stream of water trickled down the hill, leaving small pools in its wake, gathering patches of debris from the road. The earth smelled rich that morning and the ground was soft and friendly to the tread and I was high with expectation as the sun began to climb into the sky above the sea to give the town its hottest day that summer.

Halfway up the hill and who was coming around a bend to-wards me but the ragged, elfin form of Christy Plunkett. I sneered. Ever since my fight with his brother, he had been avoiding me, no doubt, feeling responsible and fearing repercussions. He no longer accompanied his grandmother to Calgary, for she still made regular social visits, but according to Sam he still made persist-ent efforts to court her, using means as diverse as they were ineffectual, but which didn't include trying to ingratiate himself with her older brother. I had expected trouble since my fight with Patsy and the resulting ten stitches in his head but we were well into the summer holidays and nothing had happened yet. But I was on my guard. Shonti often looked at me meaningfully, and I knew that there were still unforgotten scores to settle.

We spotted each other simultaneously from a distance and Christy would have avoided me if he could, but where we would meet high hedges and undergrowth made avoidance impossible. Christy was hurrying and sweating heavily and would have passed me by if I hadn't accosted him by grabbing his arm, 'Big hurry, Christy.'

'Meetin' me brothers,' he replied nervously.

'Collecting money owed to my father,' I told him portentously

He wiped his forehead with the back of his hand. 'Jeez it's hot.'

'A job I often do for my father. He gets bad payers and has to send me.' I showed him the envelopes. 'Bills for a hundred pounds in here get two pence in the pound.' I tried to do the calculation in my head but struggled. 'That's about fifteen bob.'

'Jeez it's hot,' Christy complained, mopping at his brow again.

'Fifteen bob,' I mused, 'might get a new pair of shoes. Don't know though,' I added thoughtfully. 'Haven't worn those I got last Christmas yet. Remember them?'

The boy squinted down at the shoddy shards that he was wear-ing as if I might have been unfairly alluding to them and, screwing one foot uncomfortably into a small mound of mud, said, 'Got to go, meetin' with me brothers.'

'Where?'

His green eyes shifted from his foot and over my shoulder to the north: 'On Bray Head.' His eyes dropped to his foot again and he took a couple of backward steps down the hill. Matted with sweat, tufts of hair sprouted above his head like a cockerel's comb. The heat plucked at little globes of perspiration on his brow, nurturing them until they were fat enough to roll unhindered down his cheeks. He was agitated and wanted to be on his way. His shifty posture, his agitation, his eyes, unable to meet mine, made me suspicious and for the first time I wondered how much Nugget Nolan could be trusted.

'You and your brothers climbing Bray Head on a day like this?'

'No, we won't be climbin'. It's somethin' else.'

'Something else, what for then?' my voice was controlled, disguising a rising alarm. Was he meeting with his brothers at the ruins? Had Nugget Nolan been talking to the Plunketts?

'We're goin' shootin' lions.'

My ears had deceived me. "Shooting lions?'

'Yeah, shootin' lions whit Shonti and Patsy.'

'SHOOTING LIONS?' I expostulated.

Suddenly the boy took flight, running down the hill as fast as he could. Resisting the urge to race after him, I called out for him to stop but it was too late. What did he mean by 'shooting lions'? It just didn't make sense. I puzzled as I began my upward journey again. If I had been warned about Brother Brady, Gruff Duff and the Russian madman, surely someone might have warned me about mountain lions on the loose. I pondered his words, but there was no question in my mind, other than, had I heard him correctly? I was worried; they were not fishing and they couldn't be shooting lions, so why was he meeting his brothers? Well, I couldn't do anything about it now. Any action I might take would have to wait.

I was troubled. Was I deluded in thinking that I alone would share in Nugget's secret? The thought of panicking Christy running down the hill to meet his brothers nagged at me. Was 'shooting lions' Plunkett cryptology to throw another off the scent? Would a Plunkett have the brains to think of such a thing? The answer was 'no'; surely, my impotence was making me anxious. I allowed the hot sun to relax my mind. First, deliver the bills and I began rehearsing the nonchalant manner I would adopt when handing the money over to my father.

I set off again and half-an-hour later, I had reached the big wooden gate leading to Mrs Keogh's farmhouse. I rapped on the door, just knowing that I wouldn't get an answer. I rapped again, loudly, feeling cheated at the unrewarding resonance echoing within. I was about to leave when a mongrel dog loped into view and I was apprehensive; farmyard dogs are not noted for their sunny dispositions. It stopped and sniffed the ground then, eyeing me, gave a half-hearted bark of territorial apathy, before cocking its leg and wetting on a pile of reclaimed pan tiles. I made friendly clucking noises and it responded by lowering its head submissively, wagging an encrusted tail and waddling towards me, where it settled like an old, black rug at my feet.

With the dog for company I would wait a further five minutes for I was loath to make the long walk back to Greystones empty-handed. Sleepily, in the warmth, I traced my eyes along the grass beside the gateway. A band of mercenary chickens came my way, but when nothing was on offer, they looked at me with beady, accusing eyes and dispersed. The dog twitched and yawned and a broken cloud drifted across the face of the sun, freckling shadows on the farmland.

In the village a clock struck noon. I must have drifted off to sleep. Rising quickly to my feet, I disturbed the dog, who opened one sad eye, sighed deeply, closed the eye and fell back to sleep, gently snoring. I hammered the knocker one last time and left.

The sun was at its highest and brightest and the day was very hot. The leaves and grasses so upright on my assent had yielded to the heat and now drooped a little. The small streams of rainwater had dried already, leaving only languid pools and muddy patches. There was little sign of wildlife and as I began my downhill trek, there was only disappointment in the air.

I would have better luck with Mrs Darling, I told myself, but first I would visit Frank. I was relying on Mrs Darling and Frank to cheer me up.

Although there was a small group of children already chattering merrily on the forecourt, the glass doors of the cinema were still locked. I was not prepared to wait any more that day, so I hammered on the glass until Frank came hurrying from a staff room on the right. An intense, fidgety man with a shock of jet black hair and a face the colour of a ripe plum, the lines of tension around his eyes did not ease as he saw that it was me and would be a grille of stress before the day was out. Frank was far too conscientious for his own good. He looked at his watch. 'We don't open for another half-hour yet,' he mouthed through the glass.

'A minute only,' I mouthed back, signalling the bolts at the bottom of the doors.

'Too busy,' he signalled. 'Sorry.'

This really was a bad day. 'Ok Frank,' I conceded. I had set out with such high hopes that morning. No money from Mrs Keogh and the two envelopes stuffed in my pocket now creased and flaccid. How could I hand the likes of them to Mrs Darling, an envelope, soggy with sweat from my groin? Bad omen meeting a Plunkett, Frank hadn't the time to talk to me, it was too hot and Reardon and Donoghue were upon me and I simply couldn't do with them right now. 'Not goin' to the matinee,' Reardon observed.

'What on a day like this? You'll be breeding maggots in there today. Anyway it's about an invisible rabbit,' I said despairingly.

'Well, Liam can't go next Sunday, he's been picked to row in the regatta,' Donoghue said.

'Got business to attend to,' I said, fishing in my pocket and flourishing the envelopes which by now looked like slices of wet bread. 'Already been to Mrs Keogh's, she wasn't in.'

'Saw you pass the house on your way,' Donoghue said. Donoghue lived with his family, halfway up Coolagad Hill, on the way to Delgany. His house was illuminated by oil lamps and during a time of friendship he had shown me how to brighten and dim the light by control of a knob attached to a wick. His house belonged to another age and had a wonderfully strange atmosphere with firelight competing with oil lamps and shadows moving everywhere; even when nothing in the house was moving, shadows were. Low, oak beamed ceilings, cast iron fireplaces with turf and logs beside them and polished timber floors and all the time, the shadows, transient, ethereal, ghosts of the past observing life within the walls from dim penumbra.

Reardon clapped his hands gleefully: 'Next Sunday regatta day. Uncle Jimmy is rowin' in the big one. Me, I got picked for the juniors. Wait all year for regatta day.'

I was jealous. I was hoping to get picked for the juniors. Reardon was better than me, but not much. He would make up a team of four and I should have been one of them. His father constructed boats and skiffs in a workshop beside his house and, whenever I could, I loved to watch him at his work, marvelling at the way he shaped timbers by soaking them and wedging them between beams and benches to get the required curves. And the words he used, like ribs and breast-hooks and knees made me think of a medical man rather than a carpenter. He specialised in skiffs, sculling boats he called them. Rowing was in the Reardon blood and that was why his son was better at it than I was.

'The filum next week is *Winchester 73*,' Donoghue said. 'My Uncle Pat is after seein' it in Dublin. Said it was the best cowboy filum he's ever seen. That's the one that Liam's gonna miss. There's a bad guy in it called Waco Johnny Dean an, my Uncle Pat said, he was the best bad guy that he's ever see. He must come from Waco in Texas. I got a map o' Texas an' looked it up Waco is a town in Texas.'

'Ever seen a film called *The Treasure of the Sierra Madre*, with Humphrey Bogart in it?'

'Nah,' Donoghue answered, 'but heard of it. The Sierra Madre is a range o' mountains in California. I looked it up.'

'Hey, ever find out what them periods were?' I asked.

The two boys looked at each other and laughed. 'Nothin,' seems it's something women can get from ridin' bikes.' Donoghue volunteered.

'Had any more love bites lately?' I asked of him.

The two boys looked at each other again and laughed. Donoghue eyed me with a sideways look as if unsure of my worth; it was condescending and I didn't like it, but if I wanted the kind of stuff that Donoghue had to tell, I was going to have to put up with it. He turned to his friend. 'Show him, Liam.'

Reardon pulled down the collar of his shirt to reveal two fading red marks, more on his shoulder than his neck. 'These cudda been yours,' he said.

'Yeah, they cudda,' Donoghue concurred. 'Remember my mott had a friend an' I asked you to come. You wouldn't an' Liam came instead. Sure he's been gettin' them things ever since.'

'A lot more than them,' Reardon boasted.

'More than sticking your tongue in a mott's ear and getting your neck sucked?' The way they kept looking at each other and laughing was annoying me but it was just too hot to get annoyed.

'He ain't ready yet, is he, Paddy?' Reardon sniggered.

'Not ready!' I cried indignantly. 'I'm eleven, nearly twelve, same as you two.'

'Nearly twelve,' Reardon replied dismissively and I knew that whereas I was talking years these boys were talking experience and the sideways looks that I was getting were a measure of the divide. I wanted to know who the two motts were, but daren't ask; the way that things had gone so far today, one of them was bound to be Cora Casey.

I was beginning to feel uncomfortable. The heat was oppressive, but in addition, these boys were poking fun at me. I had an easier relationship with them as individuals, but paired up, I felt they threatened me. Like Rooney and Cronin, they each had enviable qualities of leadership and also like Rooney and Cronin, when hostilities reared, their origins were invariably nationalistic and were as unwonted and ridiculous, as all such conflicts are. Particularly so in my case, for although my sympathies now lay comfortably alongside republicanism, I was overt in my support of British imperialism for fear my enemies might take credit for my change of heart. Was it any wonder people didn't understand me when I really couldn't understand myself?

But just now hostilities were suspended and long may the adjournment last. I luxuriated in Donoghue's sexual avowals, and racing Reardon over the sea in skiffs was something I couldn't do without that summer. Time I was moving on because together these boys could be provocative and I sensed that they were heading that way now. I was wary of them because combined they were a formidable force, and they were wary of me, my history of bearing grudges being well-documented. Considering a permanent absence of supportive combatants, the timing of my retaliation could never be easily predicted but its unequivocal ferocity could, and both of them knew it well.

'Hey we'd better get a move on,' Reardon advised. 'We're gonna miss the start of the first filum.' They began to walk quickly towards the cinema.

'Shooting lions,' I blurted after them.

They stopped and turned. 'Wha?' they both enquired.

'What does shooting lions mean?'

They eyed each other blankly. 'Lions?' puzzled Donoghue.

'On the way to Delgany this morning I met with Christy Plunkett and he told me he was meeting with his brothers on Bray Head and they were going shooting lions.' The start of the first film forgotten, the boys were walking back towards me. I tried to read their faces; was that mischief, eclipsed by inscrutability?

'Say that again,' Reardon demanded. Their faces were straight, too straight and I felt my body stiffen with suspected but unknown stupidity, but if there was going to be ridicule, surely it must be heaped upon the head of Patsy Plunkett.

'What did he mean?' Inscrutability was melting into something else.

Reardon nodded. 'Shooting lions,' he agreed with affected enunciation. 'It's the season. August is always the start of the lion-hunting season in Wicklow. Sure the Wicklow Mountains is full of 'em.' He was still trying to keep a straight face but the sides of his mouth were twitching with suppressed laughter. The two boys were looking at each other, the film forgotten, and the nuances of mockery in their eyes were unmistakeable.

Donoghue put an arm around my shoulder, the sarcasm in his voice heavier than his arm. 'Big game hunters come from all over the world,' he explained patiently. 'Jaguar huntin' on Jeeney Hill is a big favourite.'

'Well, of course I knew it couldn't be…' I blustered in desperation, before denial was felled by peals of laughter. The boys could not contain themselves any longer and as I tried to join them in the hope that the laugh was on Christy Plunkett, my laughter faltered in an empty charade. The laugh was on me.

Reardon was almost on his knees. 'Jesus, I'm after hearin' everythin' now.' He slapped his thigh and kept repeating 'shootin' lions' over and over. This wasn't poking fun, this was unmitigated ridicule and I could no longer pretend to be amused. Whatever the mistake was, it was mine and I was seething with rage at being the object of such hilarity. Christy's words had been quite clear and I still had absolutely no idea of the joke. The boys were holding on to each other's shoulders now and, emasculated, were trying to tell each other about that 'jaguar' on Jeeney' Hill. My anger was at boiling point but could not explode without some kind of rationale.

'Ok, ok, I made a mistake.' My voice sounded cracked and stupid through its rage.

'It's fishin',' Reardon managed, when he had regained sufficient breath to speak. 'Oh God, I must tell this one at home, wait until Uncle Jimmy hears this one. Shootin lions is fishin', it's the way we say it. We shoot loyns out to sea of an evenin',' leave, 'em, then we go back in the mornin' to see if we've cot anything. Or we shoot loyns in the mornin' an' go back in the evenin'. The Plunketts have places on the Head where they shoot lines from, fishin' lines.'

My smile at the news was strained to the limit. Of course the Plunketts had fishing sites on the Head; one was directly beneath my den. The way these stupid people talked, motts for girls, toys for ties, loyns for lines, how was I to know that the youngest of the fish-faced gob-shites was taking about fishing and not hunting? The boys were still laughing and I knew my face was flushed with fury. It could no longer be contained and would be released upon them. My fists tightened and all my muscles with them.

The two protagonists, sensing the tension and happy to laugh rather than fight, turned and walked briskly towards the cinema. Smouldering, I let them go. To pursue the issue now would only make me a look a bigger fool, but then I heard unbridled laughter at the foyer entrance. The boys were telling another of my foolishness but I could do nothing. I was melting in the heat.

My fury now was choked with impotence as I saw them among the throng at the ticket kiosk and could imagine their hoots of disparaging laughter. My humiliation would be avenged, but would have to wait. Sick at heart and consumed with thoughts of the wretchedness of the day, I was shocked to find myself suddenly on Mrs Darling's doorstep. I had walked a mile and had not been aware of it. I was not aware of ringing the door-bell either but I must have done because, through an opaque glass panel, someone was coming in response.

The door opened to my forced, good-natured smile of greeting and Mrs Darling took the proffered envelope from my hand between two fingernails and handled it as she might a dead rat as it all but disintegrated at her touch. The folded bill inside, in better shape, she scanned remotely, without acknowledging my forced smile or my apologetic explanation for the state that it was in. I was not hopeful, tall and still as a statue, her air of indifference implied that both my father's missive and the son who bore it were beneath her reckoning.

I looked for something in her handsome, heavily made up face, but all I saw was barren eyes mirroring her barren heart. She turned her back and was lost among the dark oak panels of the hallway but, lingering after her, that sensuous aroma that I knew from morning Mass.

She returned so quickly I felt it could only be to dismiss me for being so disrespectful but, to my surprise, she handed me another envelope, a new, crisp one and as she closed the door on me, I flicked it open to reveal three white five pound notes and my heart leaped like a gazelle.

'Thank you very much, Mrs Darling,' I fussed to the disjointed shape behind the opaque glass. Warming to the woman and with her scent still swimming in my head, I thanked the door again and turned for home.

'No one in at Mrs Keogh's,' I told my father dolefully. Then, when disappointment had registered on his face, I handed him the crisp, new envelope. 'But fifteen pounds from Mrs Darling.'

A lousy day had turned out well.

Chapter Seventeen

*D*ays later and Mrs Keogh was not at home again. Was she laid dead inside the house – anything to avoid paying what she owed? Anticipating another absence, I had taken a loaf of stale bread, so at least this time, while I waited on the steps, I would not be bored and listless. My knocking on the door had alerted the resident chickens and a flock of local opportunist starlings, which I fed until the bread was gone. After about fifteen minutes and neither the old witch or her crusty farmyard dog had put in an appearance, I dusted my hands, stuck the bill through the letterbox and set off home, much less dispirited than before.

It was a dull overcast morning, but warm and as I made the long downhill journey to Greystones, I couldn't decide whether to go to my den or spend the morning swimming. The afternoon was taken care of. Mr McGrath, as a financial experiment, was putting on matinees all week, the film to be shown was not to be advertised until an hour before the doors opened, something of an adventure in itself. I chose swimming from the pier.

On the pier there was a gathering of St Jude girls. A quick glance told me that Cora Casey was not among them. A group of youths and one or two St Luke's boys were swimming from the steps and as I was wearing my swimming trunks beneath my trousers, I wasn't long in joining the swimmers.

Later, I saw a young man called Stan begin diving over the back of the pier wall into the open sea. Stan was a stylish diver and the pier emptied up on to the high wall, to watch him, girls cheering every dive. After a dozen jack-knives and swallow dives, he tired and began drying himself off with everyone returning to the lower level to gather around him, chattering.

That pier wall was no more than a yard wide, a concrete drop on one side and a thirty to forty feet drop on the other side into the open sea. When I saw that Stan had finished, I got up on the wall and walked its full stretch on my hands, but although many on the pier must have noticed me, no one applauded. This was something I couldn't understand, because what I did was much cleverer, much braver than Stan's diving, but no matter however many times I hand-walked that pier wall or however many people were on the pier at the time, no one ever applauded me. Once, a watching couple, I think they were English tourists, told me 'not to be so silly'. They had no admiration in their expression, no regard in the tone of their voices, only an aura of censure, very disheartening, for I always went to great pains to look unselfconscious about it all.

Homeward bound to get ready for the matinee; I was leaving the pier on the narrow gravel stretch above the slip, when coming towards me was a lone Cora Casey. We would pass within a matter of a couple of feet.

What happened? Head held imperiously high, and radiating sublime self-assurance, the girl was upon me without registering the remotest sign of recognition. And then she was gone, passed me by to join with the other St Jude girls on the pier; passed me by with about as much regard as she would have given to a stray dog.

Such poise and such contrast to my own pathetic demeanour, the moment I perceived her my heart shrunk instantaneously to the size of a pea, my throat dried, my innards turned to water and my eyes were downcast to the gravel path. Of course the girl ignored me; I was beneath contempt.

A girl like Cora Casey might stop and chat with a boy she felt her equal; she certainly would have stopped to chat with Stan. She might even flash her eyes and flirt with a boy of bearing, a confident charismatic boy, with a ready rapport. What that girl would not do was waste a glance on a shuffling, feeble skulker without the nerve to look her in the eye, a faint-hearted short-trousered excuse for a boy, with knees like a horse's hocks, a moral wreck astir on feet of clay. A boy, who could brave a pier wall on his hands, yet couldn't face a schoolgirl.

Report of a second fool's errand and my father's generous sixpence did nothing to lift my gloom, my misery so abstracting me that I didn't even thank him. Oh, the ache of Cora Casey, so severe a wound I thought that I might die from it; words hurt, but so often it's the absence of them that hurts the more.

For a little while, I brooded on the beach, listlessly skimming stones by the breakwater, then, recalling the earlier satisfaction of Mrs Keogh's chickens, I returned to Calgary for the metal bucket. If this bucket of food and the feeding frenzy to follow couldn't lift my spirits, then nothing could. I wouldn't even go to the matinee, for fear of seeing her again.

Making my way to the back of the house, I stood motionless beside the empty chicken coops and, with the bucket behind my back, waited. Recognised as a reliable source of food, the worldly-wise mother hens gathered around expectantly, while their naive and less mercenary offspring grubbed about in the hedgerows. Then, when I felt that I had sufficient inattention, when even the mother hens had grown impatient, I lifted the bucket aloft and began to beat the sides with a wooden spoon.

Nothing in the avian world is guaranteed to generate more frenzy than a drum roll such as this. No orchestration can cause such fervour as can a tin bucket and a spoon. Pandemonium from the four points of the earth came upon me then, in a cacophonous explosion of life, a phalanx of feathers, propelled on yellow twiglets, alternating at the speed of light. Headlong they hurtled through the impenetrable, assailing the unassailable, somersaulting the impregnable, a giddy troupe, whirling, twirling, pirouetting and defecating madly with excitement to the tune of a bucket and a wooden spoon. And how my spirits lifted, with a scatter of food to the left, a little to the right, more over my shoulder and a whole handful to the capricious winds, and, as I was assailed by a seething, scrambling, squawking, multi-coloured choreography of hunger and greed, I knew I would make the matinee that afternoon.

Feeling better and clearer in my mind as to how to conduct myself in any future encounter with Miss Casey, I resolved a whole new strategy. Next time, I vowed to throw caution to the winds, take her by the hands, swing her off her feet, catch her as she fell and come up with something quick and witty. The something quick and witty might take weeks, but I would make sure that it was very quick and very witty. And with this new determination, I set off for the matinee. But as I neared the cinema my resolve melted in fear that I might bump into her again. Best for me was to dismiss her from my life.

Yes, I would take my cue from Burt Lancaster, who this very afternoon was looking at me from a poster. Mr McGrath had chosen *Sorry Wrong Number* for his matinee and Burt, opposite a busty Barbara Stanwyck, was promising the thrill of this and every other lifetime. Could I smile like Burt, a rock-hard handsome face with rows of teeth like tombstones? Well, yes, I could have tombstone teeth, if it wasn't for the gaps between them.

Amongst the crowd gathering outside the doors, Donoghue and Reardon were talking to Rogan. They were probably talking about lion-hunting but I still had to face them, so it was up to me to make the first move. I caught their eye, nodded and making my way across to them was pleased to find them friendly. But Rogan's plump, pink face was grinning mischievously, and alluding to an earlier conversation, he winked at Reardon, saying, 'What's this about what you promised to Donnelly and Flanagan?'

'What's this then?' Reardon enquired slyly.

This was embarrassing, but at least I knew what they were talking about. I hesitated, thinking on my feet, then, covered up by joking, 'Just winding them, got Flan's snot running down his chin at the thought of naked women, Donnelly as well.' But I was annoyed at them being so indiscreet.

Rogan winked at Reardon again. 'This is yerman for drawin' naked wimmin.'

'Well, you're a good drawer, no doubt about it,' Donoghue said. 'So it's true then, you can draw naked wimmen?'

'Can I walk? Can I breathe? Can I draw a naked horse, a naked man? Of course I can. It's no big deal. Course I can draw naked women, but wait until I see them two blabbing little shites, if Father Fallon gets wind of it, I'll be excommunicated.'

'That what you're gonna do when you leave school, be an artist?' Rogan asked seriously.

'Nah, don't know what I'm going to do but you wouldn't believe what my parents want me to be; a priest. Imagine it, a priest.'

'Called you Christian to give you a head start,' Donoghue remarked.

'Brother McBride said I was Christian by name and Christian by nature,' I parried.

'O' Farrell's gonna be a priest, that's why he does no wrong at school. Ever remember O' Farrell gettin' strapped? Even Warthead daren't strap O'Farrell.' Rogan spat on the ground and worked the spittle into the mud at the injustice.

'O'Farrell will be pope before I'm a priest,' I commented wryly

Donoghue's eyes danced. 'Has its good points, like listenin' to a mott's confession.'

'Never thought of that,' I admitted as, with crosses in the air, I consecrated the cinema, the crowd around me and Frank Moore, who was opening the doors. 'What I'd like to be when I leave school is a writer. Create a character like Lemmy Caution. You lot ever read a Lemmy Caution book?'

'Gotta have an education to be a writer, 'Donoghue reminded me dolefully.

Reardon laughed shortly. 'Course he'll have an education. Doesn't he know his catechism from back to front?'

Rogan laughed. 'An' some lessons in Gaelic, he loves his lessons in Gaelic.'

'An' every Irish rebel song ever written,' Donoghue added laconically.

We were all laughing as we joined the large undisciplined queue gathering at the cinema doors. 'When I go for a job I'll tell my employer that I was educated by the Irish Christian brothers and what more in the world could a boy want?'

'An' you can show 'em your bruises to prove it,' Reardon remarked gaily as we waited our turn at the ticket kiosk.

In the kiosk Frank was selling tickets. 'Frank wants to see me after the show,' I told the boys. 'Don't know what he wants but said for me to be sure to meet him after the show, said it was important. Me and Frank like talking about films, directors, stars and stuff. We're good friends me and Frank.' Behind us was a group of girls and without turning or hearing her voice I knew one of them was Cora Casey.

'Hi Liam, hi Paddy,' I heard her say; I put the four pence back in my pocket and left. I didn't want to see the stupid film. I didn't want to live.

Chapter Eighteen

*O*n'y a fib an' nothin' to be gettin' out o' bed about,' the fib was Dodo's, relating to missing home-made toffee, for which Grandma Plunkett was regionally famous.

Treachery, she avowed was ethnic, and in her experience of hogwash, eyewash and downright lies, Korearionians, Russians, Chinese and heathen Communists were infamous, only the Anglo Irish and America could be relied upon to tell the truth, but fibs were ok. God and the Devil could shake hands comfortably over a fib.

Following her amicable dismissal, the old lady was on one of her regular social visits and occupying the only soft chair in the kitchen. More information was wrought by wireless, than she had ever dreamed of. Why, before she got that wireless, Killincarrig was abroad. A North Korearionian cease-fire was on the world agenda and God-fearing nations needed to be very careful of far-eastern duplicity.

And she had learned recently of another blight descending on the troubled world, 'Mau Mau' black-hearted, black-faced, witch-doctor worshipping heathens with a penchant for oaths, blood drinking, satanic rites and allegiance to the Devil. All the trouble in the world, she had noticed, was caused by foreigners, and why because foreigners, by and large, were not God-fearing and therefore had no concept of peace on earth and goodwill to all men. America should recall General Doug and Senator Joe and bomb the hell out of them all before it was too late.

I was directed by my mother to make our guest a pot of tea, sparking Sam into all too familiar, but unspoken mischief as she skipped across the floor to the pantry.

'And I'll get you a nice piece of treacle-cake, Mrs Plunkett,' she volunteered dutifully.

Malicious grins were exchanged between us as I brewed the tea and Sam cut the cake. There was no way the old lady could chew her own toffee but treacle cake would give Sam and I what we were looking for, top drawer entertainment. My sister, having cut a large wedge of cake, placed it on a china plate and laid it on her lap, while I set the tea tray on the table beside her. 'There you are, Grandma,' we said courteously before stepping back in gleeful anticipation.

Our beloved Grandma Plunkett had two sets of false teeth which appeared to operate in complete independence of each other and total dissociation of the jaws into which they were precariously set. Accustomed to this incompatibility, she could normally, eat, drink and talk without much trouble, but on the introduction of anything sticky, these fundamentals became mutinous and were a source of amazement to anyone who might be around her at the time. Her jaws opening to chew would find the sets of teeth inextricably clamped together, becoming so furiously mobile in their efforts to disengage themselves that the confines of her mouth could not contain them. They could be seen wrestling madly until inevitably popping out through her lips onto her lap, whereon, being popped back, they would immediately regain their independence.

Flicking at stubborn crumbs adhered to her projecting bosom Grandma brought the last gluey morsels of treacle-cake under control and thanked my ever accommodating sister profusely for her invitation to a second helping. But as Sam hoofed across the kitchen to the pantry, my mother stopped her with a look that would have stopped a bull elephant.

'Don't think I don't know what you two are up to,' she hissed behind the old lady's back.

Clearing her mouth with slurping sips of sweet tea, Grandma, suddenly grim-faced, embarked upon another favoured diatribe, every bit to be feared and loathed as Korearionians: the harlot. 'An' sure wasn't the harlot at church agin las' Sunday, showin' off the flesh of her bosom the same as she has bin doin'all these past weeks since the first day she dared to poke her powdered nose through doors that should be ever barred to the likes o' that one. No hat or scarf o' course an' throusers so tight, you would not think it possible for her to get into them, slacks is what she calls 'em, dear God, slacks indeed, for there's nothin' slack about 'em. And wasn't there such a gasp when the hussy has the cheek to get up an' wobble down the aisle for to take Holy Communion. Wasn't people turnin' to one another an' frownin' an' tuttin' an not bein' able to believe their own eyes as poor Father McCartney was made to tolerate the likes o' that one whit her neck cranin' forward an' her tongue lollin' out like a golly in a nest. Oh imagine, why dontcha, that poor priest havin' to put the blessed host, the Body and Blood o' Christ through lips so clarted up whit red muck, it must o' seemed to him as if he was droppin' the blessed lamb o' God into the gapin' jaws o' Hell. Then watch her chasseyin' back down the aisle whit the blessed host stuck in the corner of her mouth like a wad o' gum an' don't be lookin' for her to genuflect, ah no, genuflect an' she'd split them throusers from one side of her rump to the other, slacks indeed, can't genuflect so she gives a little kind o' nod towards the tabernacle, as if she an' the good Lord are best o'mates and after Mass she'll be meetin' him in Dan's bar for a laugh an'a jar.'

Earlier that morning, she had been blown down our path by the beginnings of a summer gale and now, mid-morning winds from the sea were lashing sheets of rain at the windows. Denied our covert mockery, Sam and I were paying attention to the worsening storm and were eager to be out in the middle of it, so, when we were instructed to escort the old lady home, we agreed immediately and dressed ourselves in rain-wear and boots.

'And no fooling about,' our mother warned.

Day or night, was there anything more exhilarating than wading through the tumult of a coastal storm? Night storms were the preferred; night was scary and more fertile to the imagination; the wild shoreline, the wind-whipped tree-lined roads, raw nature rewarding us with her most turbulent productions. Looking through the window, Sam and I assured each other that this storm could last well into the night and if it did, well, we would be out again as soon as it was dark.

Other children might be tucked up safely in their homes in such black weather, but not Sam and me. My abiding reason was a delight in scaring the life out of her, and Sam's abiding reason was the love of it. Oh, she would return home from such excursions complaining bitterly at my stories and antics, but come the next night-time storm and she would be first at the door with her boots on, wanting to be scared half to death again.

I had different horror strategies. In a maelstrom of darkness, wind and rain, I might tell her about the bizarre relationship I had with the banshee who haunted the Protestant graveyard, or portend the shadow of Rasputin holding a sack, behind a tree. Or, it was great fun to stop suddenly in my tracks, ostensibly to remove a stone from my boot or investigate mysterious rustlings in a ditch, only to vanish in an instant behind a hedgerow or over a farm gate, to leave her lonely on a black and empty road. What a laugh it was, her not knowing when or where I would overtake her and lie in wait. What a joke when I pounced out on her with blood-curdling shrieks, then, be made to promise not to do it again, a promise she knew that I could never keep.

Sometimes though, I would come unstuck. Once, on a particularly wild night, as we passed the Protestant church, I heaved her over the wall into the graveyard as a gift to my friend, the banshee. What I had not taken into account was a screaming fit that would overwhelm the storm. Neither was I to know that the tall iron gates were locked and that I would have to climb over the wall myself to help her out and so stop her fearful screaming. How humiliating to find that I couldn't get out myself without negotiating the spiked gates. How galling for me to have to beg her to go for help and how frustrating when my solicitations through the iron bars were blithely ignored. So being forced into climbing the gates, I slipped and badly lacerated my shin on a rusty spike. How furious to have to limp homewards with blood gathering in the folds of my sock. All the way home I harangued her bitterly, telling her that tetanus was not only inevitable but fatal and, because of her refusal to help me, tantamount to murder. But the prospect of life imprisonment for the murder of a sibling left her singularly unmoved and I found incredibly irritating her feigned concern at my death struggle home and her enquiries, far too gleeful, as to exactly how much my shin hurt.

As my mother called us, warning again about foolishness, a wave smashed into the breakwater blanketing the sky. 'Make sure you escort her all the way home and see her right into her house. No play-acting, no silliness. Mrs Plunkett is an old lady and you are responsible for her safety.'

The wind almost tore the door off its hinges as I opened it.

Wedging the old lady between us, we battled into sheets of rain. The woman being such a wide catchment for the wind, we had to hang on to her arms to prevent her being bowled over. As we bent forward against the buffeting, she scarcely uttered a word, saving what breath she had to call on Jesus, Mary and Joseph to help propel her homeward. Deliberately, we took her the longest, wildest route by the sea, but we were mindful of our mother's warning, sheltering her as best we could and helping her through puddles.

It was midday before we reached her small council house by the railway station and the wind now was at its most furious, whipping the branches of trees upwards in points of warning at the sky. Low sheets of slate-grey cloud, weighted with rain massed across the sea so that the sea and the sky were impossible to distinguish one from the other. Inland, well beyond the mountains to the west, a strange radiance threw pale light in a feeble protest at the path the storm was taking.

'Jesus Mary an' Joseph,' Grandma wheezed as she fumbled in her purse for the key. Inside, we ignored her appeals to take off our wet clothing. 'But stay a while an' warm yerselves,' she puffed.

Sam shook her head. 'No Mrs Plunkett, honestly we want to get back out there.'

The room was dark and cosy and packed with small ornaments and bric-a-brac. Faded black and white photographs in cheap frames stood on the mantle of a cast-iron fireplace. The fire in the hearth was out but the room smelled faintly of smoke permeated from earlier down-draughts.

'But sure I must make a fire for yous to warm yersel's before yous set off back,' she insisted as she busied herself at the hearth. 'An sure you must stop for a cup o' tay.'

'Please don't bother,' I answered hastily. Sam looked at me meaningfully, as outside the house the storm raged, reaching new levels of ferocity. I led Sam towards the door.

The old lady struck a match to paper beneath kindling and, as pale yellow flames took a tenuous hold in the grate, a sudden quiet fell upon the house. The wind ceased and the rain stopped beating against the windows and there was stillness. The round, black bundle at the hearth muttered, 'Jesus, Mary and Joseph,' and crossed herself, there was a low painful moaning from the chimney and emergent flames began dancing wildly in the grate.

Sam's fingers entwined in mine like snarled cord as something slammed into the house, shaking it to its foundations. Sam paled. The battering on the house must surely be the sea's waves engulfing us. The old lady's eyes dulled with fear as the solitary light bulb swinging above her head fused, as did the lights over a large part of the Wicklow coastline.

'The Lord save us but there goes the 'lectrics,' Grandma murmured fearfully.

Sam released my hand. 'But we're not frightened of storms,' she proclaimed bravely. 'Where we come from in Cravenvale there are no storms like these, no mountains, no rough seas. We're going before we miss it all.'

'We got you home safely,' I reminded the old lady.

Grandma got up and peered tentatively through the rain-washed window as the house shook again. 'Oh, please don't be goin' back by the coast, will yous?' she implored. 'Sure, I'd never forgive mesel' should anything happen to yous, after yous have been so good to me.' She kept her face to the window, nervously fingering the buttons of her cardigan.

'Exactly the way we are going,' I answered boastfully.

Sam opened the door, allowing the wind to crash into the room, scattering everything not weighted down. 'It's all so wonderful, so wild and wonderful, especially the wild, wild, sea,' she announced ostentatiously, throwing her arm through the open door.

Pushing her before me, I closed the door and we were out on the road and, wind and rain in our faces, we were making purposefully for the coast.

'Let's dodge waves,' I cried.

'No not today,' Sam cried back, 'too rough for that today.'

Powerful gusts whined and whistled in overhead wires and the sea was frenzied. Dodging waves was one of my favourite pastimes but I agreed with Sam, not today, the sea was very rough and what was more, there would be no one about to watch me. On the coast road, the sea-spray and rain had formed a misty waterfall and, weirdly, the sky had closed in on the sea and there was a strange darkness as if the sun had forever disappeared from the sky.

Opposite Marine Drive, a little, red figure by the wall of the Garda station, 'Is that Poppy Boyle?' Sam asked herself.

We crossed the road to the girl. She was chewing bubble gum and looked uncharacteristically downcast. 'Poppy, what is it?' I asked. She blew a bubble, the bubble popped, masticated gum adhering on her lips. She tried to free it with the tip of her tongue.

'Were you looking for us?' Sam asked. The girl nodded.

'How did you know where to find us?' I was intrigued.

Poppy spat the wad of gum to the ground and stared at it

meditatively. 'You're Mammy's after tellin' me,' she answered. Scraping at gum on her top lip with a fingernail, she continued moodily, 'I'm in trouble. I went to your house. Your mammy was ok with me; she told me where to find you, she said you would be walkin' by the sea. She said to tell you, you're not to be dodging waves. She really meant it. No dodgin' waves, she told me to tell you.'

She was wearing a red raincoat with the hood tied down beneath her chin with a bow. Her little face was wan, much paler than usual and the freckles on her cheeks were bolder, standing out like the wet, pink petals of a tiny rose, wet ringlets of hair peeked out from beneath her hood and were the colour of old gold. She looked small and vulnerable and her blue eyes were anxious. I put my arm around her shoulder and pulled her to me.

'Why were you waiting on us?' Sam enquired, concerned at her friend's demeanour.

Poppy hesitated, poking at the ejected bubble gum with the sole of her shoe. Something here was very wrong. This was not a girl to hang her head dejectedly. A freakish wave slammed onto the rocks and the wind wailed as if in pain. This was something serious. Poppy had knocked on the door of Calgary, knowing well of our mother's antipathy towards her.

'Come on, Poppy, what is it?' Sam asked.

'I'm in the shit,' she said forlornly, pressing flat the ball of gum with her foot.

I laughed. 'But you always are. It's where you choose to be.'

'Yeah, but this time, I really am.' Somewhere behind the Garda station, slates loosened by the wind rattled to the ground and the sea swelled and roared at the rocks in celebration. She tried a smile gum still adhered to her lips. The smile didn't make it. 'I've been expelled.'

'Expelled from where?' Sam and I asked simultaneously.

'School,' she answered glumly. From the police yard, Sergeant O'Neill on his bicycle sallied past us down the slope. Turning left, the wind caught his huge, black cape, sailing him uphill towards

Trafalgar Road. He glanced at us but didn't speak. He had never spoken to me since the night I knocked him off his bicycle as I was running from the dock.

'No one has ever been expelled from St Jude's,' Sam argued. 'Mother Superior threatens but it never happens.'

'The on'y one Mother Superior threatens to expel is me, and this time she's done it.'

'School hasn't even started. How can you be expelled during the summer holidays?' Opening my coat I stood close to her, wanting to protect her from the wind, from Mother Superior.

'Well, I have,' she answered miserably. 'We start back to school on Monday and I've been told not to be there Monday morning. Not that I'm too bothered about school, but I'm gettin' absolute hell from Mammy, an' even Daddy's goin' mad with me, an' my sister Mary, she hasn't spoken to me since it happened.'

Poppy was seriously upset and so were we. Sam bit into her bottom lip. St Jude's would not be the same school without Poppy Boyle. 'Then tell us what happened,' Sam suggested gently.

'Sister Joseph is rehearsin' for a concert. Ten of us have been picked for the main parts. Can you believe it rehearsin' for a November concert in August? Sister called at the house. The first rehearsal was last Saturday. "Of course Sister, Jennifer would love to take part." Poppy mimicked her mother. "Oh, Sister it's an honour so it is, isn't it Jennifer?" says Mammy. No, it isn't says I. I'm not goin' to school durin' the holidays for no rehearsal. "You are," Mammy says. Of the ten of us I was on'y one who didn't want to be there an' I showed it.'

'But you were there last Saturday,' Sam said.

'I was made to go. I had no choice. There should be a law or something against making kids go to school during their holidays.' Sergeant O'Neill returned, leaning on his pedals. He got off his bicycle beside us, ignoring us again.

'Nearly killed him once,' I told the girls proudly, nodding at the Garda's back. The rain was intermittent now, but if anything the wind was fiercer and, standing talking, I realised just how cold it was. 'Let's get some shelter,' I suggested.

We started walking up Marine Drive with Poppy Boyle complaining. 'I was on holiday an' should o' been left alone. The other girls were kissin' Sister's bum but they was kind of eggin' me on, they kind o' knew there was goin' to be trouble an' there was.'

'But surely you didn't get expelled for that,' I said.

Sheltering by a high wall of the burned-out Grand Hotel, the storm was forgotten as Poppy related her part in the story of the only girl ever to be expelled from St Jude's Private Girls' School, Greystones. 'A pencil-case,' she started.

'A pencil-case?' Sam echoed.

It was a long, thin, wooden pencil-case and a girl was saying something that was supposed to be funny that was part of the play, except that it wasn't funny and everyone was supposed to laugh. Poppy told Sister Joseph that she found it impossible to laugh at something that wasn't funny but volunteered to rattle her pencil-case instead. Sister Joseph got red in the face, a condition she was known for. But Poppy had to laugh along with everybody else, whether she liked it or not. Poppy didn't like it and she didn't laugh, but she rattled her pencil-case instead. The funny thing, as all members of the cast agreed afterwards, was that the rattle of the pencil case sounded just like real laughter. But at the time Sister Joseph just got redder and redder and something had to give.

Huddled close beneath the high wall, Poppy told us the rest of the story.

An incorrigible maverick, Jennifer Jane Boyle had become the first girl in the history of St Jude's to be expelled. Perhaps 'expelled' was too strong a word, for, as the story unfolded, it became apparent that her plight was more of a conditional suspension pending arbitration of religious and secular representatives, which Father Fallon, the parish priest, was sure to chair.

The allegation that Miss Boyle had rattled a wooden pencil-case instead of laughing was indisputable, as the girl herself admitted most readily, but how can a girl be expected to laugh at something she did not find funny? Also, repeated entreaties from the frustrated stage director for co-operation, could not be denied either, but then, hadn't the girl been shanghaied while on holiday, to perform in a concert containing unfunny jokes? Really, what else but disharmony could anyone expect?

Anyway, understandably, Sister Joseph finally lost patience and attempted to divest the girl of her unwanted accoutrement which led to a struggle, then in turn, to a veritable tug-of-war, Jennifer Jane with characteristic determination hanging on to one end of the pencil-case, while Sister Joseph, a lady of similar brimful resolution, was hanging on grimly to the other.

Much to the awe and covert amusement of the spectators, the struggle went on for some time, with neither side prepared to give an inch, that was, until Miss Boyle allowed an innate sense of humour to determine a mischievous and mercurial outcome. She let go.

With this sudden release of tensile tension, the bountiful cleric shot backwards, to fall in a heap with her legs in the air, bringing a free-standing blackboard and easel down on top of her. There she lay, stunned in an undignified tangle, to the scarcely stifled giggles of the concert crew. Yet this indignity in itself was not the issue to exacerbate the conflict, for the humiliated lady, seizing the moment, clambered to her feet, waving the pencil-case aloft in triumph. It was what Miss Boyle said next that caused the trouble. 'That pencil-case Sister, you can stick it up your duck run.'

Rehearsal abandoned, Mother Superior was disturbed for heated debate with an outraged subordinate. This girl's insolence was beyond the pale, something finally must be done. An irate Mother Superior convened to her office with Jennifer Jane Boyle summoned to appear before her, where she was scolded at length, received a final warning and was ordered to apologise. But when remorse and apology were resisted, the aptly named Sister of Mercy was forced into a second, time and tested strategy, the leathering of both hands with a belt; and this during a girl's holiday. And that was where it should have ended, but it didn't.

Jennifer was told to re-join her concert class and do as she was told in future but, with sensibilities smarting at the injustice every bit as much as the palms of her hands, she was in no mood to be cajoled. Sister Joseph, smiling smugly, presumed an act of conciliation by attempting to put a comforting arm around the shoulder of the prodigal. 'All over a silly pencil case,' she said, her graciousness hardly concealing a smirk of satisfaction. 'And how you can come out with such nonsense, I really don't know. You really are a silly goose.'

'I was just being polite, Sister.'

The nun snorted. 'Polite! What you said to me, young lady, certainly wasn't polite.'

'It was, Sister. I was going to tell you to stick it up your arse.'

Sam and I were laughing. We wanted to commiserate, but we couldn't for laughing. We wanted to invite her back to our house, but, even though our mother had been polite to her earlier we were sure the courtesy would not be extended to hospitality beyond the threshold and no way could we guarantee that there would not still be laughter when we got home and be required to tell our mother of its origin. I was beholden to Poppy ever since she intervened in my fight with Patsy Plunkett and I had vowed then to help her where and when I could.

'It'll blow over like this storm,' Sam said, still laughing.

Chapter Nineteen

I was reporting back to Nugget Nolan with an account of recent surveillance. 'Nugget, I'm fed up of following him. Nothing ever happens.'

The cobbler, sitting at his bench stitching a boot, smiled slowly. 'Surveillance takes patience. The one thing Chief Superintendent Thomas Nolan was famous for was patient surveillance. Watch a cat stalk a bird; if you want results you gotta be as patient as a cat.'

'But you've no idea how slow and boring it is following him.'

Nugget pushed a needle into the side of the boot and made a stitch in line with other stitches. The needle was long and thin and the stitching very neat. All of Nugget's work was neat, in contrast to the detritus of his craft, littering his bench and the floor beneath. 'That was the deal, folley him and report back. Remember, we're in this together as friends and collaborators. Might take weeks afore somethin' comes up but we got to stick together, you an' me an' see it through. Think o' the risk I took showin' you that note.'

'The other day I watched him for an hour. All he did was smoke his pipe and cough.'

'You need to remember who the man is.' The cobbler swept a hank of thin coppery hair from obstructing his eyes, back over his mottled crown and nodded his head reflectively. 'He didn't see you, did he? For God's sake don't let him know you're on to him. That was the mistake that Uncle Thomas made.'

'Nugget, surely you don't think… '

Nugget worked another stitch cautiously. 'Well, let's say I've allus had me suspicions. Never mention me though, mention me an' me days could well be numbered for he knows well that I'm the nephew of his great adversary.'

It was raining gently. Through the window, the sky was overcast and the sea calm. Brother Mulligan and Brother Ryan, wrapped against the weather, were walking past, talking earnestly. I was glad they didn't come inside.

Laying the boot aside, the cobbler looked up and said, 'Don't even question him, just keep watch, then I'll tell you when the time comes. I'll tell you when to get him to them ruins. Tell you when to grab him by the lapels an' make him tell you where they are, sayin', "Where's them crown jewels, you louser? In the meantime, patient surveillance an' nothin' else." '

This was something I just couldn't do and I looked closely into the man's face to see if he was serious. He was. 'Nugget, you haven't told anyone else about this, have you? You know, about that note, about Mr Malone, your Uncle Thomas? You haven't said anything to any of the Plunkett boys?'

Nugget picked up the boot again, nursing it together with a hurt expression on his face. 'We're in this together, just you an' me,' he said plaintively. 'How could you think such a thing?'

Worried that I had offended him, I was quick to apologise. 'It's nothing. I'm sorry, Nugget, we're in this together, you and me.'

The door opened and Donoghue and his brother, Paul, came in. Paul was carrying two pairs of shoes by their laces.

All I wanted after that summer holiday was to return to school wearing long trousers. During the weeks leading up to my twelfth birthday in August, I kept dropping hints to my parents. Whenever I saw a boy of my age wearing long trousers, I would remark on how smart he looked. How such attire gave bearing, self-esteem and dignity to a young man and was bound to encourage him to walk with head held high and shoulders back, a posture to which my father continually ascribed. Such a boy would never be found, teasing and tormenting younger sisters, why, long trousers could well influence a boy to become a priest.

My birthday had come and gone and I was still wearing short ones but Paddy Donoghue, grinning all over his face, wasn't. He was wearing long ones and didn't he just know it.

Refusing to acknowledge the new-found status which his trousers gave him and while he discussed with Nugget the work required on the shoes, I chatted with his brother, Paul, disguising with some jocularity a molten fury ravaging my soul.

Recently, researching historical leadership and concerned at my lack of it (looking for that essential yardstick, by which leadership can be measured), I had concluded that all leaders (great leaders) were either very good or very bad. Using Jesus of Nazareth on one side of the scale of rectitude and Adolf Hitler on the other, I was pleased with this hypothesis, although I had difficulty equating it with Reardon, Donoghue, Rooney and Cronin as none of these boys was anywhere near as good or bad as either of my glaring archetypes.

And then it had dawned on me, the one essential that all leaders possessed, yet was denied me, long trousers. Discounting Jesus who had preached to Galileans in a dress, every other great leader I had come across had one thing in common, they all wore long trousers. Who was going to follow someone with purple knee-caps on permanent display?

Seeking anything to avert my eyes, my attention from his insufferable brother, I asked of Paul, 'You ever read a book with Lemmy Caution in it?'

The boy shook his head uncertainly.

'Well, Lemmy Caution is a character in books by a guy called Peter Cheyney. Books with great titles, like *This Man Is Dangerous*, *Dames Don't Care*, *Don't Get Me Wrong*, and *I'll Say She Does*. You can buy them at the station bookstall for two shillings. I bought one, it's called *You Can Always Duck*. I keep it hidden behind a board in the coalhouse. See, I'm not allowed to read them until I'm older. Well, my dad reads them and my mum too, they keep them locked in their bedroom, along with other stuff I'm not supposed to read but I know where they keep the key and I sneak in and borrow books one at a time, so they never know. The one I bought has got a gorgeous dame on the cover. And does that dame on the cover look good or does she? I'll say she does. That's the way Lemmy Caution talks, he talks tough. He is tough.' I knew that I was gabbling but I couldn't help it.

Paddy joined us, leaving Nugget to return to his stitching.

I continued frenetically, 'Telling Paul about this character called Lemmy Caution. He's a "G" man, wears a slouchy hat and a trench coat. Know why he wears a trench coat? No, cos he's got a machine gun hidden under it. No one messes with Lemmy Caution.' My talk was getting faster and I knew I sounded silly.

'What's a "G" man,' Paul asked.

'He's an FBI agent, you know Federal Bureau of Investigation. Maybe G stands for gun, gun-man, because that's what he keeps hidden under his trench coat. He's in books I nick from my parents' bedroom.'

'Think the "G" stands for "Government"?' Paddy said, pretending to be interested as he wiped at an imaginary mark close to the razor sharp crease in his right, trouser leg.

I would have to go. Donoghue was now, very carefully, removing brand-new fluff from out of his turn-ups. Remembering something important, I left the shack without saying goodbye to the cobbler. Unfortunately, the boys followed me.

I had to cut the elder brother down somehow without being too obvious. 'Paddy, you know you was telling me about that mott sucking your neck, well I was wondering, did you do the same to her?'

Donoghue's face darkened and went blank, he hadn't heard me.

'I was thinking, if you did it on her neck, then her mammy would notice. I...'

'We don't talk about stuff like that in front o' children,' he reprimanded haughtily, nodding towards his younger brother. 'By the way, Patsy and Shonti Plunkett are looking for you. Saw 'em yesterday an' they didn't look too pleased.'

'Looking for me?'

'Want to talk to you about something an' they didn't look too pleased.'

Just what I needed, as if I didn't feel bad enough.

Chapter Twenty

Although my parents did not discuss our family's worsening financial situation in front of their children, I knew that things were bad. Bob, the one surviving member of my father's workforce, had been laid off and, summer holidays over, I had not been given a single day's work. And I couldn't help but notice, subtle changes in my mother's running of the household. Socks were darned now where once they would have been thrown out, patches were appearing on trousers and dresses and I was surprised to see Tam wearing hand-me-downs from Sam and, Dodo wearing hand-me-downs from Tam. We didn't use the car for trips into the Wicklow Mountains now, and behind the clock, the mantle was growing thick with unpaid bills. Most disturbing of all, once I thought I'd heard my mother crying.

Back at school and waiting for the whistle to sound, boys wasted no time in badgering me to join in my next lion-hunting expedition. Months earlier and I would have likely worn myself out taking violent issue at such incitement but, having been force-fed school survival techniques since my arrival, I made the most of the very best of them. 'Sorry, but all safari expeditions to Bray Head are currently fully booked,' I parried. 'Try again next year.' And, as self-parody cannot be parodied, my antagonists withdrew and so did I, to a step beside the bicycle sheds where I sat watching the beginning of the new term.

Boys jostling for pecking order like Mr McCarron's chickens

and Christian Brothers mingling, smiling and bending an ear to accounts of holiday escapades, a demonstration of coexistence which everyone made the most of, knowing well it would all end with the first shrill of a whistle.

But not so Brother Brady, he stood by the main doors disliking what he saw. He had a body and bearing more fitting to the jolly and avuncular but this veritable Friar Tuck had no time for coexistence, not even for a few minutes at the beginning of term. He belied his larger-than-life aspect with a narrow, unerring eye for misdemeanour, a mean-spirited mental acuity of critical observation, razor-sharpened by vigilante years of schoolyard and schoolroom surveillance. It was this characteristic, together with his more infamous one, his unequivocal commitment to penal judgement that gave him his legendary reputation. While the other brothers mingled, smiled and rolled their eyes, Brother Brady's only thought was to roll his sleeves.

At that time, Catholic schools in Eire were not all grim holes of rampant tyranny as so many subsequent tales of harrowing childhoods would have us believe. By and large, boys and girls knew where they stood, were happy with their boundaries and, well-disciplined, were contented in knowing just how far to go with teachers, be they nuns, brothers, monks, priests or secular. Children were seldom cheeky, disobedient or provocative (Poppy Boyle being a singular exception), a uniformity agreeable to all, but great diligence was required to maintain this symbiotic status-quo; children always need to be corralled and controlled.

And so it was with Brother Brady. For him to turn a blind eye to a wrong-doing, however trivial, was to condone it, and to condone it, was to invite repetition until repetition became routine, the die cast and the child lost.

Brother Brady prided himself on nipping in the bud. Imagine, if you can Brother Brady entrusted with a child's tutelage and spiritual salvation, viewing himself in the mirror of a morning, knowing he had lost a child to whims of wilfulness through a neglect of discipline. It was something that he could never allow to happen.

To the mid-century ecclesiastical fraternity of Eire, there was no war of nerves with their charges, only observance of duty. Crossed leather belts lay on one side of the scales of childish variance, while obedience, good behaviour and subjugation lay on the other, detente resulted and everyone was happy, especially parents. It had proved a highly efficient and workable system, enforcement on one end of the scale, pain on the other, the only other compelling aspect of this coercion being the deportment of the cleric on the retributive end.

A teacher could be as arbitrary as he liked in degree of punishment; talking in class and a kid could get six of the best or two of the best, a reprimand or nothing at all if you were promised to the priesthood. A lot depended on who was doing the talking and who was doing the punishing, an unfair managerial system some might say, but eminently reliable.

A neutral, observing the teaching principles of St Luke's, would see that, to the Head and Brothers Ryan and Molloy, the role of vindicator was just another mundane facet of school life, like a history or geography lesson or a rough and tumble on the playing field. With such savants, severity was wholly dependent on levels of misbehaviour and the observer could not fail to recognise a certain empathy with the victim, making proceedings understandable and justifiable, agreeable even.

Brother Mulligan was different. To this cleric, punishment was a mutually painful duty he could well do without and its moderation was in keeping with the weary resignation with which it was administered. The fist that clenched the belt aloft went just as high as any other fist but never fell as fast. Why, following a Mulligan thrashing, a kid could use a pen or pencil again within a matter of minutes. Brother Mulligan would much prefer to thrash the desk in front of him than he would a child.

But not so Brother Brady: if Poppy Boyle was the exception in the rank and file, then Brother Brady was the exception among the executive. Remonstration and reckoning for its own sake was not enough. Punishment could be nurtured and prolonged into an art form, into his very own, little piece of theatre.

> 'Grasshopper Green is a comical chap
> He lives on the best of fare
> Quaint little trousers jacket and cap... '

Then on the fourth line the belt came down, the breathy exertion behind it and the resounding crack on the outstretched hand making incomprehensible the end of the rhyming stanza. And as the fourth line was drowned out, then so was the eighth and in turn, the twelfth, until the poem was over. The prospect of getting a thrashing from Brother Brady to the rhythm of 'Hiawatha,' gave me nightmares.

With Brother Brady, chastisement could often be deferred, often with unspoken promise of forgiveness or forgetfulness. It was entertainment for a captive audience, sometimes prolonged, even until school time was over for the day, a spectacle of two stars, one the predator and one the prey and, for each boy in the audience, the paramount sense of relief that he was not the latter. Awe and fear were expected from the spectators, a little rapport and a few giggles, answers to rhetorical questions and outright laughter, but the drama was not conducive to applause, applause was not encouraged or expected and had never been known to happen. Applause would be in such bad taste.

Christian Brothers, as we all knew, had an unalienable right to chastise for unruly or bad behaviour. Was not the very garb they donned each morning, integrally equipped with the means? Renegade action against just deserts was unheard of and tore at the very roots of detente it upset the status-quo. If self-determination was allowed to go unchecked it could lead to anarchy, an inclination in schoolboys often warned of, especially by Brother Brady.

The whistle blew and I joined my line for class. Brother Brady was inspecting us, moving so lightly on his feet, he might have been a silent thundercloud. As he neared I lowered my eyes. 'Ah, if it isn't Otello back with us again,' he said.

'Good morning, Brother,' I replied.

Sitting at my desk, I put my head in my hands. Who or what the hell was an Otello? No one in town was called O'Tello so it wasn't an allegorical reference to some parochial buffoon. The nearest I could think of was O'Toole, the town's poacher; maybe he could help or maybe one day I would muster enough courage to ask the man himself.

An hour later, I had been called 'Oliver' by Rooney, 'Christian' by Brother McBride, 'Gilla Christe' by Brother Mulligan and 'Otello' by Brother Brady. Surely I must get 'English dog' by dinner-time.

I couldn't wait to leave school, but I would have to wait a year until the next summer holidays, children couldn't leave at twelve. One evening I had eavesdropped on low voices coming from the kitchen. I was to leave school as soon as I reached thirteen, get a job and bring some money to the home, a prospect that delighted me, although I couldn't help but nurse resentment that I must work to keep my sisters at private school.

Chapter Twenty-one

*T*hrough the dull damp air of a September morning, and, early for a change, I was slowly making my way to school. Passing The Ormonde, Frank's bicycle was parked outside, plenty of time for an early morning chat. I hadn't seen him for a while, so there would be lots for us to talk about, anyway, the doors were locked and wherever he was inside, he couldn't hear my knocking.

In the school-yard Shonti Plunkett was hustling Dermot Coyle towards me while his brother, Patsy, shifted uncertainly in the background. I was agitated. The Plunketts were looking for me and I had been avoiding them. They had a score to settle and Coyle's smile of linkage was insincere. 'Maybe I shunt, but I've bin tellin' Shonti an' Patsy…' Coyle began.

It was dinner hour and Shonti's breath smelled of raw onion. He had edged Coyle out of my way and his face was uncomfortably close to mine. 'What you was tellin' him an' Flan in Pennicook's,' he swallowed hard, 'like what you can draw.'

I faced him with a vacant expression. 'Pennicook's?' I puzzled.

Fearing I was about to contest or deny his story, Coyle chipped in quickly. 'Remember, in the cafe, we was eatin' chips an' you was tellin' me an' Flan what you could draw.'

'Draw,' I wondered vaguely.

Shonti looked about him warily as Patsy began to edge closer. 'Naked wimmin,' he breathed toxically.

'So. What about naked women?'

Patsy was looking to close in, wanting to be party to the conversation I was having with his brother. I ignored him completely. We had hardly exchanged a word since our fight outside the school gates but his resentment was still palpable. I remained the victor and would continue to remain so, as long as I kept my distance. I had been very lucky that afternoon, no one knew that better than Patsy and I knew that I could not expect to be so lucky again. 'So what, anybody can draw naked women,' I said expansively.

'Well, I can't,' Shonti grunted.

Patsy had wormed his way beside me. 'Neither can I,' he tried to confide.

I had never expected to be able to act contemptuously so I made the most of it. Turning away from them, I addressed Coyle shortly. 'This was something I told you and Flanagan in secret. It wasn't something I wanted blabbing about the school. Reardon and Donoghue were even on to me about it. Who else have you been blabbing to?'

'Sure it's Flan what's been blabbin, honest.' Coyle could not hold my eye.

'Well, can ya?' Shonti demanded gruffly.

I ignored him. If a Plunkett wanted something from me, he would have to pay, starting with a little homage.

'Me an' Patsy want you to do some for us.'

'Do some what?'

'You know naked wimmin.'

'Artwork, you would have to pay,' I bargained tautly.

'We'll pay,' Shonti answered readily, his tone unexpectedly congenial.

The prospect suddenly excited me, but I was cautious. I didn't like the Plunketts and they didn't like me; neither did I trust them one iota. 'So I draw naked women for you, you show them to somebody and they ask you where you got them from, what are you going to say?' I probed astutely.

Askance, the brothers looked first at each other then at Coyle and then at me, horror in their eyes at the imputation. Seizing the

187

initiative, Patsy opened his account. 'Shop a frein'? Tell on a frein'?' He began shaking his head slowly at such an outrageous suggestion. 'You don't know the Plunkett boys, the Plunkett boys have never ratted on a frein'.'

'A sacred thrust,' Shonti assured me, his indignant face close to mine, his breath making my eyes water. 'You think Patsy an' me would go… '

'A sacred thrust,' Patsy cut in proudly.

All thought on the matter was suddenly spiced with greed, the law of supply and demand hitting me like a bolt from the blue. Supply was not a problem and if boys were prepared to pay, then demand was, surely, incontrovertible. 'I would want a shilling each,' I mused

'A shillin' each,' Shonti spluttered.

'Jesus wept!' his brother yelped

'I haven't got a shilling,' Donnelly moaned.

I shrugged dismissively. 'Please yourselves.'

'A shillin' each an' we would want specifictions,' Shonti decreed in a businesslike manner.

I had heard the word before. My father used it a lot when talking with colleagues and studying plans. 'What specifications?' I quizzed uneasily.

Patsy thrust his chin forward, his words slipping unctuously over the hump of his bottom lip. 'He means different positions an' the like.' His eyes glowed. 'Different poses like in magazines, 'cept this time the wimmin will have no clothes on.' He was grinning lewdly, one hand in his pocket investigating his crotch.

'I'm gonna start savin' up,' Coyle resolved.

'One shilling each, specifications required,' Shonti finalised portentously. Patsy's lips had grown in size and had reddened with lasciviousness. Drooling, Coyle was gnawing at his nails.

What a lucrative negotiation this could turn out to be. The huge smile of satisfaction wanting to burst forth was put in place by an implacable poker face; this was the commercialism of the market and I had to be equal to it. 'You want a naked woman standing on her head, it's yours,' I remarked cleverly.

'A deal then,' Shonti said solemnly.

I took a pencil and a fold of paper from my pocket: 'How many?' I asked.

The brothers raised eyebrows at each other, Shonti being the first to decide. 'I want three.'

An entrepreneurial dawn was bursting upon my horizon. A shilling each was big business and I couldn't believe how easy it was. Laying bricks in the teeming rain, digging footings in the snow, was that business? My father thought it was. Already I knew more about business than he did in fact, I was already streets ahead of him. My family would be saved by my endeavour and a another Jaguar car was negotiating slip roads in my mind, a Mark VII, 31\2 litre and in silver.

'Two for me,' Patsy said as his older brother stuck out a hand and clasped mine in a 'done deal' manner. Patsy rubbed his hands together and, salivating, said, 'Mine's gotta have big tits.'

'I like big tits, too,' Coyle commented mournfully, 'but I can't afford a shillin', I on'y get a tanner a week an' that's if I'm lucky. I'm completely broke.' He shoved his hands deep in his pockets and wriggled them around to substantiate his claim.

'A shilling is no problem to me,' Shonti boasted grandly. 'Work Saturday mornin' whit me da an' I get three shillins. Shoot lines Sunday, a good catch an' I get three more. I'm gonna start whit three drawin's an' I might have a lot more, providin' they're done to proper specifications.'

'Yeah, proper specifications,' Patsy concurred, showing me his hand as his brother had done. I declined it by turning my attention to Coyle.

'What about you then, Dermot?'

Coyle was sulking. 'I can't afford a shillin'.'

He was talking to a hard-nosed businessman. 'Take it or leave it, that's the price.' Opening up the fold of paper, I rested it on the low coping of the bicycle shed: 'Now about these specifications.'

Instantly coy, his sexual predilections for my ear only, Shonti pressed a shilling in my hand and whispered, ' A deposit, listen, one facin' front, one facin' backwards, an' one sidewards, an' I'm not bothered about big tits, ordinary ones'll do.'

Apart from having to endure poisonous breath, I was enjoying myself as I carefully noted his specifications. A bustling Patsy replaced his brother at my ear. 'I've changed my mind, I on'y want one, can't afford two.'

I raised an uninterested eyebrow: 'Any specifications?'

'Big tits.'

After jotting down Shonti's requirements, I pencilled, 'Patsy' (1) B.T.

Coyle was pulling at my sleeve anxiously. 'I'll give you sixpence on Monday an' another sixpence the Monday after.'

I frowned. In business a man must start as he means to go on and stroking my jaw thoughtfully at the proposition, I let him squirm. 'That's hire purchase, not a good idea to get stuff on the never-never.'

'Just draw one tit then," he ventured hopefully, 'one now and the other when I've paid up.'

I continued to stroke my jaw. Coyle must know I wasn't an easy touch.

'Think of all the comics I've lent you,' he reminded me.

'Ok,' I relented and dexterously added to the paper, 'Dermot (1) O.O.T.,' quite surprised at my own ruthlessness.

'Make sure it's a big one.'

'I'm not bothered about big ones,' Shonti told his brother primly then, squinting at me through knitted brows, asked, 'An' when can we expect 'em?'

Carefully folding the paper on which the specifications were written, I put it in my pocket and answered firmly, 'Monday morning, first thing.'

I left them then, dreamily contemplating a new role in life, one promising to be not only immensely enjoyable but financially rewarding, too. This role of manufacturer and vendor of illicit material was untapped and could give me credibility hitherto undreamed of. In my dream-like state I saw queues of boys wanting to do business with me and I saw myself accepting some and rejecting others and best of all was heaps of shillings being changed for five-pound notes at the post office and along a highway through my mind, my father at the wheel, the silver Jaguar was gaining speed.

The whistle was blowing for return to class. Coyle was beside me. 'Long legs,' he winked.

I winked back: 'Two of them,' I promised, as we marched into the schoolhouse.

Before starting on the enterprise that same night in my room, I pondered the lack of initiative in those, every bit as capable as I, those present at St Luke's now and those that had gone before, years of horny boys, probably all but O'Farrell, desperate to feast their eyes on forbidden fruit and not a dirty picture to be found in the whole of Ireland. Was I the first boy ever at St Luke's who could draw? Of course not, yet I had found myself, was it by accident in a veritable cornucopia of financial opportunity. This was far easier than searching old ruins for jewels and I couldn't wait to get started.

Retiring early to my room, after complaining to my parents about the amount of homework expected of us, I propped the door open with a book and alert to approaching footsteps on the stair, began my new career.

Assisted by one remaining horror comic from the coal shed, I copied form, posture and faces until satisfied that they accorded with all specifications required. Tall, nubile, smiling, pouting, winsome and profane, five beautiful unclad maidens lay exposed before me and in my artistic fervour I had to stop myself from giving Coyle a second tit.

Glancing at the clock on my dressing table, I couldn't believe that they had taken but little over an hour to complete and for the remainder of the second hour, I congratulated myself, feasting my eyes upon my own unexpurgated creations. Five shillings for just over an hour's work, enough customers and I could retire by the time I was thirteen. Was it a sin? Yes. Was it a mortal sin? Probably, but I cared not; whoever gave heed to sin when held in the deadly, heady, twin embrace of greed and lust?

The next morning with three envelopes secreted at the bottom of my satchel, I avoided the schoolyard throng but Coyle found me and raised his eyebrows in silent interrogation. I ignored him. The drawings had been promised for the coming Monday.

Playtime we shared with Shonti's class, so in the corridor, after giving Coyle a knowing wink, I doubled back to the classroom where Brother Mulligan was working at his desk. I approached him, ostensibly feigning interest in a subject he had addressed earlier, but knowing well that by now Shonti and Coyle would be scouring the schoolyard in spry anticipation.

Refusing to be drawn into any clarification by Coyle fidgeting beside me, it was dinner-hour, and, taking my satchel with me, I continued to avoid everyone by sneaking around the back of the school house and eating my lunch, alone, by the playing-field. I preferred to eat alone anyway, seldom joining with others during dinner-hour.

At St Luke's and St Jude's and, I suspect, all other mid-century Alma Maters in Eire, there were many unspoken and unwritten prejudices of order and class among the children, determined by generations of social chauvinism, which although not necessarily understood, were accepted as readily as the quality of footwear a child was given to wear to school each morning. Paramount among these precepts was the way one spoke and dressed, one's good manners, a father's employment and status, the location of the family home, and of course, above all, where one's family was seated at Sunday morning mass. But there were many subtle mores too, one of these being the quality and presentation of the pre-packed school lunch, boys from 'poor families' being made to do with chunks of bread smeared with dripping, or dry bread with a raw onion, likely wrapped in newspaper. These boys would drink water from the school font. Then there were those with feet on the bottom rung of the ladder of the social spectrum; these might have jam and bread, wrapped in brown paper, and a lemonade bottle containing milk. Those of a higher social standing, to which, by my fingertips, I considered myself, to still belong, would have sandwiches of cheese or meat, supplemented by home-made cake in a proper lunchbox and we could count on tea in a flask or Bovril in winter. So dinner-hour at school was an entrenched, self-and group-imposed segregation with each faculty, not scorning or despising another but simply separating as easily and naturally as different species of animal on an African savannah. Nowhere, except for Sunday morning Mass, could social divisions be seen to be more clearly and potently defined.

Sitting on a stump behind a bush overlooking the hurling field, I ate my 'upper class' lunch slowly and sipped hot sweet tea from a flask. The day was cold, the chill wind carrying shrill voices from the schoolyard. Although hidden from view, I was still self-conscious, knowing I was the quarry of Coyle and the Plunkett brothers and knowing, with sweet tremors of sensibility, that trapped between my ankles was money to be made from naked breasts, long, bare legs, rounded buttocks and looks of innocence and brazen insolence. I did not see or even hear their approach but, sensing their arrival, responded without surprise to the light touch on my shoulder from behind. Coyle and Shonti then faced me while Patsy squatted beside me on the grass. Shonti was first to speak. 'Dermot said you done 'em already,' the smell of onion again, very likely the same onion as yesterday.

Swallowing the last of my sandwich, I nodded.

'Where are they?' Shonti demanded.

I gestured towards the satchel at my feet.

'You done 'em quick,' Patsy's breathe also smelled strongly of onion.

'Well give us a howl o' them,' Shonti ordered curtly.

'Money first,' I demanded.

There was no argument. Shonti handed me three shilling pieces. 'My one's in whit that,' Patsy said quickly.

'Four shillings whit the deposit,' Shonti reminded me as I pocketed the coins.

'Sixpence on Monday, an' sixpence the Monday after,' Coyle piped excitedly. 'But sure seein' as you're after doin' 'em, I might as well have mine now.'

I was so ecstatic to have so much money in my pocket and earned so easily that Coyle's suggestion was ratified immediately. 'Well, give us a howl o' them then,' Shonti insisted, his squint narrowing suspiciously.

'They're in separate envelopes in my satchel,' I replied coolly. 'Look, I'm not taking them out here in the open. We'll walk casually back to the school and I'll give them to you outside the lavs, but don't show them to anyone, don't talk about them, look at them in the lavs, then hide them when you get home.

The boys agreed readily and by the ablution block I handed over the envelopes and they disappeared inside. Through open fanlights, I heard lavatory doors closing and I smiled to myself as I imagined them gloating over my handiwork. The coins rested reassuringly against my buttock as I ferreted in my satchel for pad and pencil. Further orders were certainly to be called for. No, this would be a mistake and I returned the pad and pencil. Better to be coy at this stage, better if I wasn't around when they came back out, let them look for me again. I was on the way to my classroom when I was stopped in my tracks by a derisive hoot through one of the open fanlights. Unmistakeably, it was the hoot of Shonti Plunkett and I was dumbfounded at its dissent.

What the hell was wrong? The women had been drawn exactly to specification. Shonti's hoot was followed by one from Patsy and two doors slammed simultaneously, then another it would be Coyle's. Shonti appeared, visibly irritated, followed by Patsy and Donnelly, muttering petulantly to each other. Patsy overtook his brother and, thrusting his face forward, pursed his flaccid lips together in disgust. 'Forgotten somethin', have we?'

Coyle's face was equally disagreeable, 'You're not gettin' no tanner deposit for this,' he sneered, waving his envelope at my nose.

I was baffled. Had the three of them suddenly gone mad? Why would I not get Coyle's tanner? Furrowing my brow, I swept their faces with condescension. The Plunkett boys were not noted for brains, whereas Coyle, although clever, was easily led. If the Plunkett boys were dissatisfied, then Coyle would be, too. 'I haven't forgotten anything.'

'You know well enough what you forgot,' Shonti snorted. 'Grown-up wimmin was what we specified.'

'They ain't been done to proper specifications,' Patsy claimed, shaking his head from side to side slowly in disgust.

'I don't know what the hell you're talking about,' I countered sharply.

'Hair,' Patsy spluttered his nose an inch from mine, his breath worse than his brother's, making me want to retch. Sticking his envelope inside my shirt, he said, 'An I want me shillin' back.'

'An' if you can't do 'em proper, I want me three shillin's back.' Shonti's voice was bitter, his face laden with recrimination.

I kept my calm. If I must humour them a while, then so be it. All five girls had been beautifully drawn, exactly to specifications, taking particular pains with their hair. Each one had been individually styled and shaded for colour, one with a fringe, one with a pig-tail and a third with ringlets. Patsy's had a pony tail and Coyle's had lustrous tresses hanging to her waist. With one brain cell between them, the oafishness of the Plunkett boys was incontestable and they had bullied Coyle into joining them. They were deliberately complaining in the hope of getting the five drawings for nothing. So this was the unacceptable side of business. What an affront to an honest business man, to be hassled by such unscrupulous idiots.

'My one's tit's not the on'y thing that's missin',' Coyle leered.

What fraternal insanity had visited these boys? 'Something make 'em go bald in the shit house?' I asked sarcastically.

'You a friggin' eejit or wha?' Patsy yelped.

Stunned, it suddenly struck me what it was they were talking about, but surely they wouldn't have wanted me to include something so unsightly. 'It just doesn't look nice,' I protested.

'What doesn't?' Shonti's eyes had narrowed into slits.

'Underarm hair,' I explained.

'Underarm hair,' Shonti echoed incredulously, 'you takin' the piss?' and, shoving his envelope inside my shirt to join with Patsy's, said, 'We're not talkin' armpits, you friggin' eejit.'

I lost my patience. These boys were raving lunatics. 'Where the hell do you want it then?' I shouted and pulling the envelopes from my shirt, thrust them in the face of Shonti. 'You want moustaches, a big, black beard? How about a hairy chest on Coyle's, there's enough room?'

Collectively, on their faces, something had dawned. 'Their minges,' Patsy said quietly.

'WHAT?'

'Not on their heads, not in their armpits, their friggin' minges.'

With a thud of realisation, I grasped the sheer extent of their folly, the enormity of their collective stupidity. Shonti's vacuous bucket nut, his piss-hole eyes and his gormless brother Pollack Gob, the nearest Greystones had to a village idiot and Coyle, nothing more than a sycophantic, yellow-toothed rat. I should just walk away and leave them wallowing in their mindless ignorance. Why waste time on imbeciles? Gently, I took hold of the envelopes and, extracting the drawings, fanned them open in my fingers. I would keep my temper, explain things rationally and without rancour. I wouldn't even patronise. Keep my temper, and I would keep the shillings. I had earned them.

'Women don't have hair down there like men do," I articulated clearly and, smiling self-consciously, elaborated further. 'It grows on men at a certain age, as well you know, tell you the truth, I'm starting to get some myself down there, just now. Well, with women, it's different.' My smile broadened as I saw three jaws drop as one. 'See, women don't have hair down there like men.' How gratifying it was to see them choking at my disclosure, but quite honestly, I was astonished to find them unaware of such a universally understood anatomical fact. 'Tell you the truth, lads, it's something I thought you would have known.'

Shonty appeared uncharacteristically humble. 'How do you know all this?' he asked respectfully.

He looked so crushed, I couldn't help but patronise. 'Sisters, Shonti, I've got sisters.'

'How old is yer sisters?' Patsy asked pointedly.

I wasn't going to answer a silly question. Patsy knew well how old my sisters were. Suddenly his nose was an inch away from mine and with breath that could peel paint said, 'Well, me an' Shonti. We got sisters too, they're seventeen, eighteen and twenty-three an' they've got more hair down there than there is up Brady's sneck.' Grabbing the drawings from my hand, he hailed a gathering of eavesdroppers I had failed to notice. 'Come here, yous lot, an' have a look at these, why dontcha?' Patsy fanned the drawings in his hand and a ribald circle formed around them. Snatched and sniggered at, they were handed around, comments in general lewd and complimentary, but a consensus firmly in accordance with the Plunkett critique. Donoghue also joined the circle, a bemused look on his face. Something unquestionably was wrong with those drawings and whispers like wind began shifting my certitude and doubt started creeping on me like a stalking cat.

Somehow, it was my mistake, a big one, and far from being the grandee of the schoolyard, as I had fancied myself, I was an object of ridicule, even assailed by Coyle, the little rat, tutting his teeth and tossing his head disdainfully and loudly cancelling his order. I felt faint and stupefied, wrestling to comprehend how wrong I'd been.

Pulling Donoghue from the jostle by his sleeve, I harangued him. 'Paddy, all that stuff you've been telling me how could you have missed that out?' I was so frustrated and humiliated, so disappointed, I was nearly crying. Donoghue was smiling wryly. I took him by the arms and began shaking him. 'Paddy, how could you miss out something so—so—important?'

He shrugged: 'Thought you'd o' known.'

'Well, I didn't, I didn't.'

He shrugged again: 'Women same as men in that department.'

'Well, maybe I should have known, but I didn't.'

Shonti had collected the drawings and was shoving them in my hand. 'Put 'em friggin' right.'

'Ok, ok.' Four of the five needed rectifying and, squatting on my hams, I laid the drawings on the back of my satchel and with my 'accounting' pencil poised above the first of them, I was ready to do as he had ordered, but what, and precisely where?

'Jesus, not as much as that,' Shonti growled, snatching the pencil from my fingers, 'It doesn't go up to their bloody belly buttons.' With the rubber end of the pencil, he erased my over-compensation and shaded in an appropriate, respectable but quite generous hirsute V. He handed back the pencil, as Coyle's misshapen beauty came to light.' Here, do the rest yersel'.'

How can something six-feet-four inches tall and weighing nigh on twenty stones materialise out of thin air? Even more incredible, how can almost two dozen eyes and ears, blessed with the optimum of vibrant youth, fail to see it coming? What kind of hocus-pocus, sorcery, demonic intervention or plain bad luck can spirit a black-garbed harbinger, the size of a block of flats, out of emptiness in to the epicentre of a group of wily boys, without one of them getting wind of it?

A huge, fleshy hand was descending from above and, quite gently, removing five drawings from my fingers. It was a witch-finder. Was he sent by God or Satan? I looked up fearfully into two bushy blowholes amid a moonscape of pink jelly and at eyes that had been dead for years. Brother Brady's face assimilated all colour from the faces of the boys around him, all now petrified in a stricken silence. Cowering beneath him, unable to fully comprehend the sheer awfulness of my situation, my first instinct was to run, but I couldn't. This manifestation towering above me had sapped every atom of spirit from my blood, leaving only husk.

Brother Brady levelled the drawings neatly, folded them once into a smart crease, placed them in one of the torn envelopes, then secreted them in the deep folds of his soutane. He did not speak or even glance at anyone, but swivelled delicately on his heel and started gliding towards the schoolhouse, his soutane sustained in the draughts of air preceding him.

'It was Gilla Christe what done 'em, Bru,' Shonti Plunkett shouted and, getting no response, sprinted after him. 'It was Gilla Christe what done 'em, Bru.'

Coyle burst into tears, calling loudly after the cleric, 'Oy done nuttin' dorty, Bru.'

Then I was completely alone and stricken with shame and guilt and shrinking against the rough pebble-dash of the ablution block wall with the awful truth of Shonti's accusation still ringing in my ears.

Yes, it was Gilla Christe what done 'em, Bru, Gilla Christe, caught red-handed. My spirit swooned, not at thought of punishment, not a flogging, no, a flogging, I would welcome as expiation and accountability, a flogging would normalise my life again. My spirit swooned at the shame I had brought upon myself, my parents and my little sisters, the innocent ruin behind my bestial portraitures and guilt consumed me.

And what of the Christian Brothers, the priests, who had so diligently guided me towards the love of God, what would they think of me as evidence was declaimed? What of the Sisters of Mercy at St Jude's, the girls of that school, among them Cora Casey? Would they speak slyly among themselves of my disgrace? Would they gossip? Or worse, draw a discreet curtain of respectability over something too shameful to talk about, too disturbing for the quiet waters of polite society? Whether it would be brushed under the carpet, sniggered at or shouted from roof tops, everyone would know about it just the same.

I wailed and, dragging my fingernails down the pebbledash, I sought relief in the pain and anguish.

There was someone at my side. 'Listen you, I want me friggin' money back.' It was Shonti.

Chapter Twenty-two

*H*ad I being given the choice to live or die as I watched Shonti slither back into the schoolhouse, I would have chosen death. I was so aware of my miserable existence that September afternoon, I did not want to live. All around me, commonplace schoolboy activity, a cacophony of coarse voices, as if from another world, an innocent world in which I no longer played a part. Oh, I cursed myself for the greedy unworldly fool I was, childishly congratulating myself on initiative and commerce and counting stacks of shillings in my mind. What worth those miserable millstones in my pocket now? What a disappointment I was to everyone, most of all to myself.

Soon the whistle would blow and I would have a choice to make. Turn right towards the schoolhouse and face consequences too appalling to contemplate, or turn left, and run. There was no choice, I would run, hide somewhere, my cave-den on the mountain, escape from clouded faces, hushed voices and an issue too indelicate for righteous people to speak of. I would join with Poppy Boyle; as fugitives from a world of social grace, we would survive together, comfort each other as the rejects that we were. Thought of escape consumed me.

Soon the whistle would blow and I would have a choice to make, I had made my choice, I would run. But first, back to the hurling field, where, in another age, I had eaten lunch and bargained, full of pride and expectation. For the first time I felt pain in my bleeding fingers where I had torn them on the wall. They were sore as I fingered the shilling coins from my pocket and threw them as far as I could into waist-high grass. Not as an act of atonement, no, I would tell the despicable Plunketts exactly where they were and let them look for them.

Veering away from the schoolyard, I made for the gate. A whistle was blowing and I could not bear the thought of enquiry, interrogation and disgrace. The gate was in sight and I was running fast. With or without Poppy Boyle, I could not live the winter in a cave. I would return to England and live with demurring relatives, a pariah's life infinitely preferable to what I would leave behind. I was stopped by Brother McBride turning through the gateway. 'And where do you think you are going, boy?'

I wasn't going anywhere. I was going back to classes like everyone else. A whistle, I hadn't heard a whistle. And then a boy was by my side; he was from my own class but I didn't know his name. His voice was disembodied, as if calling to me from a troubled dream. I was wanted by Brother Brady in his office. Of course I was wanted by Brother Brady. The boy's eyes were downcast as if he already knew my fate and in the corridor, lots of boys with sad eyes, who couldn't bear to look at me.

I opened the office door without knocking and fell inside. 'Sorry, Brother, I'm sorry,' I heard myself blurting. I wanted a thrashing, equal to the fabled one that I had got before. I would hold my hands out all day long and never flinch. But what I got from the big fat man behind the table was disregard and silence.

Just as every boy had a story to tell about the mountain madman, so they had a story of a summoning by Brother Brady. A boy could be made to stand worrying for the duration of playtime or even longer before cold eyes even noticed he was there. Cronin had once missed an entire lesson standing in front of the man as, muttering and sighing, he fussed through a pile of paperwork, searching for a non-existent file, knowing well that the deferment was deliberate. A boy could be reduced to a nervous wreck just standing there, some even bursting into tears before a single word was spoken. In Cronin's case, when the boy began to fidget and whimper, the cleric had looked up, surprised to find that he was still there and asked him what he wanted. How many times had I vowed never to give Brady the satisfaction of seeing my spirit broken, my unfounded tears. However grievous my crime, then I would take punishment without complaint, even slink through life shamefaced, forever furtive in dishonour, anything rather than fall prey to this man's cruel psychological trickery.

If there is no hope of mercy, then you may look judgement in the face for indication of your fate and, in such a situation, the lightest nuance can tell you all you want to know. Once you know your fate, then immediately, and no matter how awful it is, you can start to prepare yourself to face it. But cruellest of all is not-knowing and not being given the chance to know and that was what Brady was doing to me now. He was not ignoring me as he had done with Cronin, he was looking me directly in the eye, but his eyes were expressionless, no anger in them, no disgust or loathing and searching them for something I found nothing, not even threat.

Presently, he stood up and, taking a file from the cabinet behind him, he placed it carefully on the table, its edges corresponding exactly with the edges of the blotter. I saw that it had my name on it and my heart lurched. He sat down again and, fingering inside its covers, he manoeuvred the contents until the corners of five white sheets appeared, only corners, but the precursors of a sickening exposure. I knew that he was looking at me again but I could not meet his eyes, examining instead, my shoes, dusty from the playing-field, and strange spots like little pearls which had appeared on the toecaps.

Now he propped the file upright on the table and appeared to be absorbed with what he saw inside, his mouth tightening grimly. There were more pearls on my toe caps and I was stunned to see that they were teardrops. How long had I been crying? The cleric closed the file and laid it down squarely in front of him. 'You know why I have called for you?' he said grimly.

I nodded, for I could not speak for the shame and terror at being confronted with my wickedness, yet his expression had changed, no longer blank, no longer grim but a cynical contemplation of my plight. Then he had taken out of the file five sheets of paper and at that moment I felt that I must die.

The cleric eased his chair backwards, allowing his girth to bulge forward. On the table in front of him, five pages of my handwriting. He said, 'Been meaning to have a word with you about these for quite some time, a bit flowery in places, but in general quite expressive. One I liked best was "A Winter's Day". I declare to goodness, made me feel quite chilly.'

I knew that he was talking about my essays but I didn't know anything else, this world of rights and wrongs and rebus was not for me, I was too small and stupid and wicked for this world. The only thing I understood was my ugly knees and the teardrops on my toecaps.

Without further ceremony, the cleric stood up and put my file back in the cabinet, every movement so easy, so precise. He said, 'You appear to be a little upset about someting. Maybe it's not a good time to discuss your essays.' Then he swept past me to the door, turning as he exited. 'Remain exactly where you are, I tink Brother Mulligan wants a word.'

Minutes later, Brother Mulligan arrived, looking upset and weary, his movements quick and nervy. Shoulders slumped he sat down on the chair and, putting his elbows on the table, laid his head in his hands. 'Oh Gilla Christe,' he said softly into his hands.

He took his head from his hands and his tired eyes cast about the room and seemed to settle on the transom of the door behind me. Somehow the ceiling seemed lower and the filing cabinet and decking towered and tilted like never before. From the corner of the cabinet a tiny spider swung on a single thread, wafting to and fro in the draught from the partly open window. Not daring to look at him, or the brown envelope he had put on the table in front of him, I kept my eyes transfixed on the spider. When the teacher spoke, his voice was laden with disappointment and he didn't look at me. 'Gilla Christe, what were you thinking, boy?'

Through the open window I could hear the voice of Brother Ryan, assembling my own class for Gaelic football, then the distant voice of Brother Molloy, calling from the playing field, beneath the window Dermot Coyle answering someone, 'No, not me, oy done nuttin' dorty.'

With a deep sigh, the cleric got up and closed the window, then sat down again, heavily. The spider had vanished; vaguely I looked for it to be caught up in the folds of his soutane. I was no longer crying but my eyes were stinging and it would take little for me to start again. With a gesture of his hand, the brother bade me sit down in front of him and with a thin finger poked the envelope further along the table and, for the first time, met my eye. 'What you have done is very, very wrong,' he said. 'This is hard for me, for as in all my years as a teacher I have never before had to deal with anything like this.' He poked at the envelope again. 'I don't even have to ask you if you are responsible because I know you are. When Brother Brady told me what Shonti Plunkett had said, I hoped he was mistaken, but when I saw, when I saw…' His words stumbled and he shook his head. 'I knew that it was you, I knew that it couldn't be anybody else.'

My nose was running and fresh tears were pricking behind my eyes. Rummaging in my pocket for a handkerchief, I didn't have one but the cleric, sensing my discomfort, took a clean rag from a drawer in the table and handed it to me. I blew my nose and dabbed at my swollen eyes. The cleric did not seem to know what further to say to me and kept shaking his head and sighing. Then after about a minute without saying anything, he began a counselling so unhappily grave that I felt he might begin to weep himself.

He spoke of how lucky I was to be born into a good Catholic family and to be able to go freely to church and school and did I know that in this troubled world there were places where such commonplace activities were prohibited on pain of death. So easily could any one of us be born in a Communist state, denying even the very existence of God, where a boy might live its entire life without being given the opportunity of God's blessing and the chance for the eternal salvation of his soul, did I appreciate what I had? Did I realise how lucky I was? For if not, oh, how I would if it was suddenly taken from me. His words flowed now, lenient, and his blue eyes shone with something deeper than understanding, warmer than candour. It was as if he could feel my pain himself and I was no longer cowed.

He continued, 'There comes a time in the life of every boy when he must leave childhood behind and begin a new life, a life he knows very little of. Before we are born, how much do we know of this life and in this life that we are now living, how much do we know of the life that awaits us after death? Don't rush this life you're living, don't try to become an adult overnight.'

He continued so tenderly that the weariness left his face and the furrows eased in his brow, leaving only the sadness in his eyes, that strange pain of his. He even tried to make a joke about my tearful state, causing me to raise a smile to my puffed and sagging cheeks but although he spoke with tenderness, gravity remained because soon he would have to face the issue that bedevilled him, a brown envelope a sickening reminder to us both.

It was common knowledge that Brother Mulligan could not utter the word 'sex' without sounding hysterical. He would use the word 'lust' instead, because it was one of the deadly sins, an essential part of the church's doctrine, about which it was his duty to inform us. 'Sex' was quite something else and if he couldn't bring himself to use the word, then I prayed that he could not comfortably open up that envelope and allow sex to flood across the table in a lurid pool.

'Oh, Gilla Christe, you are a lucky boy this day. You were on the wrong road and how lucky you were that Brother Brady should find you there and rescue you and you must thank that man from the very bottom of your heart.'

He paused, scratching at his ear and stared again at the transom above my head and I sensed another train of thought, anything to defer the mutual embarrassment of the envelope. 'Companions on that wrong road, yes, that's another thing, so it is. A boy must be so careful who he chooses as a fellow traveller. Ah Johnny there, sure he's a bright fella, knows all the answers, the one to lead us from the wrong road to the right one. It is not the case; the know-it-all fella is sure to take you further and deeper down the wrong road until you are surely lost. Now I know you spend an awful lot of your time in that shop of Nugget Nolan. Now I do not say that Mr Nolan is the type of chap to lead a boy deliberately astray, but I do wonder at the difference in ages and what on earth the two of you can have in common and the shop itself, dear God what a dump it is, really, is it a place that a young lad like yourself should be spending so much time in? Not at prayer, not at study, not playing football, not even playing with other boys, but stuck in a smelly cobbler's shop on the edge of a council tip.'

I was shocked that he should know so much about my life outside of school. Often I had seen him walking past the window of the shack, secure in the knowledge that he would never see me through a filthy window. Then how did he know so much about me. Who had told him? And why should he find Nugget Nolan so undesirable? He was my best friend, the shop, a dump, yes, but not the man himself, surely?

For sure, he gimped around town, in and out of the bookies, in and out of Dan's often with a jar or two inside him, often with a lot more, but he wasn't on his own there. He stank to high heaven but then, on hot days, so did Brother Brady. But there was nothing too unsavoury in his conduct, language a little risqué sometimes but nothing I hadn't heard before. No, the cleric had Nugget Nolan wrong; he knew nothing of the man's pedigree, his genealogy of heroes and achievers.

How often had the cleric himself, during history lessons, proclaimed consanguinity of all Irishmen from kings? Well, knowing what I did of the cobbler's illustrious lineage I could think of no one else in Greystones more likely than he to have royal blood coursing through his veins. The cleric was wrong, but this certainly was not the time and place to put him right.

Reading my doubts, the cleric continued hastily, 'I'm not saying Nugget Nolan is a bad man, ah no, that would not be right, what I'm saying is, that as a cobbler, he is better suited to dealing with the soles of shoes than the souls of men. He has a lot to say for himself and I wouldn't take too much notice of all he tells you. A broad mind, you might say. Oh, I hear so much nowadays about the 'broad mind'. On the wireless even, a broadminded man, you'll hear said, as if it's a great compliment. Well, what I say is, the broader the mind, the more rubbish to fill it with. Oh the devil loves the broad mind because he has just the stuff to fill it.' He smiled at his own reasoning, allowing the smile to linger on his lips long enough to make me feel included. 'A narrow mind filled with God's grace is the broadest mind of all. And what broad mind inspired this, I wonder?' he added, flicking at the envelope with the back of his hand and, in so doing, raising, at last, the dread purpose of our one-sided engagement.

I sniffed and found that I could not lift my eyes but inspected closely a small wart that had recently appeared on the knuckle of my thumb. This was it soon I would know my fate.

'What a terrible thing to do, to draw such stuff as is in that envelope. What in the name of God possessed you?' he continued unsparingly. 'And then hawking them around the schoolyard, corrupting innocent boys, pictures – drawings – the product of a corrupting mind, well... ' He let his words trail away as if he had neither the words or the willingness to chronicle such iniquity. 'Lust,' he said quietly, prolonging unhappily the single syllable. 'As you poised your pencil above that first blank sheet of paper, did you not consider for one moment the Virgin Mary at your shoulder and the anguish in her eyes? Were you aware that at your other shoulder was the devil, laughing, guiding your hand, urging you on?' Suddenly his posture altered and his eyes were imbued with an evangelical fervour, for he knew, as well as

I, that he had won the battle for my soul. 'Gilla Christe, as those first ruinous lines appeared on that paper, so the Blessed Virgin wept and Satan clapped his hands with glee. Oh yes, how Satan and his legions rejoiced, how they danced with joy to see a young boy fall to the deadly sin of lust. Where a young boy is concerned it is the devil's most insidious and deadly weapon. Did you not hear legions rejoicing from the depths of Hell, did you not hear the weeping of angels? Gilla Christe, Servant of Christ, another angel fallen into Hell.'

My eyes had dried and I felt contrite and humble at the brother's impassioned saving of my soul, yet I also felt deep resentment at those 'innocents' corrupted. How unfair that I should be taking all the blame. Yes, I had done the deed and I was sorry and deeply ashamed, but what of the cajoling, the bribery that had led me to it? Should not my shame be diluted with the oozing guilt of other? Both Shonti and Patsy Plunkett, both older than I, what fine examples of innocence they were. Why were they not here with me now? And snivelling Dermot Coyle, whining his puny mantra, 'Oy done nuttin' dorty', he should be here too.

'It wasn't just me, Brother,' I managed weakly. 'Those other boys, they were not so innocent.'

'Forget those other boys.'

'But it was them that put me up to it.'

'Forget them.'

'But...'

Forget them? It was so unfair. At this very moment, truth and lies in malicious abandon would be spread around to others. The subject, one so dear to every schoolboy's heart, sex, the stuff of ribaldry, lust, harnessed and corralled, ameliorated and exaggerated, a powerhouse of calumny, spread to vilify me and glorify the perpetrators.. 'Please, Brother, it's only fair. Let me tell you about Shonti and Patsy Plunkett, about Dermot Coyle.'

The cleric leaned forward a little and I caught again the familiar odour of sweetness on his breath. "He takes funny little cashew things," Corrigan had once whispered, as if imputing some well-kept secret vice.

'When Lucifer fell, Lucifer, an archangel like Michael and Gabriel, he brought many angels with him into hell. Even angels can find themselves on the wrong road, following the wrong man. That heritage, Gilla Christe, before the beginning of time is with us still. When man falls he seeks to bring others with him, pool the evil of his deed so that he might be found responsible only for the measure he is sinking in. He gains nothing in fact he has compounded the sin and multiplied its gravity by every soul he's tainted with it. A good man will do the opposite. Remember Jesus, an innocent man, yet without blame, he died for the sins of the entire world. It will do you no good to implicate others.'

I understood what he was saying, but it did not make me feel less bitter. They would all pay one day for this betrayal.

The teacher now sat upright in his chair and ran fingers through his greying hair. He was not angry with me, he had never been angry with me and somehow I knew that the issue of the drawings would go no further than this room. My heart was uplifted; this man's soul was great. His face shone with a kind of spirituality, a light that shines only in men who have no idea that it is there. He glanced scathingly at the envelope, ugly, at the table end. 'And the body of man, of woman, what are they but the holy vessels of the soul, containers for the everlasting soul and blessed in their own right as they have been fashioned in the image of God. To make much of the body is to diminish its purpose and to reproduce it as a spectacle for lewd and sinful musing is to reduce it to animal state, a corrupt vehicle for the whims of the devil. Jesus says that if your eye offends you pluck it out; by that He means that the eye is there to be used to view the wonders of God's universe and is but a vile and useless thing when used to gloat upon the world of Satan.'

My heart was moving forcefully at the rapture of his words as they began to nurture once again my withered soul. I had been on the point of rejecting God and the church, my family and everything that I held dear for a few shillings and a trifling slice of schoolyard popularity. The tiny spider appeared again on the cuff of the cleric's shirt and began to explore the blue veined texture of his hand. I watched it as it manoeuvred through the thick, black hair at the cuff's edge, a forest to the tiny thing, then swing on a strand to the table below where if disappeared beneath the envelope.

'Brother Brady and I have discussed this matter and feel that it is in the best interests of the school to take it no further. This disgusting stuff I will now burn in the school furnace and that will be the end of it. The Head will be told, of course, I will do that now and I will assure him of your promise never to do such a thing again. Am I right?'

My ordeal was coming to a close and the block of bitter tears, frozen behind my eyes, began to melt inwardly. 'Oh Brother, such a thing will never, ever happen again.'

The cleric paused and grimaced, as if there was one last troublesome impediment to be expunged before the matter could be laid to rest, finally. 'There was one drawing in particular that Brother Brady and I were most disturbed by.' He paused and glanced at the envelope in disgust but did not continue, wanting me to intercede with an explanation, to save him more embarrassment.

I knew immediately what he was referring to, something difficult to explain, to even talk about. 'That was a kind of joke, Brother, something between me and Coyle.'

'One most peculiar drawing,' he did not look at me but at the spider that had reappeared and was scurrying from beneath the envelope, as if what it had found there was distasteful.

'See, Bru, I only got paid for one.' Words repressed for so long, queued to tumble from my lips. 'That's what I was trying to tell you those drawings were done to specifications they were paying me. Coyle was going to pay… '

The brother's hand shot up to silence me, the topic needed immediate closure. 'Enough,' he said abruptly. 'All you need now is to be ever thankful to Brother Brady for his vigilance. You have a lot to thank Brother Brady for.'

Never would I thank that man for anything. He did not save souls, he played with them. His game with the essays was unspeakably cruel and forced me to break my vow, never to shed a tear in his cause. 'Yes, I know that, Brother,' I submitted weakly.

The cleric now stood up and, bracing himself picked up the envelope and stuffed it in a pocket of his soutane. Cocking his ear towards noise from the schoolyard, he said. 'Your class is on its way to the playing-field, but one more thing before you go and join them. As you know, school confessions are on Thursday. Examine your conscience, and consider if, or not, you are in a state of mortal sin. No one can judge that but yourself but I strongly advise you to confess this sin as a matter of great priority,' and he tapped his pocket, in case I had doubt as to which sin he was alluding.

He continued with bold insistence, 'Confession on Thursday, Holy Communion on Friday. Dedicate both sacraments to the Blessed Virgin and to the precious Body and Blood of Christ, and with this awful stuff behind you,' he tapped his pocket again, 'you are on a new road, with a new life and with the love of God flooding in your soul.'

Stepping from behind the table, he opened the door and gestured for me to precede him. With small steps I followed him to the doorway. I had learned a bitter, painful lesson and vowed henceforth to live within the Holy Spirit. At the doorway I hesitated, wanting so much to thank him. Sensing the reason behind my hesitation, he smiled and said, 'If you have anything to say before you go, then go ahead.'

'Bru, Bru, Bru, Bru, Bru, Bru, Bru, Bru, Bru,' came from a classroom. I waited until the noise subsided. I had to say something, something appropriate, profound. This man had lifted a huge weight from my shoulders and was sending me on my way with forgiveness and good will. I had a few seconds, before we went our separate ways, in which to express my gratitude. Emotionally, I was exhausted, ripped apart, that heady experience of sex and sin, of sudden wealth and popularity had taken its toll. Such a fleeting visit to be fragmented so soon at the confluence of promise and denial, oh, how I would have loved to have lived that dream a little longer. Could I ever forgive Donoghue? How could he have omitted from his awesome disclosures so primal a facet of pubescence that everyone knew of it except for me?

'Bru, Bru, Bru, Bru, Bru, Bru, Bru, Bru, Bru.' The noise was louder still. What could I say to this kind man whose smile was fading now but was still apparent in the tissue of his eyes this warm, weary cleric who didn't have to, but chose to raise his tired spirit and re-construct my soul, his words of understanding and compassion, to be with me all my life? He wanted to close the door, yet he waited. What could I say to him before he was gone and I was in the cloakroom for my football boots? Not a flaccid 'Goodbye, Brother' but generous words of gratitude, and not the silly childish words he might expect from a Plunkett or a Coyle. I needed words to make him respect me and admire me again. And as I stepped out into the corridor, they came to me as if from heaven sent. ' "Come what come may Time and the Hour runs through the roughest day." '

And as I laced up my football boots in the cloakroom, I felt a strange victory.

Chapter Twenty-three

A restless night shifting between sleep and wakefulness with voices calling faintly from behind the faint light of the landing then from behind the curtained window, a shrieking woman came that night. She was covered in coarse brown hair and, appearing at my side, shrieked at me in a language I could not understand. Then, hovering in the faint light, she beckoned me to follow her. But I was powerless in a limbo between dreamland and reality and, although I could see her clearly, I could not open my eyes. I fought to open my eyes and banish her, but she laughed and told me that this very night I had been chosen to become one of the hundred thousand who were to die this day and that she had won the battle for my soul. I tried desperately to call out because I did not want to die, but found I could not move a muscle or even lift an eyelid and there was nothing I could do except drift into a void I knew was death.

Then from the ceiling, floating into the sleepy paralysis of my brain, a saviour came. It was Coyle's woman with long, copper hair and one breast, surely she was there to release me from my seizure, but as I tried to raise my arm to her, she breathed brimstone in my face and said, huskily, 'Gilla Christe, it is I who won the battle for your soul.' Then, like witches, the two women clung to one another and, cackling, began to dance around my bed and at the fetid stench of their breath, I awakened suddenly in a sweat to find them gone, and relieved that I was not dead, but then remembering 'confession' I wished I was.

I was awakened from one hell to find myself in another. 'Confession,' the word and everything it represented, centred in the pit of my belly, a ball of anxiety, sending shoots and tendrils throughout my body, to emasculate me as ivy would a dying oak. From the window, in the early morning sunlight, the horizon was a pale gold which made me think of heaven but, as I lifted the catch with fumbling fingers and opened the window, the cold air and the strident calling of sea-birds awakened me fully to reality and it was just the morning of another awful day.

'Confession': my sick stomach could not face food and I declined the breakfast served to me and even before I began the walk to school, I had fed the contents of my lunchbox to the chickens.

'Confession': my leaden brain could not absorb lessons, numbers and letters like strange hieroglyphs and the voices of the teachers, alien. Only the ticking clock made any sense, each tick making the ball in my belly bigger. Everybody shrank from me. Coyle slid away from me along the bench until he was halfway across the adjacent aisle. No one spoke to me, no one wanting to be tainted by the guilt of association, and 'filthy pictures' was a whisper going around.

And the behaviour of the brothers was beyond my comprehension; the enigmatic smiles that Brother McBride had directed at me that morning in the schoolyard, Brother Brady's elaborate courtesy in the cloakroom and Brother Mulligan, so kind and understanding during my ordeal in the office, had not yet afforded me a word or glance.

Indelibly imprinted on my mind, Brother Mulligan's urging of Confession and Communion, forgiveness, penance and the acceptance of God as solution to a millstone of sin, but no omission, no prevarication; how often had we been warned of the dire consequences of such equivocations. To withhold a mortal sin or depreciate its gravity in the confessional was to multiply iniquity a thousand fold. Confessional dishonesty and St Peter's rock would crumble underfoot and Satan's legions camp at heaven's door.

Brother Mulligan was addressing the class. 'Ok boys, collect your caps and jackets, and the boys from Bray your satchels and homework and assemble in the yard, we are going to march very smartly today and I'll be watching carefully for any boy stepping out of line.'

Boys with no soles to their shoes were exempt from this obligation and allowances were made. The brothers knew who the boys were and nothing was ever said to them, but boys with good shoes, if they stepped out of line, they could be certain of a hefty clout of re-adjustment. I followed others into the cloakroom for my cap and jacket, and took my place in the line of boys outside. While others giggled, shuffled, nudged and whispered, I stood immured in my own gloom, it was as if some sad derelict had gained entry to my core and squatted there. Ascending Jeeney Hill, I felt no ground beneath my feet, no breath of air in my face. I was moving through colourless grey, seeing nothing on the way, no bird or animal, no leaf or blade of grass, no other human, except those marionettes whose heads were bobbing up and down in front of me. I heard nothing, saw nothing, it was neither light nor dark, nor day or night, but a dream-like, sullen journey through preoccupation. I must have put one foot in front of another and kept in line and I must have swung my arms in semblance of uniformity, because at no time, as far as I could remember, did I receive an adjusting clout from a flanking brother. My perception of the gloom around me was so stultified by apprehension that if Brother McBride, leading our ranks, had veered over a cliff's edge, then, none the wiser, I would have followed to my death. I had no sense of being, no potency, no will to live, only an intolerable burden of sexual sin and an all-consuming fear of confessing it to Father Duff.

St Killian's church loomed, a towering edifice, an Irish Notre Dame, and I the skulking Frollo. The two confessionals stood wall-side like upturned coffins and my heart lurched to see that the name plates were missing. Had one of the brothers, Brother Brady, or even Brother Mulligan, taken them down deliberately to punish me? Yes, it was not intended that I should know the identity of the priest awaiting me. Once I had a terrifying nightmare of being buried alive in a coffin with Father Duff as slowly, he putrefied, while absolving me of sins. With whom, I wondered pityingly, would I be entombed today?

Directed by the brothers, one by one, the classes genuflected and took their places abreast of their appointed confessionals. They crossed themselves and, on knee pads, knelt in silent prayer. When the classes were in place, the church fell silent except for the clinking of rosary beads and breathy murmurings from the lofty void above. My class had taken rows to be served by the first confessional. Please let it be the one occupied by Father McCartney.

With grievous sins to tell, McCartney was to Brother Mulligan what Duff was to Brother Brady. Gruff Duff would not take kindly to the news I had for him today. The sliding of slats and the confessionals were in dual operation. Two boys in unison genuflected and through the velvet curtains, entered the box at opposing sides. One penitent first, then following his absolution, the priest would swivel on his chair to the second, while a third boy took the first one's place. I watched the first boy leave, head down, soulful, to the back of the church, there to recite his penance, the third boy then disappearing behind the curtains. Where was I in the order of things? Counting back I was the thirteenth and this was no coincidence, I had seen Brother Mulligan hold a boy back and speak to him, so that the ill-fated number was sure to be mine.

A fourth boy and then a fifth, no curmudgeonly grunts as yet, there was still hope. Soon it would be my turn. Would Father Duff be there to meet me?

Everything began to fall into place, the sinister smiles of Brother McBride, Brother Brady's inordinate courtesy, Brother Mulligan strange and distant since I left him at that office door. How naive of me to think that I could be allowed to escape with such leniency. Yes, through staggered heads, I could see a bulge at Brother Brady's waist band, the missing name plates. I turned my head, yes, two pews behind me, Brother Mulligan smiling secretly and I was next and had to quell a panic that would have me bolting from the church.

I had made my mind up, whoever was behind that shutter, I would blurt out my sin immediately and get it over with. The twelfth boy was leaving the box, pale-faced and pious and I almost barged into him, such was my hurry to take his place. I knelt down in total darkness, thank God for total darkness. No, in the blink of an eye, as if summoned, fingers of meagre light were creeping upon me from a small lattice, high in the confessional and the shutter was being opened and more light, a muted, corporeal glow, coming from the priest himself. This was an irradiation; miraculously bestowed at a priest's ordination, designed to put a face to sin.

What use lowering your head and mumbling through barely parted fingers. A priest knows who you are the moment he opens the shutter, knows your parents and your family history before you have time to clear your throat. But that inner light of Holy Orders is also light enough for you to know the priest. It was who I knew it would be, Father Duff.

I was bent so low, I was almost sitting on my heels and knew that only the tip of my forehead was visible through the hatch. One warning filled my mind, 'get it out quick', 'get it done with'. 'Bless me, Father, for I have sinned, I have been drawing impure pictures.'

There it was out, it was done and I dared to tilt my head backwards a little and raise my eyes to judgement. Above my brows, a misty face inclined towards me. 'What was that, again?'

'I have been drawing impure pictures, Father.'

'ONLY THE LOWEST OF THE LOW DO THAT SORT OF THING.'

It was the loudest, most disgusted voice that I had ever heard. A thunderclap of condemnation and in its bitter timbre, unequivocal repulsion, and in this hallowed place, this house of God, it echoed, the vaulted ceilings reverberating, so if there was anyone who doubted their ears, then they could hear it again and again.

My mind exploded. I may well, in anguish, have blurted other sins. I may have made an act of contrition and received absolution, but I was not aware of it. All I was aware of was a priest's voice that wouldn't go away and a penance, harsh and punitive. Legend had a boy getting a whole rosary as penance, but that was for setting fire to the school. But no one had ever got 'the 'stations of the cross' before. This was a first; you had to be the lowest of the low to get 'the stations of the cross'. No one in the sacerdotal history of Ireland had ever got 'the stations of the cross'.

I had no recollection of leaving the confessional or making my way to the rear of the church, where the first 'station' was positioned. On a stone pillar between two stained glass windows I became aware of our saviour being condemned to death. I was aware of old people, too, mostly women, stooped and wheezing over rosaries but so sickened at what they had heard from the confessional that they could not raise their eyes to me.

As a penance, 'The Way of the Cross' not only embodied requital and atonement but assimilated all the secondary deserts of disgrace as well, exposition, notoriety, isolation and scorn. To attend each of the fourteen stations individually was to cover the length of the church, on each side, in full view of a congregation, consisting, for most part, of my teachers and my peers.

I was being made an example of. No boy now would ever again hawk filth in the playground. What a fool I was to think that I had got away with it. Brother Brady, Brother Mulligan and Father Duff had cooked this up between them Brother McBride might well have been party to it too.

Dizzily treading air, not daring to look to right or left and every eye upon me, I fastened my gaze upon the first slate-hewn evocation of Christ's terrible journey and so began my own, my spirit shrivelled, fires burning on my cheeks, 'Only The Lowest of the Low', a stigma forever to shroud my life.

Oh, that poor priest, that much maligned man, who many years ago had decided to devote his life to God, compelled by vocation and duty to ingest the issue of the ungodly and profane. Yet even with all his years as minister of his church, nothing had prepared him for that sin of mine. I had caused him to renounce the sanctity of that sacred sacrament of Confession. I should have done as I had always done before, infused the sin with a few graceless short-comings, disobedience, late for Mass neglected prayers. How selfish and misguided of me to think I could just blurt it out and get it over with, blaze into the confessional and announce that I had drawn impure pictures, as if it was something to boast about. No wonder the poor man was shocked.

Oh, but it was never my intention, he had misunderstood me, taking me for a brazen braggart, flaunting sedition in his face and in the face of profound Catholic propriety. It was not I, who, with Pilate, had condemned our Lord unjustly. I could never be a soldier, muted and cold, to oversee His torment, a sinner, yes, but. I was genuinely sorry and infinitely more so now.

Anchored to the tiled floor, how long had I been pondering the dilemma of Simon of Cyrene? I swam in panic. How long had I been there with Simon? It was time I moved on, as Simon did.

Blurring images, the weight of the cross, whip-torn flesh, thorns piercing the skull, blood seeping into rags and voices rejoicing in barbarity and in misery and shame I was there on that road to Calvary. My head was swimming and I must have moved, for suddenly light through stained glass radiated the aisle to halo in yellow warmth the gentle face of St Veronica. A simple act of instinctive kindness, a fragment of humanity on that journey of redemption, she was handing Jesus a towel with which to wipe His face.

For the first time, I dared to lower my eyes over the heads of those boys still waiting in the pews. Close to each other, the two Plunkett boys, near to the second confessional. Not for them the rage of Father Duff or the agony of debasement. Would they confess the role that they had played? Of course not, ignorant of most things, they would not know the true measure of sin and evasion in the confessional would be grist to the mill for them. There was a terrible absence of justice in this church.

Plain to see, to anyone who looked closely, the angular impression the missing nameplates made under the cloth of Brother Brady's soutane, fitting nicely in the fleshy wedges of his gut. The sight of his bulky back and thick, red neck filling me with loathing and a few seats behind him, the meretricious Brother Mulligan, smugly fingering rosary beads, so much for his forgiveness and kind counselling; now, if I wanted, I could tell my mother a thing or two about a certain 'holy' face and the shabby duplicity that lay behind it.

I now faced the stations on the opposing side of the aisle. Pews here were empty and, with my back to conspirators, I could join the weeping women on Christ's dread journey, the kind of women, to which, henceforth, I would devote my fevered love. Wanton and dissolute, the image of Coyle's woman came to me, hungry eyes and wet, open mouth, a missing breast, and I was deeply ashamed. Salaciousness would be harnessed, restrained and then denied. The female form, clothed and modest, from now on, would occupy my thoughts, these weeping women, the wholesome tenants of my soul. My fever would be cured by the embodiment of kindness, flawlessness, beneficence and virtue only these qualities possessed the strength to tame the salivating beast lurking cloven-hoofed within me, that ungodly, unwanted custodian of my soul. And that small female feature, which for a year now had been the focus of all-consuming wonder and desire, would never again be sullied by a single, lustful thought; it would become as powerless and neutral as a strip of pure linen.

There was shuffling behind me, but I would not turn my head. My head ached. I think I might have turned my head to see what the commotion was, but my head hurt too much. My eyes were settled on the lifeless Jesus and my heart was melting in contemplation at the suffering He had endured. My heart was melting and my head was aching. I said to myself, "We adore Thee, O Christ, and bless Thee, because by Thy Holy Cross, Thou hast redeemed the world."

The journey of Jesus had ended. He had not died along the way, the mob were not cheated, He had died on a cross as He was supposed to do and now Joseph and Nicodemus were lowering Him into the arms of his poor mother. Soon that slab of stone would shift at resurrection. I felt sick.

The grasp at my elbow was firm but gentle, the kind of touch that would be used to rouse you from a deep sleep. What was Brother Mulligan doing at my side? The church was swaying, the pews were empty except for old people dressed in black and they were swaying too. I felt sick and faint. 'Brother…' I began.

'Gilla Christe, you can remain of course if you wish.' The brother's voice was edged with concern. 'Do you know that you have done "the stations of the cross", twice?'

'Brother…'

'Do you feel ill?'

My body was weak and trembling. An old woman was beside me; it was Grandma Plunkett. She was looking at me quaintly; she was not swaying, she was still.

'Confessions are over. Everyone is one their way back to school,' the brother said.

My legs gave way beneath me and the brother caught me as I fell. I was sick on the side of his soutane as he and another carried me outside. Rooney had my legs and I wondered vaguely if he was about to start telling me about his dead and deadly mott. A seagull was hovering high above my head and strangely the sky was darkening, then black.

Chapter Twenty-four

By McKenzie's shop in Blacklion, Mr Archer's car was requisitioned and in the back seat, with Brother Mulligan at my side, we were driven back to school. Not even when delirious with bronchitis had I ever felt as bad as I did now. There was something seriously wrong with me, because not only were the symptoms almost intolerable, but I was laid on a couch in Brother McBride's private room, an inner sanctum to which no boy had ever been allowed before. Since my trauma in the schoolyard with Brother Brady and the drawings, I had slept only intermittently and every waking hour since I had been consumed with misery and regret, the only relief being that short period of closure following Brother Mulligan's counselling, which I now considered to be greatly suspect. During this time I had felt listless and drained, a precursor, perhaps to another serious bout of bronchitis or influenza, but this was something else. I couldn't stand the light, I was shivering uncontrollably and my head was splitting with pain.

I was informed by Brother Mulligan, who remained with me, that the Head had summoned a doctor by telephone and a boy despatched to Calgary to inform my mother who would in turn try to contact my father. Getting out of Mr Archer's car, I had vomited again and although I did not feel so sick to my stomach now, a precautionary bucket had been placed beside the couch. I had no idea what was wrong with me. My ailment in church was so sudden and unexpected I thought I had somehow ingested poison. I was shaking more violently than ever and my head felt as if it was being sawn in half. Yet I did not fear death. A robust boy such as I would die from falling off a cliff or be drowned after being washed into the sea by a wave; healthy boys do not die of sudden sickness while debilitated on a cleric's couch.

Dr Donnelly arrived quickly. I had hoped for Dr Walsh, our family doctor, who always humoured me, but I felt so wretched, it wouldn't have mattered who turned up. Dr Donnelly did not like my father following an incident in the Railway Hotel. My father had been talking with a group of men which included Dr Donnelly when the latter began boasting that 'had the Dutch Ireland, they could feed the world' and apparently, my father had answered jokingly, 'And had the Irish, Holland, they could drown their bloody selves.' Dr Donnelly did not like this from an Englishman and had never spoken to him since

Dr Donnelly was a tall, bespectacled, balding man, with a disconcerting facial twitch. Boys at school laughed and mimicked the doctor, for when making a diagnosis, he would appear to wink, so that no one knew whether he was joking or not. He compensated for this twitch by approaching everything and everybody with a most serious demeanour which was even merrier to observe. He was twitching and serious when he was examining me, but no one in the room was merry.

Kneeling down beside me at the couch, he gestured to Brother Mulligan to close the curtains against the light, then, with one hand, as he felt for the pulse at my wrist, fingers of the other hand delicately placed a thermometer beneath my tongue. On closure of the curtains, a small wall light had been switched on and although painful for me to open my eyes, I searched his face for a measure of concern.

I thought he might speak to Brother Mulligan who was hovering worriedly in the background, but he did not speak or even look at him. Spoken diagnosis was unnecessary for as he read the thermometer, the twitch in his eye increased dramatically and I knew that I was very ill.

Still without acknowledgment of the cleric behind him, he opened my shirt and pressed a stethoscope to my chest. Whatever the result of this procedure, his expression did not lighten and, removing the blanket, he examined first my back and then my inner thighs his eye still twitching.

For the first time, he spoke to Brother Mulligan, asking for a cold flannel, which he laid across my forehead. Then he spoke to the cleric again as he jotted something in a note-book, but in a voice too low to hear. He gave me two tablets which I swallowed with sips of water and then he spoke to me. 'We'll get you home, young man, and we'll keep an eye on you tonight. No better in the morning and it's to hospital in Dublin.' Then he winked and I didn't know if he was joking or not.

I passed out then and did not know anything more until I awoke in my own bed in Calgary.

The doctor's initial suspicion had proved right. I had contracted a strain of cerebo-spinal fever, a form of meningitis which can prove fatal, but in my case, luckily, had been diagnosed and treated early and it was not as virulent as this affliction often is.

'Spotted fever,' the doctor told my parents, with a wink, my condition going some way towards healing his rift with my father.

'Spotted fever' may not sound too serious, but the medical euphemism did nothing, those first few days, to alleviate the vomiting, the pain in my back and thighs and most severely, in my head. I was confined to bed in a darkened bedroom for a whole week and denied visitation by all except my parents and Dr Donnelly, who kept me under close observation.

Thankfully, anti-biotics, together with a robust immune system, did not necessitate hospitalisation and within days, in my own bed, I began to show signs of recovery. Apparently, I had responded to treatment and a diet of milk-foods and broth far quicker than was expected, and, as I was constantly reminded, a daily intake of a spoonful of execrable brandy, forced on me as a stimulant. On the third day of my confinement, expectant spots had appeared in the form of a rash. They were concentrated on my back and thighs and had my parents and the doctor nodding to each other in satisfied corroboration and reaching again for the brandy bottle.

The second week and now under the care of my own doctor, Dr Walsh saw me out of bed and starting to feel well again. I was still weak and restricted to the house, but this suited me for a time as I certainly was in no hurry to return to school.

Truth was, I was beginning to hate and fear school. The ill-feeling I harboured at my treatment had been nurtured throughout my confinement, but I couldn't bear the grudges any longer, they were too many and they weighed too much and I wasn't up to facing them. I had no true friends at school and, although I pretended to myself that I didn't want them or need them, I did. If I wanted friends I was going to have to 'start school' again, the same school a different boy.

But the third week came and outside the windows of Calgary, moody October was preparing the way for the frosts and storms of winter and I longed to be out on the Head again. I had grown tired of painting pictures, teasing sisters and reading books (even though one was a new Lemmy Caution) 'borrowed' from my parents' bedroom. I was missing the cliffs, that towering stack and my secret den. And I longed to see again my only friends, Frank at The Ormonde, Mr Malone, and, of course, Nugget Nolan. It was over three weeks since I last saw Nugget and he would be concerned about me, wondering where I was and missing me, as I was missing him.

Chapter Twenty-five

*I*t was a cold, sunny Saturday afternoon when I first got permission from my father to leave the house and as I vaulted the gate, I turned immediately onto the unmade road and set out for Nugget's shack. Sometimes on a Saturday he would not turn up for work, too much porter the night before, but as I neared his works, I could see a shape behind the window, and I was excited.

He would be wondering why I hadn't reported to him on my surveillance of Mr Malone and I was most eager to tell him about the illness I had just recovered from, how serious it was and I had remembered words like meningitis, and cerebro-spinal especially to impress him, but I wouldn't mention spotted fever because it didn't sound serious enough. No doubt his older brother Dr Aloysius Nolan the surgeon would have heard of the condition, so Nugget would have tales to tell himself. I smiled as I imagined his reaction when I burst through the door. He would leap backwards in mock alarm clutching at his chest and saying, 'Dear God, sure you nearly gave us a heart attack burstin' in like that. Where have you been all these months? Sure, I thought you must o' emigrated back to England.' I would reply, 'Nugget, I've been suffering from meningitis, a serious cerebro-spinal condition and I could have died'.

Head bent low, I sneaked beneath his window and, smiling broadly, threw open the door and leaped inside.

Everything died, my smile first. What were Cora Casey and a

pretty-faced friend doing in Nugget's shack? These were Burnaby girls, St Jude's girls, high class society girls, Cora's father owned a hotel in Bray and the other girl, well her father was Dr Donnelly, the man who had saved my life. This was a sunny afternoon in October. What were they doing in Nugget's shack?

I froze on the spot as no one acknowledged my flamboyant entry. Why didn't Nugget greet me? Why, oh why had I not done as usual and peep through the woodwork first?

'Hi, Nugget,' I managed.

The cobbler didn't answer. What was wrong with him? He hadn't seen me for weeks, why did he not speak to me, what had I done? The girls didn't speak to me either, but then, Cora Casey had never spoken to me and Dr Donnelly's daughter, well, she would probably only know me by sight. I knew instantly that my sudden entry had been both untimely and unwelcome and I should have turned on my heel immediately and left, but I didn't. I was still frozen in disbelief that Nugget was ignoring me. This man was my best friend. Ok, I was interrupting something and I should have left but I couldn't; my heart was beating madly and I found myself shuffling into a corner where some dusty magazines were stacked, the top one proving to be of great interest.

A conversation, interrupted by my entry, resumed and was both animated and frivolous. It was obvious that the girls were here for something more than a quick purchase or an emergency shoe repair. The three were laughing loudly at something that Nugget was saying and looking up from the magazine I joined in the laughter.

Oh Nugget, please acknowledge me, I exist, I am your friend. Don't you want to know where I have been, what's been wrong with me? Don't do this to me in front of Cora Casey.

He didn't know me and didn't want to know where I'd been and the conversation and laughter continued unabated with Nugget's ginger moustache working overtime; cock-a-hoop with his illustrious company he positively radiated self satisfaction.

I was deeply hurt. I had dreamed many times of being in a

claustrophobic situation with Cora Casey but Nugget Nolan's sweat-smelling, refuse-reeking, dilapidated workplace had never been the milieu of my dreams. I felt so uncomfortable, so uneasy; my battered spirit having recovered a little during my three weeks of confinement in Calgary was taking an unmerciful battering again. The Donnelly girl was slim and pretty, lovely to look at, but it was the closeness of Cora, which unnerved me so. I had been close to her before, in queues and the foyer of The Ormonde, and on swimming and sunbathing days on the pier. Once, while walking on my hands, I had deliberately fallen, brushing her with my legs and apologising profusely. She hadn't noticed me then and she wasn't going to notice me now. The closeness of Cora was completely draining me and I really should leave, but I simply couldn't; somehow, I was trapped.

Buried in the magazine, 'Nugget', I beseeched inwardly, 'don't do this.'

The cobbler was grinning from ear to ear at something Cora was telling him about the Donnelly girl and in a state of high excitement he began gimping about the shop. Feet splayed, thumbs extended, he skipped over a cigarette end, grabbed a skin of leather from a shelf before spiralling back to his bench. 'Ah Nora, you're the sly one, so you are. What Cora's after tellin' me I know to be true so don't be tryin' to deny it.'

'Nora, that's her name,' I told the magazine.

Now Nugget was telling stories of his father's music-hall friendship with George Formby, good stories, full of lively anecdotes and mimicry and dutifully I laughed loudly at 'turned out nice again' and 'Ooo Mother' but to no avail; this introduction of myself wasn't working either. Shaking the dust off another magazine, I opened it at random, finding this one even more compelling than the last.

There is nothing worse in life than to feel of no account, nothing so demoralising as to feel every fibre of your being sink into a pit of uselessness. If Nugget was upset that I hadn't been to see him for almost a month, let him give me a moment to explain, I could use words like cerebo-spinal, it would make interesting conversation. He could tell the girls about his brother Dr Aloysius and his work as a surgeon. Nora Donnelly would be interested, both with respective family members high in the medical profession. But I wasn't being given the chance. I had thrust open the door of my friend's workplace and might as well have fallen in a well. Only a few words and my friend could get me out, but today, Nugget Nolan only had eyes, ears and words for two St Jude girls. He was doting on them, drooling over them. Nora complained of cold, so he bent down to the paraffin stove beneath the bench and began adjusting the flame, tinkering with the knob, his face mobile with concentration, his fingers dexterous with the stove's supposed complexities.

'Oh, that's better,' Nora said, as Nugget rose to his feet, beaming on her. Thin bars of autumn sunlight infiltrated the cabin walls, segmenting its rubbish-strewn floor. In a corner of the furthermost yellow stripe, the movement of a mouse and an opportunity to insinuate myself by adroitly introducing its intrusion, an opportunity to get reaction from the girls, but my courage failed me and the mouse disappeared behind a scatter of tins and boxes.

Nora warmed her hands on the stove She was slim and pretty and, provided she didn't inherit her father's twitch, would grow up very beautiful, but Cora would grow up even more beautiful than Nora. I wanted to comment on the warmth given by the new oil stove setting but it was too late now. Anything I thought to say sounded gauche and foolish when rehearsed in my mind and could only add to my wretchedness. The deepest wells are those you dig for yourself. I had stayed too long to just leave without a word. How humiliating to say goodbye to those who could not be bothered to say hello.

And Cora Casey had grown. Pubescent girls grow faster than pubescent boys, seems the only things that grow bigger in pubescent boys are knees.

Nugget was so full of himself. Tending to a shoe on a last, I could see that he was using a variety of unnecessary tools with the touch and sensitivity of an artist and explaining to the girls just how important each extravagant procedure was. Now he was cavorting around the shack, friskily chiding Nora about a boy he was alleging to have seen her with.

'Ah now, Miss Donnelly, a dark horse, so you are, an' I'll be havin' a word with your da, tellin' him what you do be gettin' up to for I seen yer more than once at it, so I have.'

'Nugget Nolan, a scandalmonger so you are, describe this boy to me,' she temporised craftily.

'A right evil lookin' blackguard, seen yous in the back seats o' The Ormond, says yer Da to me, look out for that girl o' mine, will you, Mr Nolan. Says I to him, I will, Doctor, immediately, if not sooner, and says he to me, Mr Nolan, I'm forever in yer debt.'

Nora grinned coquettishly at her friend. 'He tells a good story, so he does.' The sun went behind a cloud, the cabin darkened and the stove glowed orange in the shadow beneath the bench. I picked up a third magazine but could no longer pretend to be interested. The cobbler flicked back a lick of hair, swelled his chest and winked at Cora.

'Ah yes, Cora, I seen 'em right enough, I seen her with the same young fella back o' the Garda station when I was deliverin' mended shoes to me good friend Sergeant O'Neill. Says I to him, there's somethin' goin on behind them bike sheds, Sergeant, an' says he to me, sure it's on'y Nora Donnelly, who does be there all the time with one fella or another.'

'Sergeant O'Neill does not know me,' Nora contested defensively.

'Ah sure, you're more well known than you think, more notorious than you think, with all yer shenanikins. It was the same fella right enough, the same fella as The Ormonde.'

The girls giggled and looked at each other meaningfully. 'So what did this fella look like?' Nora insisted playfully.

'He looked as if he's just escaped from Mountjoy jail an' there's you an' him canoodlin' as if there's no tommora.'

'You might have seen me with a boy at the Garda station, but there was no canoodling and you've got the wrong end of the stick,' Nora answered, a little stiffly.

'Young love, I thought to meself, young love. Ah it's a grand thing, young love.'

Cora gathered her brows and disputed lightly. 'What you saw there, Mr Nolan was not a boyfriend at all but a cousin visiting from Cork. He has relatives at the station and was staying there, Nora's cousin and all above board, a cousin only.'

'A likely tale,' the cobbler countered.

'No, the truth,' said Nora.

'I seen 'em whisperin,' goaded Nugget crisply.

'Can a girl not whisper something to her cousin?' Cora enquired archly.

'Not with her tongue in his ear,' Nugget sniggered.

'Never, never,' Nora cried in spurious outrage. 'Mr Nolan you'll be giving me a bad name.'

They had been playing a game, Nugget teasing and the girls enjoying it, but he had gone too far. The girls' faces were closed against him. Acting quickly to restore his standing, Nugget pushed his grimy chest out ostentatiously and said, 'On'y messin,' Nora, on'y messin', although I must never forget my religious an' moral duty an' me promise to yer da.' He pulled an old beer mat forward, then, edging it over his bench, flicked it with his thumb, and as it twirled in the air, he caught it between his teeth.

It was a trick I had seen him try many times before, mostly unsuccessfully, but this time it was managed to perfection. The girls, laughed, easing the tension and Nugget glowed with pride. I was both fascinated and repelled at the transition in the man. How could he be so unfair to me? And I now viewed him with implacable distrust. Brother Mulligan had been right about him and I very wrong.

That noble and masterly lineage in which he gloried was being put in serious question as he postured like a hollow Judas. What were those two lovely girls doing in his stinking shack? What was I doing? Today Nugget Nolan stank of rotted fish and I was consumed by a smouldering hatred, so powerful it momentarily overcame my wilting sense of insignificance. What he was doing was cruel and undeserved; a single word of recognition and a heavy veil of injustice would be lifted, a friendship restored and long-awaited rapport with Cora pioneered. I couldn't expect Nora to welcome me, she didn't know me, but Cora must know me. Had she never sensed my all-consuming love for her? Surely she must know me as the boy always walking on his hands. Maybe she knew me better upside down, I figured bleakly.

The heavy, cast-iron last beckoned to me from the bench. If I crashed it down on Nugget's freckled skull, would they notice me then? It would serve him right for toadying to Burnaby girls who would likely never step inside his septic tank again.

The squeal of an animal sounded from the tip, alerting the girls to a small window at the back of the shack where they tried fruit-lessly to peer through the dirt-encrusted glass. Dutifully, the cobbler pirouetted across the floor and cleared a patch of glass with a damp cloth. Sunlight shone through the opening in the dirt, framing brightly Cora's perfect face.

The scream was that of a rat and I thought to tell them, but once again my courage failed me. At night, the tip face teamed with hungry rats, their squeaking cries a cacophony of commerce, but during the hours of daylight they stayed hidden until disturbed by boys with catapults who hounded them. Cronin or Rooney or Keogh would have scored a hit.

Cora was the first to lose interest, shrugging her shoulders and averting her eyes from the sun's glare. She had the most perfect profile and above the nameless magazine which I still held in my hands, I devoured the burnish of her auburn hair and pale, flawless skin. The half-smile on her lips faded then opened in shock as Nora turned from the window and whispered something to her. 'But surely, it can't be,' she exclaimed.

'I'm afraid that it is true,' Nora answered gravely.

They began speaking of a nun, Sister Dominic, who was very

ill. I knew of Sister Dominic because I had heard Sam talking about her to my mother.

'But did I not see her only a few days ago?' Cora said. 'Well, maybe it was longer than that. Yes, it was in the holidays that I saw her and she looked fine, her decline must have been very quick.'

A hardy late bluebottle blundered its way into the shack and began to zigzag crazily as Nugget lashed at it with his cloth. 'Oh, I can't believe the poor sister is dying,' Cora lamented as Nugget splattered the bluebottle on the window-sill.

'Yes, Daddy told me that she was taken to hospital last night where she was given the last rites by a priest. Daddy has been attending to her for some time. It is so sad,' Nora said.

'It is an illness you do not hear too much about,' Cora said.

I thought of the strange malady that afflicted Sister Dominic. Cancer of the bowels I had heard Sam tell my mother, and I thought of the poor woman receiving the last rites and what an awful thing for a nun to have, bowels.

'Brother Mulligan,' Cora observed thoughtfully, squinting through the window that overlooked the trail to the Head.

'Is he coming here?' Nora asked the cobbler.

Nugget straightened his tie. The sack of dross was actually wearing a tie. 'Oh, very likely, the clergy do be callin' in here an' takin' up me time a lot. The brothers an' the priests, Father Fallon himself, forever wantin' my views on the parish, can't get rid o' him sometimes. Says I to him, on'y the other day, Father Fallon, says I, you're a darlin' man an' doin' a gran' job without the help o' Nugget Nolan.'

I hoped that the brother would call, but he often walked alone on the Head, so I wasn't optimistic. He had cautioned me about the cobbler and the amount of time I spent with him and would not be pleased to see me in his shack, but he would not ignore me. He would enquire about my recent illness and when I was expected to return to school. Moreover, it would give me the opportunity to leave with him as he left.

Ignoring the approach of the Christian Brother, the cobbler broached the subject of Nora's suitors again and another he suspected might be receiving her favours. He started bandying names until Nora laughed at one name and spluttered fierce denials.

'Brother Mulligan has passed by,' Cora observed. Whereas I was disappointed, the cobbler seemed pleased.

'An',' you, Cora, a dark horse if ever I spotted one, quiet ones are allus the worst. Cannot help but notice that you're very quiet on the subject o' boyfriends, a pretty girl like you, a name please,' he enquired mischievously.

'A name of what?' Cora asked demurely.

'The fella you have in tow, a pretty girl like you must have a fella in tow.'

Cora smiled knowingly at her friend. 'Well, I might have'

'Well, a name then, so's I might consider his suitability.'

'I won't give his name, Mr Nolan, because he is known to you and we all know the mischief you can cause.'

'Ah, a local boy then,' he deducted, smiling.

'He's from "around",' Cora replied mysteriously.

I dreaded to hear a name. I would not have thought it possible for my heart to sink any lower, but with her coy riposte it plummeted to new depths because the boy she had in mind certainly wasn't me. How much more of this torture could I bear?

'Serious is it, tongues an' all?' the cobbler leered.

No longer demure, Cora took on a haughty look. Mellow and jokingly friendly towards the man, like Nora, she took exception to his sleaze. It was apparent by her change in demeanour, that when she wanted she could change, a potentiality making her even more alluring. These girls were no more than twelve years old and I was truly disgusted with my former friend.

'He's not from around, he's from Greystones,' Nora chided, giving Cora a playful shove and immediately relieving the tension.

Cora dropped her defence and, nudging her friend, said in mock distaste, 'Take no notice of this one, like yourself, she's forever making mischief.'

I would leave and I would leave with something, an exquisite hatred, every bit as potent as exquisite love. I must leave because nothing saps vitality like indifference; it murders-self esteem, leaving only ego, false and vulnerable. Hatred is as vital to life, as love. Putting down the magazine, I stepped towards the door.

Voices outside the shack and I immediately thought of the rat-catchers, then, following an enormous bang on the side of the cabin which made us all start, the laughing face of Patsy Plunkett could be seen through the cleaned square of glass in the tip-side window. The door opened and Shonti strode in, followed a couple of paces behind by little Christy; the three Plunkett brothers, to make my day complete.

Once again, I should have left but didn't. Looking to Nugget I expected displeasure at the intrusion, but far from it, the welcoming expression on his face could only be genuine. Patsy swaggered in then, wearing his first pair of long trousers, not hand-me-downs either, these trousers were smart. Long trousers and smoking a cigarette, Patsy Plunkett had become adult overnight and, making for the girls, he began demonstrating his new-found maturity. Shonti and Patsy Plunkett presenting themselves to St Jude girls in long trousers, me and little Christy still in short ones and I began to hate my parents along with everybody else.

'You foun' 'em then,' Nugget's question to Shonti was guarded but loud enough for me to hear. 'Dear God, but didn't I know you would.'

The boy touched his nose and, nodding, said hurriedly, 'Yes, the hooks, the hooks,' then, turning to the girls and tipping at a non-existent cap, said, 'Afternoon ladies.' Patsy shook hands with each of the girls in turn and with his cigarette perched on his droopy bottom lip like Humphrey Bogart, he cornered them. Christy stood silently beside Shonti, listening, as his brother began a whispered conversation with the cobbler.

'Hello, Patsy,' I offered in the voice of a whipped child.

Patsy half-turned and that was all.

'Hia Christy,' I tried.

'Hello, Christian,' the small boy answered honestly enough.

I was straining to hear what Nugget was talking to Shonti about but all I could hear was mumbling. Nugget slapped his thigh and, laughing gaily, danced a jig on the spot. Still laughing, he stopped his jig and with his eyes shut tightly appeared amused and delighted at what must have been appearing like a film strip in his mind. 'Sshhhhhh,' Shonti cautioned, lighting the stub of a cigarette and, after inhaling deeply, let muted dialogue issue with the smoke. I figured that they were talking about fishing.

Thumbs hitched in his braces to show how tough he was, Patsy was allowing his cigarette to smoulder in his lips. I was buried in a magazine again and, ostensibly to get more light to whatever was on the printed page, I moved a little closer to the window, but the acoustics of the shack with its creaks and moans and Patsy's raucous laughter were not conducive to eavesdropping and to lip-read would mean having to look someone in the face.

'Oh no, pleeeeeese,' Cora squealed in alarm as Patsy drew back from her and twanged his braces, mightily pleased at her reaction, I wondered what he had said or done to her and I lived again the glorious moment I had felled him with a punch, hearing again, the delicious sound his head made, cracking on the pavement.

With the unexpected arrival of the Plunketts, I would have expected the girls to leave, but they were relaxed and happy with their new company and had entered readily into banter with Patsy and with his cigarettes and long trousers, Burnaby girls held no fear for Patsy.

Also, I would have expected resentment from Nugget at Patsy pushing his nose out with the girls. Far from it, Nugget's parley with Shonti, although still covert, was clearly good-humoured and intense. Christy had edged between his brothers and was trying to listen to both. I made one further attempt to engage Christy in conversation, trying to get his interest by talking about my sister Sam, but it failed; Christy was far more interested in what his brothers had to say.

Now Patsy was entertaining the girls with his mother's disapproval of her son's drinking, smoking, thieving, swearing and fishing on a Sunday. 'Oh, an' leadin' little Christy 'asthray'. 'Asthray' he chortled, 'sure it does be Christy leadin' us asthray. His cussin' an' his swearin' sure he does be teachin' me an' Shonti new cuss words every day.'

Flattered at the oblique praise, Christy preened himself for the girls, saying, 'Give us a smoke, Patsy. Give us a smoke.'

Cora was laughing loudly, while Nora, acting a little more re-fined, was eyeing both boys with mock hauteur but she was still smiling, none the less. And Patsy, well, his gigantic bottom lip was now a veritable crescent of charm.

Nugget nodded and I caught his eye glancing my way over Shonti's shoulder

Patsy was displaying a levity and confidence I had never seen in him before. Lighting a second cigarette from the glowing stub of the first, he inhaled deeply, hung forward so that Cora was trapped in a corner, then gently blew smoke directly in her face. When she recoiled and complained, he smiled and, taking another drag, aimed the smoke down the neck of her blouse.

Patsy would get his comeuppance now and I waited for the haughty look of detraction I had seen her use with Nugget. Surely this modish, unblushing Burnaby girl would not tolerate such disrespectful behaviour from someone so manifestly her inferior, someone whose grandmother, until recently, had been 'our' maid.

But how bitterly she let me down, when she said, 'So give me a fag then, Patsy, so that I might do the same to you.'

This was a signal for Christy to badger his brother again. 'Give her a fag, Patsy, owadath, an' give us a one, too.' Raising his eyes like an expectant spaniel, he admiringly beheld his brother's face. He revered his older brothers and was proud of his recent elevation to a smoking, fishing, cussing Plunkett. Now he needed Patsy to endorse his elevation with a cigarette, but Patsy didn't feel be-holden to endorse anything.

'You're not havin' one o' my smokes an' that's it.' Fiddling in the pocket of his trousers he produced a twenty packet of 'Sweet

Afton' which he generously proffered to the girls. Nora screwed her nose and declined politely but, to my horror, Cora sweetly accepted, deftly slipping a cigarette from the pack and artlessly centring it between her rosebud lips, which she then provocatively pouted at Patsy for a light.

The boy took two matches from a box and, holding them tightly together between finger and thumb, flicked at the phosphorus tip with the thumbnail of the same hand. Cleverly and dynamically, the flame flared and, as Cora leaned forward for a light, she unnecessarily cupped her hand around his and as their eyes met, said huskily, 'Well thank you, kind sir.'

Could this rubber dinghy-lipped, fish-faced, single-brain celled Pollack gob, be Cora's secret love, the boy who mysteriously, lived 'around'? Then if so, this world had gone raving, stamping mad and I would go this very day to my mountain den and waste away 'til death.

Christy pulled at Patsy's sleeve. 'Come on, Patsy, give us a smoke.'

His brother relented and, lighting a cigarette from his own stub, handed it to the boy. Christy inhaled greedily.

The dialogue between Nugget and Shonti had become very low and more intense, their foreheads touching, each braving the other's halitosis. A fly hovered above them, appearing intoxicated in a miasma of body odour and breath. Christy started choking and collapsed in a fit of coughing.

Cora was inhaling slowly to show the choking boy how it was done and, although her eyes watered, she was determined not to cough, smoke trickling out from her parted lips until it covered her face like a veil.

Patsy was blatantly imitating Jimmy Cagney, strutting around his convulsing brother, laughing and twanging his braces. Cora Casey was his moll now, a hussy, a shameless trollop.

Recovering, Christy picked at a particle of cigarette paper stuck to his bottom lip and wheezed amiably, 'Jeez, smoke down the wrong way.'

238

Coughing in parody of Christy, Nugget, flapping at the air with his hand and complaining of the smoke from three cigarettes, capered to the door and, opening it wide, allowed chill air to ventilate the room. 'Jaysus, there's more smoke in here than there was when The Grand burned down. We'll have the Fire Brigade from Bray here any minute.' Still in the doorway, he turned his attention back to the girls: 'Pretty girls, wha? Pretty girls, though Shonti, wha?'

Shonti looked embarrassed, the girls, too. 'Ah Nugget, don't,' he said.

Nugget's chest was out again. 'I allus say Wicklow girls, is the prettiest in Ireland, the garden of Ireland grows the prettiest girls. You'd bear me out there, Shonti?'

The boy flushed a little. Not as forward as the younger Patsy, he shuffled uncomfortably, his mouth hanging open stupidly. 'Ah Nugget, sure how would I know?'

'Wicklow girls an' Dublin girls, best in Ireland,' Patsy attested, because of course, with a cigarette in his gaping gob and long trousers flapping around his spindly legs, he would know.

His manner overbearing, his tone unctuous, Nugget left the shack door open and said, 'An' shapeliest too. Nice figures on these two though, Shonti, wha?'

I hated to hear the cobbler talk like this. I was surprised, too, but then I had never been with him in the company of schoolgirls before. I had never imagined an adult talking to schoolgirls in such an unsavoury manner. Girls who had hitherto appeared so prudish and refined, counselled and cherished, as they were, by the nuns of St Jude's, should never have to listen to a grown man's crude and shabby insinuations. Particularly distasteful was the cobbler's remark about Nora's tongue in a boy's ear, which had reminded me about what Donoghue had said about such a practice. As always, Donoghue was right.

'An' now I have it in me head to fix the four of yous in a foursome in the back seats of The Ormonde. Now I'm noted in this town for a great number o' things, an' match-makin' is one of 'em.

Many's the pair o' young lovers foun' walkin' down the aisle thanks to Nugget Nolan's intervention.' His scrawny chest was so far expanded that some of the congealed deposits on his shirt were cracking and flaking.

'Give up owadath, Nugget,' Shonti pleaded.

Cora looked irritated and Nora unsure. 'Stop the stirring now, Mr Nolan,' Cora said acidly.

Unabashed, the cobbler advance his theme. 'If not the back seats o' The Ormonde, then the Cherry Orchard, as I understan' more courtin' an' canoodlin' does be goin' on there than in The Ormonde.' He found this notion hilarious, for he burst out laughing, slapping his thigh and with his tongue lolling out like a Labrador, he rocked his head from side to side.

Patsy was revelling in his older brother's discomfort and sang to the tune of 'Frère Jaques',

'At the Cherry Orchard
At the Cherry Orchard
Meet your mott, Meet your mott.'

A light, shone green and reckless in his eyes. Cora Casey was his choice in any foursome to be arranged and, with a leering smile, he laid claim to the girl by clasping her tight about the waist. She appeared to welcome the boy's attention, but still viewed the cobbler with distaste

I winced at Patsy's arm around Cora's waist and deplored her making no attempt to remove it. Nora, still looking a little unsure, was gazing out of the window thoughtfully while Christy began badgering Patsy for another cigarette. The best opportunity I had to leave was now. The door was slightly open and I could walk through it relatively unnoticed.

Nugget must have sensed my intention, because he looked at Shonti meaningfully.

Slyly, Shonti looked up from the bench with a mocking eye and at once I knew what the whispering had been about.

I grabbed Christy's shoulder and swung him around to face me. 'You've found 'em, haven't you?' I choked. My despair was beyond reckoning and I swept the brothers' faces for an answer. All looked mystified. I was not coherent; no one understood me. I had been a body propped in the corner that had just awakened like some aberration from a 'B' grade horror movie. There was a heightening of tension. The eyes of both Shonti and Patsy were mocking and full of gloating vengeance. The two girls took a step backwards in alarm.

Then they were in a huddle, all of them, Shonti's voice strangled by mirth, Nugget grinning broadly. Shonti was doing the talking, the whispering, with Patsy interceding with snippets of his own. 'A shillin' each,' I heard Patsy say.

They couldn't, they couldn't be telling Cora Casey and Nora Donnelly, about the drawings, but yes they were, for I heard the words 'Brother Brady' and 'schoolyard' clearly.

Shonti could hardly contain himself, wheezing with suppressed laughter. All were laughing except for Cora. Christy turned to me with a simpering look. At least Cora wasn't laughing. Then, Shonti fixed me with his eye and whispered loudly in Cora's ear, 'Sixpence with one tit.'

She turned and for the first time in her life she noticed me and started laughing.

I bolted for the door.

Chapter Twenty-six

I burned as I plotted revenge down to the last meticulous detail. Dreaming of revenge is useless, all those wasted days and nights, what was needed was a cold and simple plan and the determination to see it through, and both of these I had, the latter in abundance. The Plunketts first Nolan later and if they thought me powerless, I would prove them wrong. I had a weapon they couldn't even imagine. So I had gained a reputation for delaying retaliation until all was thought to be forgotten and forgiven, ok, now to live up to it.

The bright October sun had lifted clear of the horizon enamelling The Sugarloaves in a lucid glow. I was on a mission, fiercer than any on recall and I galvanised my purpose by gripping tightly the handles of a spade and crowbar. Early morning and I had been waved off by my mother as, ostensibly, I set out to walk across the Head to Bray, there to attend Mass, then to walk back. It would take all day, but hadn't fresh air and exercise, been recommended by the doctor to complete my recuperation before returning to school? But I would not arrive in Bray to attend Mass instead; I would pick up tools I had hidden in the night.

A cold, fresh, Sunday morning and no one to be seen on the beach, the road or the mountain paths and in the early light only a few lamps were visible in town, my mission had begun. I had no idea how long it would take but, once started, it would be finished. As I passed the place of my humiliation, I averted my eyes.

I could not bear to look at the shack but could not avoid the laughter of yesterday, permanently resident now and for all time, in the steaming humus of my mind.

Nolan, the biggest rat on the tip, a preening nobody whose time would come, Cora Casey, hated now but loved more than ever with a perverse and frightening intensity and the Plunketts, oh the Plunketts...I gripped the spade and the crowbar so tightly, my knuckles showed ivory through the skin. And I burned.

A stiff wind threaded through the mountains and skinned my face, but as I began the climb, I throbbed with warm anticipation at the task that I had set myself. The spade I carried with carefree nonchalance, for small spades were often carried by people to dig up flora for their gardens, but I concealed the crowbar beneath my jacket. I was too far from the shore to be turning rocks for crabs. It was unlikely I would meet with anybody at such an early hour, but I must not arouse suspicion if I was to finish what was on my mind.

I was under no illusion. An awful lot was called for; secrecy, cunning, tactics and hard work, but I had bitterness as incentive, bitterness tempered with ice-cold determination. As I reached the onset of the trail, questions jostled for priority in my mind; how much digging? How deep? How wide? How long would it take? And what to do with the excavated earth, for many times I had marvelled at the unbelievable piles of earth from a simple foundation trench. I would need props, how many? And a rope, what length? How strong the props and where would I get them from? And the work itself, it would have to be carried out unseen and unheard. Was this possible? Above all, no suspicion must fall on me, and crouching beneath an awning of bramble, I moved slowly upwards towards my target.

I was no longer upset or angry at the Crown Jewels being in the hands of the Plunketts. Through Nolan they had got to old Malone, but I had not been betrayed by the man, he would always be my friend. I wanted those boys revelling in good fortune as the huge rock fell. How fitting it would be for them to be gloating over jewels at the time.

I was closing on the stack. At some time in the distant past this rock had scaled from the overhanging cliff and impaled itself in a rare patch of soft earth some hundred feet below. It rose from the ground at least twenty feet and, hugely top-heavy, slanted bizarrely towards the sea, looking as if the merest push could send it toppling. Falling, it would spiral over the trail, taking large boulders with it, and where would it land? Why on the Plunkett fishing site, the plateau from where they shot their bloody 'lions'. How perfect, for if they chose this site for fishing then I could see them celebrating there. Oh how readily I would crystallise their jubilation by appearing above them and in their triumph, pretend to be dejected and envious. Oh, please sparkle with wealth as this slice of mountain falls on you. I had flattened Christy with a blow, Patsy with a kerbstone, now Shonti, welcome to my landslide of rocks. 'Sacred thrust,' I might call to them, 'remember the famous Plunketts' sacred thrust.'

I had reached the stack and, stopping beside it, viewed the terrain I was about to tackle. Engirdled with cliffs, crags and undergrowth, I could work virtually unseen, but I could be heard, and must at all times be aware of this. The sky had darkened, the autumn sun obstructed with deepening cloud. I would start work immediately and I wondered where I would be by nightfall.

Throwing my jacket aside, I first cut a narrow swathe through nettles surrounding the rock until I reached its base. There, with the edge of my spade, I hacked at stubborn roots and tendrils until I had formed a narrow horseshoe track seaward to the rock, with every so often stopping to ensure that I had not been seen or heard.

I started digging. The clay and scree compacted over countless years by the elements was a texture as hard and as durable as concrete but there was softer ground beneath, there had to be, or the rock could not have impaled itself in earth. After two hours of little progress, a giant blister had appeared on my right hand and the knuckles of my left hand were scrubbed and bloody. (Too much walking on my hands, I was to tell my mother.) Abandoning the spade, (its use being relatively quiet) I began to gouge at the ground with the chisel end of the crow-bar. It was more effective, but by midday I was exhausted and collapsed in a tiny horseshoe trench, viewing disconsolately my lack of progress.

Viewed from above, the ground around the rock was barely scratched, but as my sweaty body cooled, my resolve did not. I was going to need a pick-axe and patience.

After eating a sandwich and drinking the orange juice I had brought, I began again, spurred on by thoughts of gloating laughter and when the afternoon light began to fade, progress had been made. This task was not as insurmountable as I had at first thought. It was going to take time, but I had time, and I would start with an hour each day after school.

All that week, for one hour each day, I hacked and scraped at the unyielding earth with a pick axe I had brought, until, by Friday evening, the black and saturated rock bottom began to narrow towards its base; now the weekend to open up the excavation around it. After hiding the tools in the brush, I moved to my den to rest and view the awesome results. The stack was almost twice as big with its base exposed, more majestic, more threatening. It was as if a god had plucked a cone and, like a dart, cast it down to embed in a spot decreed by fate, to right a future, terrible injustice. Once, during a severe storm, I had seen it shudder, it was then that I knew that it could not be a part of the bed rock and now I had proved it to myself. Home now, because sea breezes were bringing in the twilight.

Awakening early on a Saturday morning, bright white with frost and promise, I set off again and before midday, working in softer, friendlier earth, I had a crescent-shaped trench, expanding rapidly around the rock. Only anyone standing immediately above me could observe what I was doing and, due to the overhang of rock, this was impossible and, such were the banks of insulating earth surrounding me, I could not be seen from the trail below. But at all times I could be heard and so, with ever increasing difficulty, I regularly climbed out of the trench to view the terrain beneath me. To the north, the trail was clearly visible for no more than a couple of hundred yards before disappearing behind the ridge of the escarpment and as people seldom travelled southwards from Bray, it was most unlikely that I would be discovered from this direction. To the south, a problem; here the view was clear all the way past Nolan's shack, a mile at least to the town but providing that I was sensibly vigilant, I could stop working while an approaching person was still a dot in the distance. Ironic then, that same afternoon, as work was over for the day, to see the alarming sight of Shonti and Patsy Plunkett, unloading night fishing gear on the rocks below.

I was baffled. How could they have arrived unnoticed? Of course, such had been my focus and enthusiasm for a job nearing completion I had been head down in the trench for over half an hour and was so lucky to have not been heard. Experimentally, I heaved at the stack from behind, but it held fast. I knew it wouldn't move, but it was a great thrill to have such power soon available in my hands.

It was then that the immensity of my achievement hit home to me and I had a sudden urge to share it with someone. I dismissed the thought immediately. Making way for foolish pride is triumph's greatest weakness.

I was tired, my hands were sore and I would leave for home as soon as I had retrieved the tools from the trench. Getting into the excavation was easy. I just needed to vault or jump, but getting out was becoming increasingly difficult. In spite of scattering at least half of the excavated earth down the mountainside, what was left was banked up in a semi-circular mound of immense proportions. I had made steps before, but every time I used them they collapsed; anyway, I would make one more set of steps and they would be the last.

Having thrown the tools out over the mound, I stood contemplating the best position for steps when, I could have sworn, I felt the stack above me move. My heart stopped. I had been so intent on the task, so consumed with desire for revenge, I had been oblivious to the danger to myself. In horror at my own unthinking stupidity, I dared to look up at the monolith towering above me. Had it moved? Was it moving? What savage fate; I, too, was to die, together with the Plunketts.

Was it my imagination or was the giant rock toppling imperceptibly towards me? With nothing to gauge the top of the stack against a blank, sky, I could not tell, but undoubtedly there was a sinister creaking and snapping of roots and tendrils and the rock was slowly and inexorably toppling down on top of me.

Panicking, I began scrambling and tearing at the bank sides to escape, not caring who heard me; my life was at stake but the more I clawed, the more the earth collapsed about me. Then, as suddenly as the creaking and the snapping started, it stopped and I babbled a silent prayer of thanksgiving. Gripping a root, I hauled myself out and saw that the stack had indeed moved, only a few inches, but was ready now to fall at any time.

Had it fallen, what irony, for the Plunketts had picked up their fishing gear and could be seen moving to another site.

I needed props and a rope and I needed them quickly and I swore that I would never step into that trench again.

I had had a narrow escape and the rest of that day I could not stop shaking. 'You've just got over a serious illness,' my mother admonished, eyeing me suspiciously. 'Now it looks to me as if you've caught your death of cold. What on earth do you find to do, out there all day in all weathers?' she demanded. I hated to upset my mother; she had enough on her mind. On top of our dire financial situation, we would soon have to leave Calgary and she had the added stress of moving house. 'Some boys join me and we play,' I lied.

The next day, following early morning Mass and allaying my mother's fears, I was out 'at play' again, scouring the tip. I quickly found an old plank and a length of stout carcassing, inexplicably discarded. The first journey to the site with the plank was easy, but the second journey dragging a soaking wet balk of building timber, proved to be the most exhausting experience of the whole venture. Returning to the tip to look for a suitable length of rope took me the rest of the day before I found what I was looking for.

With the two props braced at a supporting angle to the stack, I secured one end of the rope to the nearest, then threaded the other end of the rope through trampled nettles and brambles to the mouth of my den some fifteen feet away.

Exhilarated that only one relatively easy operation remained, I took time to admire my magnificent spire from different angles. It was truly a fearsome sight and, with the sun now starting to dip into the west, the long dark shadow cast marked a path on the mountainside down which the stack would fall.

Confident that the props would hold, I began cutting at the earth and tendrils already heaved up at the back-base of the rock until there was only one thick, binding root holding it in place. Bringing the chisel end of the pick down in one place repeatedly, the root began to splinter and with an almighty groan the stack inched forward and held against the props.

There, the job was done. My sense of accomplishment was overwhelming and I could not bring myself to leave for home.

Returning to my den, I wanted to stay all night, I wanted candles flickering like fireflies and to view in dim relief my misty spire against a bank of stars. Tenderly, I toyed with the end of the rope, pulling at it gently, playing with it, taking in slack until the rope was reassuringly taut against the foremost prop and thrilling at the power in my hands. But I must set off for home. My mother was getting increasingly anxious and suspicious at my long absences and it would not be long before she had my father follow me.

The undersides of the clouds were aglow as I left days of hard satisfying work behind me.

Now to wait my chance, but it would need to come while my hatred was still a potent thing, it would need to come soon. Patsy Plunkett had already made an exploratory overture of friendship which had been rebuffed with withering rejection. My bitterness towards the Plunketts was too self-indulgent to be enfeebled by reconciliation. Deliciously, my mind revelled in the recurring vision of boys fishing while, high above them, I yanked upon a rope. The Irish crown jewels played no further part in my reflections. There had been no talk at school about the 'find', no boasting, no envy or vituperation and the Plunketts were never ones to be discreet. That surreptitious whispering in the shack had been nothing more than a further dodge to tease and humiliate me and still I burned.

The sky was beginning to darken and as I neared home a worm of doubt wriggled in my consciousness. My foolproof plan, my vengeful masterpiece, so focused and brilliant in its conception, so monstrous in its potential, had a weakness. Could a high wind dislodge it from its precarious perch? Could blasting gales send my brain-child crashing down the mountain to the sea unheard, unnoticed? Would I awaken one morning following a storm, and from the veranda of Calgary, find it gone? Yes, the stack might disappear without anyone ever being witness to its creation, never knowing of the inspiration and tremendous effort that had gone into its making and I wondered with mild despair whom I could trust enough to share it with.

Reaching Calgary, I thought of Poppy Boyle.

Chapter Twenty-seven

A rumble of thunder, louder than the last, and I was anxious. 'Jesus, Mary an' Joseph, I pray the 'lectrics don't go again,' Grandma Plunkett said, crossing herself quickly.

Although no longer in our service, an old lady's habits die hard and Grandma Plunkett, on hearing at early Mass that we were about to leave Calgary for a house in Kimberley Road and knowing our mother would need help, could be seen rolling up her sleeves as she wheezed down the path.

'A few days yet before we move and just about everything is packed,' my mother told her, as the old lady, of her own volition, began dumping dirty washing in the Belfast sink.

The move was fine, she ruled, Calgary was far too close to the sea and what with the storms nowadays, she would not be surprised if one day we were all swept away. But she had reservations about Kimberley Road, as it was where the harlot lived. And talking of the harlot, she was reminded of the news that morning, red-hot from the 'BBC World Service', Pope Pius' decree that any Catholic aiding Communism would be immediately and automatically excommunicated. 'An' that's what should happen to the harlot, excommunicated and blown up along with Mau Mau, Chinese, Russians, Korearionians, Communists an' French.'

'French?' my mother raised an eyebrow.

'Ah yes, half o' them French jus' dyin' to be Communists, let 'em, then blow 'em up.'

'Our nearest neighbours before we moved over here,' my mother contemplated wryly.

Handing a dripping garment for Tam to put through the wringer, the old lady abandoned her apocalyptic propositions and, souring her expression, began complaining about the feckless behaviour of the very worst of her numerous grandsons.

Peering through a window filled with black rainclouds, she said gloomily, 'God help us an' save us, but amn't I lookin' for three lapsed Catholics. Did I see ere a sight o' them at mornin' Mass? I did not. The way they do be goin' fishin' instead of observin' their religious duties has the divil dancin' a jig. They'll be out on the Head fishin' now, I know it.'

'No fishing from the Head today, Grandma,' I told her, viewing the storm through the same window. 'And it's going to get a lot worse.' I was anxious. From yesterday evening the storm had raged and from the veranda and the open window of my bedroom, I thought I could hear a crashing landslide every hour.

The day before, Saturday, I had spent the whole of the morning, rope in hand, waiting for her grandsons to appear beneath my den, but by midday and they hadn't shown, I got bored and returned home. And I would have been back at the site today, had not strong overnight winds whipped the sea to fury. 'Every fishing site swamped with waves today,' I added.

'I'm hopin' they'll get themselves to eleven o clock mass,' the old lady said as she turned from the window and plunged her arms back into the sink. 'I've a mind to go meself an' check on 'em, the blackguards.'

'You're going to eleven Mass, you look out for them,' my mother said, nodding in my direction, then, 'Sam, will you see Grandma home when she's ready? This storm looks as if it's going to be as nasty as the last one.'

As my sister agreed, Grandma began moodily grumbling into the steam. 'Lapsed Catholics is somethin' never known afore in a Plunkett family, Shonti an', Patsy is the ones leadin' little Christy asthray. Oh, God forgive 'em.' Idiosyncratically, her top set of teeth slipped and tangled with the bottom set as she clicked them heavy-heartedly.

'Well, I'm away to Mass,' I told my mother grandly. My inclination was to miss the Mass and go to my cave. I needed reassurance that the stack was still standing but I had no choice, my father was already on his way and I was expected to follow close behind. I could have gone to the cave immediately afterwards had I not stupidly mentioned to Sam how great the Head would be in this storm. 'I'll go with you,' she had replied enthusiastically. She couldn't, of course so I agreed to meet her on the coast road when Mass was over.

'A grand boy, an' a credit to yous,' I heard Grandma say as I was going through the door.

Leaving church at noon, the storm had not abated; if anything, it was worse. Pressured by winds brewed in the Welsh mountains and with a high incoming tide as the engine, the heaving seas were powering at the coast. Dodging giant waves was such exhilarating fun, but if there happened to be a group of faint-hearted St Jude girls, including Cora Casey, watching safe behind the wash, then, the exhilaration was multiplied a hundredfold. Waves, furiously alive, could be teased and tormented into the most violent retaliation and the more they were mocked, the more furious they became. And did I take advantage of their anger? For bravery, bordering on the foolhardy, no one in town could hold a candle to me when it came to dodging waves.

I heard her laughing before I saw her. Poppy Boyle was with my sister, at the south end of Carraig Eden, close to the dock basin. Poppy, yes, if only Cora Casey could be there, too.

'Good news,' Sam mouthed, raising her thumb triumphantly.

'I'm back at school,' Poppy informed me when I was close enough to hear her voice above the waves. 'Jesus Christ, but amn't I bloody soaked already,' she added, turning from a lash of spray. It was raining heavily and Poppy's freckled face was wet and glistening beneath her red raincoat bonnet. As always she was chewing bubble gum.

'Tell him what happened,' Sam instructed.

She was back at school. Father Fallon, the parish priest no less, had decreed re-instatement, conditional on the girl's future good behaviour, a promise to the nuns, endorsed by her mother and the priest, but with only token accord from the girl herself. Her return to the fold had been unanimously applauded by her peers but not so by the Sisters of Mercy, mercy being in short supply where this young lady was concerned, Sister Benedict recommending a certain 'girls' home' in Dublin as just the place for Miss Boyle. 'But he seemed to kind o' like me," Poppy said of Father Fallon. 'An' once when Sister Joseph was givin' out, he winked at me.'

It had been reported that Mother Superior and Sister Joseph had been incandescent at news of the girl's return. 'At assembly we were made to say a prayer for the soul of Poppy Boyle,' Sam chuckled. 'It was a silent prayer. We all bent our heads and some of us were giggling and soon everybody was giggling, we couldn't help it and it made the sisters so mad.'

Poppy's face was rosy with delight. 'Look at me, amn't I soaked to the friggin' skin already?'

I was always keen to hear of Poppy's exploits. Charged with a kind of electricity, she was venturesome, uninhibited and amusing. Just the mention of her name and people's ears pricked, children smiled and adults frowned. She was the consummate rebel with a rebel's fearlessness. Throughout her life she would fail badly and succeed greatly and even now at such a tender age, she had an air of destiny about her.

'I'm glad for you, Poppy,' I said. 'Father Fallon, he's ok, he's human.'

During the tribunal, the nuns were horrified to hear the girl, voicing in her defence the very words which had caused the trouble in the first place. Every time she used the metaphoric 'duck run', which was far more often than was necessary, Father Fallon swallowed a smile and the holy sisters went apoplectic at the demure insolence with which they found themselves confronted. Anyway, the freckled faced imp was back at school, feted by her mates, but damned in general by their parents. My mother when she heard the news would be foremost among them. 'A strange maladjusted child,' she had emphatically determined.

'Yeah, he's human is Father Fallon,' Poppy agreed. Lightning flashed above Coolagad followed by thunder that shook the Sugarloafs.

'What do you keep staring at Bray Head for?' Sam questioned me. 'What are you looking for when it's completely covered in cloud?'

I was pleased for Poppy and excited at the prospect of dodging waves, but still what was foremost in my mind was hidden from view. Instinctively, my eyes kept turning to the Head and Sam had noticed. Behind that shroud of cloud, was my stack still standing? Or was it now just another rock-strewn feature of the landscape? Was it fate to meet with Poppy Boyle this day?

'Dont be doin' no dodgin' with them friggin waves,' said Poppy. 'You go too bloody far.'

What an invitation and, under my insistent influence, it wasn't long before we were laughing and screaming and urging each other further onward on to a storm-washed promontory. With spirits as high as the spumes of spray and creaming breakers, it was the first time in weeks I had been able to put my troubles and bitterness behind me . But my mind was not free of its dark and burning place, nor did I want it to be. Freedom and peace would come with the yank of a rope and again I looked to the shrouded Head.

But for now, what fun to out-run a raging sea. How challenging to laugh at air pressurised in fissures of rock, expelled in hissing anger and poke fun at booming walls of water, exploding in fury at our incitement. The spine-chilling exhilaration as we dared each other, bodies tightly sprung, to edge even further seaward, over the flat, promontory rock, laughing and tugging at each other's sleeves.

In the face of the storm, bravery was in direct proportion to age and gender. It was brave of Poppy to venture forward no further than the furthest toss of spray; after all she was a poor swimmer, whereas Sam would make it far enough to dip the welts of her boots in the ebbing wash of the last wave to hit the rock. Tempting providence and nature and always with a hopeful eye out for Cora or a gathering of girls, I would run out to the very edge of the promontory and wait until a wave was towering above me, before turning and dashing back to safety.

That I was never faster than the breaking wave, I felt, only added to my dare-devil image. I would hear the wave smash into the rock behind me then, running madly, be conscious of it looping over me like a foaming, clutching hand, happy to be caught inside its grasp, only to emerge soaking wet and grinning triumphantly. And in this way, we spent almost an hour, before the girls began complaining of cold and needing to get home to dry and warm themselves.

Sam was the first to see it, far out to sea and gathering very slowly. She clutched my arm. I saw it immediately, the one we always looked for. Every sea storm has one and usually you miss it and someone has to tell you about it afterwards. Sometimes you might wait for hours, knowing it would come, and sure enough it would come, five minutes after you had lost patience and set off for home. A corrugated snake of sea-swell and the looks between us were of excitement and foreboding, a palpable thing.

'This is the one,' I breathed as we all watched closely the slow formation of a linear mile of swell. A hundred yards from shore a wave was growing mightily, calming and feeding off waters avant. 'We can't miss this one,' I breathed.

'Well, I can.' Sam was running for the road.

I was mesmerised by what was bearing down on me. This was something I had never seen before and would never see again; this was a tidal wave, surely? The thing had come to life, slowly expanding, doubling, redoubling, a salivating beast. Just behind me, a tremulous murmur of dread. 'Oh Jesus, the sea, it's flowin' backwards.'

What was Poppy doing on the promontory? What was I doing? We hadn't moved, we couldn't move. Scraping rocks and sandy inlets with an ominous rumble, the sound of the sea flowing backwards, something beyond any wave I'd ever seen was looming over us with no escape.

'RUN, POPPY, RUN!' I bawled. My own voice was the last thing I heard before I was picked off my feet and hurled forward. Poppy's limbs and clothes were entangled with mine as a mighty surge of water swamped the promontory and swept us towards the road. Poppy was beneath me I could feel her clinging to my legs. Neither of us could breathe and Poppy could hardly swim. It didn't matter, for neither could I. We would both drown today, Poppy Boyle for certain. I tried to clutch her and drag her up for air but I was powerless. My fingers slipped on her raincoat and I was tumbling over and swallowing water. We were separated now. Then, suddenly, my head was clear of the water and I could breathe again. Wildly, I looked about for Poppy, screaming out her name. And where was Sam? Was she drowning, too? I could not see land, only bubbling, surging water and, most terrifying of all, I could not feel solid ground beneath my feet, but I could feel an irresistible drag out towards the open sea. Frantically, my feet searched beneath me, for to be swept over the edge of the promontory, there was no way back.

Something alive and floundering was clinging to my legs and, seizing clothing, I lifted Poppy Boyle's head clear of the water. Although coughing and spluttering, she was very much alive. Our frightened eyes met and we both knew that at least we wouldn't die alone.

Thrashing my arms and kicking madly, I was trying to swim, taking Poppy with me, but it was futile; we were still being taken backwards. Then suddenly, miraculously, still entangled together, we were as high as a house and flying towards the road. I could see Sam clearly on the road beneath us. We were on the great white wings of a bird. The great white wings of a second wave had picked us up and solid ground was coming up to meet us fast and, slithering forward on slippery flat rock, we actually reached the road.

Laughing and crying hysterically, Sam ran across the road to meet us, grabbing Poppy, who was thanking God with a string of expletives. Sam, unable to comprehend our survival, began counting heads. There were only three of us, but she kept on counting. And only Poppy could do what she did next; she spread gum about the tip of her tongue and blew a bubble. As long as she could blow a bubble, she was still alive. Then we crossed the road and, sitting on some garden steps, began sombrely to contemplate our lack of injury and incredible good fortune.

Air trapped within Poppy's raincoat had kept her head above water for much of the time and we were soon to realise that I had swallowed more seawater than she. Sam had made it to the road and the refuge of the steps where we were sitting now. No one was apportioning blame, we were so thankful still to be alive.

'Don't tell anyone that we was dodging waves,' I warned.

Shivering violently, Poppy took off her raincoat and began squeezing water from her clothes.

I said, 'Listen you two, don't tell anybody that…'

Sam cut in, 'For God's sake, no one's gonna tell on you. Poppy, let's get you to our house before you catch your death.' It was still raining and the sea was still crashing and I was shivering violently, too, even though I was already soaked to the skin before the wave had hit us.

'I went under an' I couldn't breathe an' I thought I was gonna die. Thought I had died, then I felt my Nana lift me up,' Poppy shivered.

'It wasn't your Nana, it was me,' I answered churlishly as lightning struck at Coolagad.

Sam looked at Poppy closely, protectively. 'Let's get to our house. It's only minutes to our house.' We broke into a slow trot, my sister, relatively dry, leading the way; thunder rolled and Poppy and I, waterlogged, slopped along behind her.

'We got caught by a freak wave, that's all,' I panted. 'We weren't dodging waves or anything, a freak wave like that could catch anyone.'

Sam had stopped running and was waiting for us to catch up with her. 'Look, home,' she said, pointing across the bay to the homely, white, squat block of Calgary.

Squelching and breathing heavily, we stopped beside her. 'I'm not for your house,' Poppy said in a matter-of-fact manner.

Rain still lashed down and lightning split the skies. Poppy and I began dancing on our feet like boxers training. Sam said, 'Poppy, you will be dry and warm and Tam's clothes will fit you.'

'I'd rather die,' the girl answered, her chattering teeth still managing to chew gum.

'Poppy, Mammy's really kind,' Sam argued emotionally against thunder to the south.

'I'd rather your mammy find me dead on your doorstep through bloody pneumonia.'

'Oh Poppy, it's just your bad language that she doesn't like.'

'She's not gonna to like it any friggin' better today then, is she?' the girl answered tersely.

'Don't be silly,' I said. She really was in a sorry state, and I was, too, but for me warmth and comfort were only strides away; for Poppy they were in Quarry Lane, still halfway across the town. The psychological stresses of wet and cold were quickly catching up with me, depressing my adrenaline. Calgary beckoned, but I could not let the girl go all the way home on her own.

Reading my thoughts, Sam said, 'It's ok, I'll go with her.'

Better for Sam to get home first and pave the way for me. 'No, you go home now, make light of it. We were on the road and we were swamped by this giant wave. It's true, Sam, that's what happened. Tell Mum I've had to take Poppy home. Tell her I'm gonna need a hot bath.'

Outside Carlisle's milk bar, my sister peeled off to Calgary, leaving Poppy and me to continue at a steady but utterly miserable jog. Blue with cold and breathing heavily, we were pleased that the rain was easing, for although it made no difference to our sodden clothing, the heavy gusts which carried it were at our backs and made going easier, but, I reflected dismally, how much more difficult it would be for me on my way back. The sea boiled, looping with high, white slashes against the murky sky. It would not be trifled with by stupid children and we had learned a severe lesson and distantly, Wexford way, thunder rumbled yet another warning.

Poppy's breathing was laboured and distressed. 'You ok?' I asked.

'No, I'm bloody frozen and I've got the stitch.'

'I'm ok, I really am.' A modicum of warm blood had begun pulsing in my veins. An old man was walking towards us. It was Mr Malone. He stopped and viewed us curiously, waiting. He would expect for us to stop and for me to tell him what had happened. 'Freak wave,' I told him as, pulling Poppy along by the arm, I increased the pace. The old man's puzzled look, I knew, followed us until we turned the bend by the iron railway bridge.

The girl stopped suddenly, and bending double, gasped, 'Bloody stitch.'

'We got to keep on running,' I insisted, jogging up and down ridiculously beside her.

'I can't,' she winced, managing a slow walk. At the other side of the road a woman eyed us judiciously, then as we drew abreast, 'Jennifer,' she called, 'what on earth has happened?'

'Freak wave,' I called back.

The woman was about to call again, but as we had not stopped, she seemed to think better of it and, lowering her head, began pushing the pram into the wind.

'That's Kitty, she'll tell Mammy for sure,' Poppy panted.

'She's going to know soon enough anyway. She'll know in a few minutes.'

'No, key is under the mat. Mammy an' Mary are after goin' to Dublin to see my da.'

This was good news I was in no state to start lying to her mother. 'Not far now,' I encouraged.

'You want to come into the house and warm up before you set off back,' Poppy tempted me.

I couldn't risk it. What if her mother returned early from Dublin to catch us warming by the fire in a state of undress? Worse still, was her older sister Mary, who for some reason had an implacable distrust of me, always looking at me with that suspicion reserved for something recently reported as having escaped from somewhere. 'No, I'll turn straight back. Poppy, Mary doesn't like me. Why doesn't Mary like me?'

'Says you show off too much,' Poppy said, far too cold, wet, miserable and exhausted to trouble with diplomacy.

'Oh, I've often wondered.'

We were in Quarry Lane and soon would reach her gate. 'I'm at St Killian's Hall for six this evening.' The relief in her voice was unequivocal.

'What's at St Killians?'

'That concert that I got into trouble over. I'm not in it, of course, but the girls want me to go.'

I studied her. Strips of copper hair stuck to her cheeks like strands of sea weed, her scarlet cheeks, the colour of her bonnet, eyes a startling blue. She began walking towards the house.

'Poppy, stop a minute.'

She turned her head. 'What?'

'I've got to show you something. There's some place you've got to come with me this afternoon. Doesn't matter what's happened, I want you to come with me.'

'WHAT, this afternoon?'

'Get dry, get changed, have some soup. Meet me by the breakwater when you can.'

She was fishing beneath a door mat for the key. 'You want to go dodging waves again?'

I was shivering violently and I felt indescribably uncomfortable, except for my feet and hands, which I couldn't feel at all. In spite of my teeth chattering madly, I tried to sound upbeat. 'Poppy, this is something real important. Something incredible, I want you to see something, plenty of time to get back for the concert.'

She had opened the door and was paused on the threshold. 'I'm not goin' anywhere.' She had recovered, her eyes were calm and I noted that she was still chewing gum. It would be the same wad of gum she had started with. In celebration, she blew a little bubble on reaching home.

'You're going to be the only person in the world to know about this apart from me. If your mammy isn't back, leave a note for her. You've gone early to see the girls at St Killian's.'

'Mammy and Mary won't be back until late tonight. I'm soaking wet, an' I'm inside this minute, thankin' God.'

'It was me what saved you. Pay me back for saving you, I didn't have to.'

'Couldn't I see it another day, couldn't I see it tomorrow after school whatever it is?'

'You don't understand, it might not be there tomorrow, it might not be there now. It's something I can't talk about, only show you. Someone's got to see it and you're the only person I can trust.' I was stamping my feet and rubbing my hands, trying to circulate blood.' I'm freezing here, say you'll meet me so's I can go. Poppy, please, I'm freezing to death.'

She peered somewhere into the dim interior of the house. 'It's almost two. If I'm not at the breakwater by four o clock, I'm not coming.'

'See you at half-past-three,' I shouted at the closing door. Running home, I got a serious stitch myself. I wanted to enter the house and face my family buoyantly, which was impossible with stitch, sodden clothes and guilt. My sisters were gathered about my mother at the kitchen stove and were silent as I entered. I thanked God my father wasn't in. My mother shook her head at me despairingly and, after an intake of breath, said, almost tearfully, 'How many times do you have to be told about dodging waves? Just how stupid are you?'

'A big wave, me and Poppy copped it, just missed Sam. I just had to take Poppy home.'

Looking to Sam for corroboration, the girl nodded sympathetically. My mother didn't believe either of us. There was soup bubbling on the stove and a cylinder full of hot water and, despite certain trouble when my father got home, it was with immense relief that I shed my clothes by the Belfast sink and escaped up-stairs. Wearing only underclothes, I went to the veranda with binoculars. The sea was still wild but the sky was clearing and the Head was free of cloud. The props had held. The stack was still standing.

Chapter Twenty-eight

Gleefully, I ran down the path to greet her. 'I knew you'd come.' She was wearing a blue tweed coat, a little big for her and a dark blue woollen bonnet with the straps hanging loose beneath her chin. The afternoon had calmed and although the waves still ran high and fast, they slumped over the pier wall as if spent.

'The minute I was warm, I was fine, still can't believe how lucky we were. I'll never, ever do that again. I had no idea a wave could be as big as that,' Poppy said.

'I don't even want to talk about it, even think about what could have been. I'll never do it again, either. I'm finished dodging waves from today. My mother doesn't believe that we was on the road just passing by. She knows we was wave dodging. I'm going to be in trouble with my father,'

'Just whereabouts are we goin'?' the girl demanded bluntly.

'I promise it's not far.'

'But how far?' She was chirpy, her expression bright but distrustful. She chewed gum with slow, methodical movements of her jaw.

I looked at her squarely and said reassuringly, 'A little way up Bray Head, that's all.' The clouds above the Head were thin and empty and, like the sea, exhausted. The storm was over and with a clear sky a frost would come.

She stopped in her tracks. 'I'm not climbing Bray Head this afternoon. I've had enough bloody excitement for one day.

Thought we might be goin' to them ruins. Thought you'd foun' jewels in them ruins. What the hell do we want to be goin' up Bray Head for?' Taking her by the elbow, I got her walking again, albeit reluctantly. She pulled at her bonnet straps nervously and her jaw quickened. A pale pink membrane appeared over the tip of her tongue, and a bubble popped. Plunging her hands deep in the pockets of her coat and hunching her shoulders, she said, 'I get scared up there.'

Prevailing, I gripped her elbow a little tighter and coaxed her forward. 'I'll keep you away from the cliffs.'

'It's not the cliffs I'm scared of, it's Ooara Moara, you know, Rasputin,' she admitted a little guiltily. 'Sometimes I have nightmares about his wife rising up out o' the bog.'

I laughed shortly. 'I'm on Bray Head all the time, every day almost, and I've never seen him there. Seen him once though, but it wasn't on the Head. He couldn't make the climb. Remember that old man this afternoon? Mr Malone, remember we passed him? Well, I know an awful lot about that man, stuff you wouldn't believe, and I know how old he is. See him tottering about, smoking, gasping and wheezing, can you see him climbing about the rocks, up those banks? of course not. Would you be frightened of Mr Malone if you met him on Bray Head? Hell no, because he's too old to do anything bad to you. Well into his seventies, eighty maybe. Know something else? Rasputin's older. And his wife, well, she's been dead and buried now for fifty years and won't be rising up from nowhere.'

She blew another bubble and started reflectively, 'Well, I never seen him, I...'

I stopped and faced her. 'Listen, Poppy, I'm going to tell you something that I've never told a living soul before. One night, about a year ago, a really dark night, I went down in to the dock. Rasputin followed me down into the dock. He made that howl of his, you know to the moon, but I wasn't scared. I couldn't see him because it was too dark, but I just remembered how old he was and strolled past him. Ok, that howl of his was scary, but I just strolled past him and up the steps, didn't try to catch me or anything, just howled away like a clapped-out old wolf. All them stories about burying children alive, they're not true. He's too old. I promise you, Poppy, there's nothing to be scared of.'

'Never seen him but I'd like to, but not on Bray Head, nowhere lonely,' she said and, chewing nervously on the strap of her bonnet, she continued, 'Think I once heard him howlin' in the quarry. That' quarry is so dark an' scary. I allus feel somethin' awful's gonna happen there. ok. But I gotta be back for the concert.' She laughed ruefully. 'Wanted to take my pencil-case to rattle but the girls wouldn't let me, said the concert would collapse if they saw me with my pencil-case. Want to get a good seat though, sit close to Mother Superior and Sister Joseph, between 'em, if I can, just to annoy 'em. Make 'em think I've got my pencil-case with me, make 'em nervous.'

We were walking slowly, close together, avoiding the huge muddy puddles that straddled the roadway, keeping to the edge of the beach where we could, where it was free from mud. Now, clear of the beach, we were skirting the tip face, jumping seepages in the compacted ground and startling foraging seagulls. The afternoon was suddenly colder, the sun bright and chill on the cliff faces, a night frost already fingering the air. Unusually, there was a light in Nolan's shack, a naked light bulb shining starkly through the dirty glass.

'Don't stop, we haven't got time,' Poppy advised.

'No chance of that,' I answered, unsmiling.

'Thought you an' Nugget were big pals,' she looked curiously at the lighted window and the stooping shape of the cobbler at his bench, 'stinks in there.'

'We go around the back so he doesn't see us.' Bile filled my throat at sight of his crouched shape. The Plunketts first, then the stinking cobbler, maybe I would bar the door shut on him, then set the shack alight. 'He's not the man I thought he was,' I said simply rather than attempt to express the loathing that I felt. But his stories were good, I'd give him that, and to keep Poppy entertained, I told her the story of Dodger Malone and his exploits. Dodger helped us to cover a lot of ground that afternoon.

We had reached the trail and there were no big-booted footprints of fishermen or walkers; we had the mountain to ourselves. Difficult to walk, we kept to the narrow, slippery verges, Poppy leading, while I supported her from behind. She grumbled as we slipped and slid and lost our feet. This trail was the sloughiest part of the journey but at least it warmed us up considerably. Out at sea, the wild, white crests had steadied to rippling carpets of foam and away to the south, breakers were no longer breeching the pier wall. What clouds were left, were moving briskly inland and, above the sea, the sky was ice blue in the autumn sunlight.

Poppy's feet went from under her and she fell. Cursing, she picked herself up, examining her mud-stained coat. Her pert nose wrinkled with annoyance and as she looked at me her eyes caught the sun in points of blue, accusing light. 'Is this what you want to show me, the easiest way to break my friggin' neck?' Her face was deliberately sour, but there was wry laughter in her voice. 'How much further is this bloody thing that's so important?'

I could see the stack from where we were and my heart thrilled. 'Another fifteen minutes.'

'You could have shown me another day, a nice dry day.' She spat out her wad of gum and, unusual for her, did not replace it.

We had reached my path, its entrance, between two clumps of furze, so small that we had to crouch to enter it. At both sides of this path, the undergrowth encroached and was wet and scratchy on our faces and on our legs where they were bare, making us mindful of nettles and trailing thorns. Poppy took off her gloves at a steep rise and hoisted herself over the mirey slope by clutching at grass sods and branches. I followed close behind.

'Poppy, do you read books?' I had sensed stiffening in her body, a reluctance to continue now my story of Dodger Malone was over, my question, a distraction.

She slipped again, the side of her coat covered in brown ooze.

She turned her eyes hostile. 'I've had enough, I want to go back home, now.'

'Poppy, do you read books?'

'What the hell do you keep asking me about bloody books for?' she snapped. 'I nearly drowned today an' I'm pissed off an' all I want is to go back an' you keep askin' me if I read bloody books. No, I don't.'

She had to keep going forward because there was no way past me on the path. 'My parents keep books and stuff I'm not allowed to read until I'm older. Well, I'm always older than the last time they told me the same thing. I know where the key is. I sneak book out of their bedroom. I'm reading one now. It's about a guy called Lemmy Caution.'

She slipped in the mud again. 'I don't want to know about Lemmy Caution, I just want to get this thing over with an' go back. Thought we was goin' to them ruins.'

Another five minutes with Poppy quietly sulking and we broke into the open. The yielding mire of the path had given way to the flatland of the hardened scree, my plateau commanded by the crazily leaning stack, some fifty yards away. From a ledge high above us, a large, black bird screeched at the intrusion.

'Know what that is? That's a raven, we got ravens here,' I told her proudly. 'On our way back, I'll show you where they build their nest.' Hanging in the thermals, herring gulls like small splatters of white as if someone had splashed a brush across the sky. 'This is my place. This is where I come. No one knows this place, no one except me knows the path that leads to it, know why? It was me what made that path.' Around us a most beautiful and savage sight, the sun's rays bouncing off the sloping sheets of magma and flashing points of silver on the quartz and mica of the cliffs. I continued with a purposeful melancholy, 'Or Some Green Hill, Where Shadows Drifted By'. That's a line from *The Wayfarer* by Patrick Pearse. Every time I'm here that line appears in my head. Maybe Pearse got to this place before I did. I like to think that he did. I like to think that he once stood where I am standing now.'

'It's a nice line,' Poppy said as I pointed to the stack, clearly visible from where we stood. Stricken, she visibly paled. 'Not that bloody thing, you haven't dragged me up here to see that bloody stick o' rock? I can see that friggin' thing from my bedroom window. We're goin' back now an' you can tell me about Lemmy bloody Caution all the way home.' She snatched her bonnet off, untidy hair sticking to her head like a cluster of wet leaves. She put her bonnet in her pocket with her gloves and clenched her little fists angrily. 'You are mad, people say you're mad an' you are. Imagine draggin' me all the way up here for this.'

I smiled. 'Madder than you think, come and look.' I started running, pulling her along until we reached the excavation. She stopped as if jerked by reins and her mouth fell open. Squatting, I waited expectantly for words of wonder. I chuckled to myself. She was barely eleven years old. How could a girl of that age have the literary elegance to express the sheer improbability of what was before her? She was lost for words. She found some.

'Jesus Christ, What the friggin' hell is it?'

'It's that stick of rock that you can see from your bedroom window.'

Gravely, she regarded the huge leaning rock, the trench surrounding it and the steep slope beneath, unsure of what it was, what it meant. 'But what's it for?'

Smirking, I stood upright and leaned my hand on the back of the stack.

'Holy God.'

'An avalanche of rocks."

'But what's it for?"

'See that rope Poppy. See the end of it going in the cave. You've seen cowboy films, imagine an Indian war party on that big, flat rock, jutting out to sea. Give that rope a tug – and –'

'An Indian war party, what else?'

Ignoring the sarcasm, 'Waiting for the Plunketts' I said with great drama.

She giggled softly. I wanted awe or admiration, better both; I certainly didn't want amusement. 'What you laughing at?' I asked uneasily.

Her face straightened as, thoughtfully, she viewed the undertaking from the excavation, to the narrow base of the rock, the props, then up along the distended shaft to the club-shaped top where, incongruously, a cormorant was perched. The cormorant would know me; all the birds around here knew me. 'You dug this out an' propped it up yourself?'

This was more like what I was looking for, the reaction that I wanted. 'All alone up here, I dug it out and propped it up.' I jerked my head towards the cave. 'The end of the rope's in there.'

Grasping the full implication of the props and rope, the girl's eyes grew bigger as they traced the expected course of the rock fall down the slope. 'The Plunkett boys,' she studied quietly.

'They fish from there.' I made no attempt to mute the excitement in my voice. 'Just imagine, Poppy, how much work it took to do this, once the bloody thing almost toppled down on me. Imagine the Plunketts down there on that rock and me up here, holding on that rope. All yesterday morning I sat here holding that rope waiting for them. They never came I got bored and went home. Poppy you gotta keep quiet about this, now and, more important, after.'

'After what?'

'After it's fallen on the Plunketts.'

She began giggling again, this time unrestrained. 'You're mad, you're quite bloody mad. You worry about mortal sins. What the hell do you think this is?' She looked up to the top of the stack where the cormorant remained, so still it could have been made of stone. 'What the hell have the Plunkett boys done to you to deserve this?'

And I told her. Told her everything, even about the drawings, I didn't go into detail about the drawings for fear she would find such talk offensive. Really, to my credit, I was always conscious of good taste. But I told her everything else and when I had finished my tale, she knew of the cobbler's and the Plunketts'

269

deceitfulness, their betrayal and how only revenge could make me whole again. But the girl still laughed. She was impressed with what I'd done but not with me, not with my story and I was disappointed. 'I'll show you my den,' I said irritably.

'But this thing could blow down any minute,' she observed. The cormorant came to life and flew off as if suddenly becoming acutely aware of the likelihood.

'Do you think I don't know? That's why you're here, to see it before it does. Least someone knows now what I'm capable off, the lengths I'm prepared to go to.' I led her to my den. It was dark inside. I lit a candle. Poppy picked up the rope and began toying with the end. 'Jesus, don't do that,' I cried, you'll have half the bloody mountain down.'

She dropped the rope as if it was red-hot and shuddered, 'To think of that thing fallin' on people.' She started laughing. 'Honest to God, I'd love to pull that rope.'

'What do you think of it, Poppy, honest?'

'It's incredible, but you're mad to even think of somethin' like this.'

So I began my story once again, just in case the first time she hadn't grasped the sheer iniquity of what had been done to me. There was self-pity in my voice which I made no attempt to disguise, but no humour or irony, no breezy self-blame. I had been crushed that afternoon and had not healed; healed and I would be stronger for the experience, but that could only come with revenge. The cruelty of the Plunketts, their betrayal, their collusion with a man, I thought of as my friend what had I ever done to Nugget Nolan that he should treat me so disgracefully? Their conduct was indefensible, and the Casey girl's sluttish behaviour, smoking and flirting with the oafish Patsy. And if that wasn't enough, I was goaded by inference that the jewels had been found by use of intelligence which I believed only I was privy to.

She was subdued a moment, thinking, then she lifted her gaze and said flatly, 'Well, everyone knew you was lookin' for them jewels, there was even talk of it at school, searchin' in them ol' ruins for the Irish Crown jewels, people was laughin'.'

'Yeah,' I agreed painfully. 'But now I couldn't care less whether they found 'em or not.'

She was quiet, still considering my story with detachment, as if I had related a passage from a book, or a scene from a movie. 'Them boys aint foun' no jewels,' she said.

She was right I had suspected it for some time and had been strangely ambivalent, yet the burden of grievance had been no easier to bear. 'Yeah, they were just goading me more.'

Some of the mud on her coat had dried. She beat at it with her hands and it fell in flakes to the ground. 'If you do it, God will never forgive you. It's gonna be an awful big mortal sin, you know?'

'I've thought of that.' Thought of it with every shovel full of earth, with every rock and every root torn from the ground, with every bead of sweat and every blister and gash to my hands, I had thought of it coming to the site and going home and above all else, in bed at night. I was committing mortal sins all the time, I couldn't help it. The death of the Plunkett boys was just another. Every lusty thought, word and deed, a mortal sin, the number of mortal sins by thought alone were countless, thought sin alone would destine me to an eternity in hell anyway. I was just not spiritually equipped to embrace the grace and goodness that the holy church demanded. The restoration of my soul had been abandoned, something else Nolan and the Plunketts had to answer for.

'Not Christy, though,' Poppy said meditatively.

'Not Christy?' I blurted. 'It was him what started it, getting tough, throwing punches, going at me like a maniac.'

'Sam told me what happened. Getting tough, throwin' punches,' she scoffed, 'poor little Christy, all he was tryin' to do was help your sister.' She moved to the cave entrance and peered at the stack, her long auburn lashes edged with gold, fluttering in evening shafts of sunlight. 'What's poor Christy done that he deserves to die?'

I felt my cheeks flushing 'Them three Plunketts, all the same,' I justified lamely. The memory of that afternoon and the telling of the story had regenerated a hatred I feared might be waning, the stack becoming not so much a functional instrument of destruction, as one of symbolic power, but after telling my story twice, I was back to hating them and wanting justice.

'What's poor Christy done that he deserves to die?' Poppy repeated.

'Well, maybe not Christy,' I conceded.

'An' Patsy playin' up to Cora, lots of boys like Cora, I can tell you that for nuthin', it's not on'y you what likes Cora Casey. You're jealous, that's all.'

'Jealous,' I spluttered, 'Jealous of that fish-faced twat. For Christ's sake, his grandmother was our maid. You should have seen him blowing smoke down Cora's blouse.'

'An' he deserves to die for that? Blowin' smoke down a girl's blouse.'

'You forget he tried to beat me up outside of school.' This girl was getting on my nerves and I was beginning to wish that I had never brought her here. 'You don't understand how they made me feel. I shouldn't have told you anything, you're too young to understand.'

She laughed shortly. 'I wonder how they felt, Christy unconscious on the north beach, Patsy unconscious outside the school gates and Shonti taking the piss out o' you over the crown jewels, I can tell you, people was queuing up to do that.' Then she turned everything on its head and only Poppy Boyle could do it. Of all the eleven- (just eleven) year-old girls in the entire world, only Poppy Boyle could do what she did next. Can a mischievous thought turn burning hatred into parody, vendetta into farce? Yes, when it enters this girl's head. Her face to mine, eyes alight with devilment, her voice hushed and conspiratorial, belied by a tiny smile, tugging at the corners of her mouth. 'Do something for me,' she whispered.

I longed to do something for Poppy Boyle.

'I want you to get Mother Superior and Sister Joseph interested in somethin'.'

I blinked with lack of comprehension. 'Interested in something?'

' Fishin'.'

She was laughing silently. Was she mocking me? Her head was in her hands and she was laughing through her fingers and I knew what it was she wanted and I was laughing, too. The cave was alive with laughter, shadows shimmered and a moth danced in the candlelight and we were laughing as never before, except maybe that hot summer's day on the beach with burning stones blistering our buttocks and my mother, baleful at the gate.

'Of course,' I howled, 'Shonti, Patsy, Christy, Nugget Nolan, Mother Superior, Sister Joseph, anybody else?' The moth was dancing, the shadows, too, and so were we, dancing.

'Uncle Bob, I don't like Uncle Bob.'

'And Brady. We gotta have the lovely Brother Brady,' I wheezed.

We rocked with laughter as I held an imaginary pen above an imaginary party list as Poppy looped about the cave in a pompous charade of mimicry. Now she was at the cave entrance blessing the stack. 'And Father Duff, we must have Father Duff, no party's complete without beloved Gruff Duff.'

We were staggering about the cave, holding each other upright, so weak were we with mirth at our comic absurdities. All the effort I had made, the evenings and weekends of hard work had not been wasted when I could laugh like this. Tears welled in our eyes as we struggled to regain our breath. Wetting the tip of my 'pen', I started a letter of invitation, it began, 'Dear Shonti, it is with great pleasure that I invite you and…'

'No, no," Poppy shrieked, 'let me.' She took over with a 'pen' and 'letter' of her own. 'Dear Mother Superior, a special tea party has been arranged on Bray Head for some very important people,' she could hardly get her breath, 'and as there is no one more important than you an' Sister Joseph, I was wonderin' if you could attend. You needn't bring anythin' with you…'

'Except crash helmets,' I exploded and we were in each oth-

273

er's arms rolling about on the cave floor as we organised an apocalyptic tea party for every curmudgeonly adult in the town and a
few undesirables of the younger generation. We had them sitting
at a table on the rocks, waited on by the three Plunketts wearing
hand-me-down dinner suits and crash helmets.

When we started arguing about which of us should pull the
rope, Poppy pleaded, 'No, please stop, I'm peein' myself.' Her face
flushed, her eyes streaming, 'I swear my sides have split,' she
chortled as we stood up and I re-lit the candle, blown out in our
whirling merriment. 'That bloody walk was worth it just to laugh
like this.' She looked at me, her eyes merry. 'Bad things go away
if you laugh at 'em enough.'

Magically, my bitterness was gone and I was surprised to find
that I didn't want it back. Blinking at tears in my own eyes, I said,
'I owe you, Poppy, but the Plunketts owe you more. I never, ever
felt so full of hate, and I can't believe it's gone, just gone, laughed
it all away.'

Suddenly her mind switched to something else and she was
sombre. 'Sure I've been so down myself. I honestly didn't think
I'd get let back to school. Mammy was cryin' all the time. What's
goin' to happen to you, Jennifer?' Daddy an' Mary was upset. I
was thinkin' there was somethin' wrong with me. When Father
Fallon was hearin' my case for goin' back to school, you should
o' heard Mother Superior, givin' out about me. "Oh, Father, the
young madam is allus doin' this," an', "Oh, but Father, the young
madam said this an' done that. There's jus' no stoppin' the way
she is, Father, we cannot do a thing with her so we can't, there's
jus' no way she can ever return to St Jude's, she's…"

I chipped in, '*The Lady doth protest too much, methinks.*'

'What?'

'That's what you should have said to Father Fallon. Excuse me,
Father but, *The Lady doth protest too much, methinks.*'

'What does it mean?'

'She's protesting too much, isn't she, Mother Superior? That
would have shut her up. Adults don't expect stuff like that from

kids. I do it all the time, 'doth' and 'methinks' really takes the wind out of their sails.'

Poppy repeated the line, twice correctly, 'I like it.' Her face lit up. 'Do you know any more like that?'

'Do I know any more? I know lots, I make 'em up. Writing and stuff, I'm the best in the class, even better than O'Farrell and he's going to be a priest. Next time I see Brother Brady or Father Duff, know what I'm going to say?, I'm going to say, *'By the pricking of my thumbs, something wicked this way comes.'*

'Oh I like that,' she beamed. 'Did you make that one up?'

'Yes, that's one of my best ones.'

She began picking at shards of clay on her boots and repeating the line. The clay came away like shreds of dead skin and was satisfying to watch. I assisted her until her boots were almost clean. 'Well, it's really good and I think you're clever.' She flicked her fingers free of grounds and said, 'I'll be in the schoolyard an' I'll have some girls aroun' me an' when I see Mother Superior, I'll say, *'By the prickin' of my thumbs, somethin' wicked this way comes."*

The lovely light of the candle flame glanced about her face, dappling her pale skin as her eyes rejoiced in mischief at the prospect. My heart melted with love for her, not the kind of love I had for Cora Casey but the way a puppy or a kitten or a small child is loved, especially, a mischievous one. Dodo had a book at home, *Flower Fairies of the Garden*, surely Poppy Boyle was 'Tulip.' A large moth appeared suddenly, fluttering at the candle flame, its shadow flitting about the cave like a plague of bats.

'Why do they call you Poppy?' I asked.

She answered thoughtfully, 'My Uncle Michael from Kerry called me that when he first saw me. I was five years old with a face full o' freckles. "Dear God," says he to Mammy, "but hasn't the child got a face like a field o' poppies." You know I only saw him a couple o' times, yet I remember him. He went back to Kerry where he died of consumption. I remember he had very kind eyes, a deep blue they were, and kind.'

'Well, Poppy suits you. My sisters, their nick-names suit them, too. Know what my nick-names are?' I continued dejectedly, 'Gilla Christe, Otello, Oliver Cromwell, English Dog and—-'

'Otello, what does that mean?'

'You tell me. Brother Brady calls me Otello, but no one seems to know what it means.'

'Ask him. Ask Brother Brady what it means.'

'What and get a clout for myself. From Cronin and Rooney, I sometimes get English Pig.'

'That's nice, and Humphrey, too,' she prompted.

I was aghast. 'What do you mean "Humphrey"? Who the hell calls me Humphrey?'

'Some girls at school, I heard 'em.'

A few minutes ago I was rolling about the cave floor in fits of laughter, now suddenly I was in the depths of despair again. Humphrey was a derogatory term. I had heard Flanagan referred to as Humphrey. 'Never heard myself called that name before,' I countered indignantly.

'Maybe I'm mistaken,' Poppy said regretfully, knowing I was hurt.

'Sure they were talking about me.?'

'Could be wrong, maybe I got it wrong.'

Blinded by the candle light, the moth flew into Poppy's face and she swiped at it, missing. It took off, dizzily swinging towards the flame to be joined by a smaller moth. They jostled as if wanting to be the first to get their wings singed.

'Think,' I insisted.

'They did talk about a kid who was aluss walkin' on his hands.'

'That's it then, that's it,' I concluded dismally,' can't be anybody else.'

'I could o' got it wrong.'

'Cora Casey, was she one of the girls?'

Poppy was silent a moment, then, taking her mud-caked gloves from her pocket, began flaying them on a smooth patch of rock. 'No, it surely wasn't Cora.'

'How can you be sure?' I demanded stiffly.

She put the gloves back in her pocket, then, sitting against the cave wall, she stretched her legs, 'Can't say I ever heard Cora Casey call you anything.'

'Humphrey, I said to myself slowly, with a hollowness of disbelief. Things were now as bad as ever. I flicked my hand at the circling moths, catching the bigger of the two and stunning it to the ground. I was tempted to crush it underfoot, but desisted. Resiliently, it shuddered back to life and, taking flight again, resumed its combat with the smaller one. My happy mood had been instantly replaced by an anxious one. The last thing I wanted was another nick-name, especially a derogatory one. 'You never heard Cora Casey ever mention my name?' I enquired miserably. I would have settled for 'English Dog', just to know I had a place, however small, however demeaning, in her thoughts.

Poppy tilted her head and looked at me sorrowfully. She knew she had upset me and was regretting it. 'Cora's older than me an' in a different class at school. I'm never with her long enough to hear her talk about anybody. An' "Humphrey", it could be because o' that filum you are allus on about.'

'*The Treasure of the Sierra Madre* with Humphrey Bogart?'

'Yeah, that one.'

A life line and my heart lurched thankfully as I grabbed for it. I'd settle for the 'Humphrey' of Humphrey Bogart any time, providing the name alluded to that gritty star. This was a Lemmy Caution type of guy, with menace in the way he spoke, the way he looked and the way he smoked his cigarette. His films were terse and pithy, *The Maltese Falcon*, *The Big Sleep*, *Key Largo*, '*The Treasure of the Sierra Madre*, and the characters he played in them, well, any kid would be proud to be identified with them wise guys. There was something really positive about the nick-name 'Humphrey' and I wondered if I should start smoking and talking with a lisp.

'I could be wrong,' Poppy admitted.

'You're not wrong,' I replied doggedly, long trousers now more urgent than ever.

She was playing with a button on her coat, twisting it back and forth, but not hard enough to break the threads. 'You know, you're in love with Cora? Well, I'm in love with someone, too,' she said wistfully, as if the thought had been trapped in her mind for too long and this was her opportunity to release it. 'Cora ignores you, well, this boy, he ignores me.' Her voice broke a little and my heart melted to hear this feisty tomboy with a sob in her throat for unrequited love.

'Who is he?'

'It's Willy Delaney,' she answered quickly and with downcast eyes suddenly looking and sounding like a fragile girl.

'Yeah, I know Willy. I'll listen out for Willy, see if he's anything to say about you. You listen out for Cora see if she ever says my name, if she's anything to say about me. Don't forget, do that for me. Listen out for my name, any of them.'

She had a quiet moment, playing with her button, then, gave a short ironic laugh. 'Willy's best friend is Paddy Ryan and Paddy's in love with me, might have a chance with Willy if Paddy wasn't so in love with me.'

I smiled at the girl's naivety. She really was a little girl with no idea of the ways of the world and I was purring inside with the easiest of solutions. 'Make Willy jealous.'

She frowned but managed a thin, wan smile. 'Make Willy jealous. An' how would I do that?'

I could not believe her innocence and laughed disdainfully. 'Start "seeing" Paddy, that's how.'

Still she didn't understand. 'But Paddy's my friend, too.'

'Exactly. Pretend to be in love with Paddy, make Willy jealous.'

Absolute shock at what I had suggested registered on her face. I didn't understand it neither did I understand the cloud of disgust which replaced it. 'What USE Paddy? I couldn't USE Paddy, Paddy is my friend, I couldn't use a friend.'

It was my turn to be shocked as I realised how different her mind was to mine. A simple emotional ploy, which to me was normal, indeed, expedient, was to her, indefensible. The shock was in knowing immediately that she was right. 'Oh, a friend, I didn't know Paddy was a friend. No, of course you couldn't "use" a friend.'

A breeze entered the cave, bending the candle flame and there was a murmuring in the brush outside. The moths had abandoned their forays into the candle-light and had settled in some dark corner. The breeze died, the flame stood upright once again and shadows stilled. There was a faint sound of music from afar.

'Oh, Jesus Christ Almighty,' Poppy yelped springing to her feet, 'That's Killian's. The bloody concert's started, it's past six o clock.' She peered past the candle-flame at the cave's entrance. 'Will you look at that? It's pitch dark we've been here talkin,' talkin', I can't believe it. We've got to get goin'.'

I was astonished to find that night had fallen unnoticed during our candle-lit exchanges in the cave. Calmly, I joined the girl at the entrance, considering the situation. It was dark but a pale full moon was being joined by emerging stars and was light enough to journey home, and, making things easier, a frost was hardening the ground. I snuffed the candle and, with the matches, put them in the wrapper. 'It's ok, we go back the same way we came.' I laughed 'Don't worry, Poppy, plenty of time to get to the concert and annoy the nuns.'

She began fumbling with her coat and bonnet. 'Oh, strike a match. I've dropped one of my gloves.' As I reached for the wrapper she was at my feet, sweeping her hand about the floor of the cave. We both heard it at the same time. 'Sshhhhh,' she whispered, 'what the hell was that?' The sound was coming from below, from where the slope met the trail. It was a crunching noise, quite distinct from the regular rhythm of the waves. Some animal or someone was trying to scramble up the mountainside. In darkness and silence, we listened intently to the sound, which, although remaining persistent, did not appear to be getting louder or nearer.

Then it stopped. 'What is it?' Poppy murmured.

'An animal.' I didn't sound convincing, yet there was no further sound, only the waves and a faint stirring in the brush outside.

We moved from our frozen immobility back to the cave entrance and looked outside. A crouched shape on the slope and, leaping back into darkness, we were stricken motionless.

'Oh, Dear God,' Poppy whimpered.

'Sshhhhh,' I soothed, 'no one knows this cave; no one knows we're here.' She found my wrist and her nails dug in. 'Sshhhh,' I soothed again, the only sound now, the rhythmic throbbing of our hearts. 'It's an animal.'

'Let's run,' she pleaded, 'just let's run for it. I know who it is he saw the candle-light, heard us talkin'.' He's after us.' We waited in silence, hardly daring to breathe, before venturing to the entrance again. 'Let's make a run for it,' she urged.

And we should have done, for remembering the tons of earth I had shovelled down that mountainside it would have bonded with the scree making the climb easier. We should have run before whatever was on the slope got any nearer. But I hesitated, desolate with fear at the image of whom it might be. Easing my head through the entrance gap, I stole another look down the slope; nothing, but nearby brush and nettles were trembling as if disturbed by concealed hands and the tilting rock was stark and terrifying, towering against a sable sky.

'We're gonna be ok,' I murmured, trying to rally my courage. 'Get ready to run.'

'Keep a hol' of my hand,' the girl pleaded.

I pointed across the plain to where a sheer rise of cliff dropped into the thick blackness of brush and scrubland. 'That's my path, keep real close behind me,' I whispered.

'Please hol' my hand,' Poppy whimpered.

Directly beneath us, I detected movement. Tension stretched my nerves like cables and I pushed her back inside the cave. Regret at lingering in the cave for so long overwhelmed me like a terrible illness. Behind me the girl was breathing in little gasps and, I realised, she was praying. I couldn't see her, but I sensed her cowering in the farthest recess of the cave. Blinking, I tried to adjust my sight to the strange, variegated light and shadow of the slope until it settled on an unmoving, black patch, where none should be. I focused on this shadow with, peripheral to it, the insubstantiality of the moon-washed landscape. Then, in a nightmare of unreality, this shadow lifted upright and I could only think of a black bird with broken wings that I had seen before, one dreadful night and I jumped back inside the cave.

'From all evil Lord deliver us,' cried the girl and we had our backs to the rock face and we were watching with trepidation for the entrance gap to fill. Terror, a third presence had joined us and the air was rancid with a smell of fear. 'If we don't go now, I'm goin' on my own,' Poppy sobbed in desperation.

'Ok, ok, we gotta go.'

'Please, please, it can't catch us if we run. You know what it is, don't you? I cannot bear to be trapped in here.' She was no longer whispering, secrecy and caution were not an option any more, only the stark precedence of self-preservation mattered now. Once again we moved to the entrance, this time with greater purpose, but peering out again for one last time, the shadow which was a living thing had vanished, as before.

'Poppy, we go fast,' I breathed. 'I can't hold your hand, but keep real close behind me and for God's sake, don't fall.' My eyes swept the vista in readiness to run. The moon was brighter and the route across the plain was bathed in added light. 'We're going, Poppy. POPPY!' The girl was gone. Where was she? Frantically, I felt behind me in the dark. 'Christ, where are you?'

A whimper from out of the blackness: 'Oh God, didn't you see it? It's out there just below the rock, it's his wife. Oh God, what will happen to us?' I fell beside her rigid body; her voice was aflame with hysteria. 'It's his wife.' We were clutching each other and sobbing unreservedly, our eyes transfixed at the entrance, waiting for it to darken. And then we heard what I had heard before, one unforgettable night, almost a year to the day. A wail of utter desolation; a madman was outside with his vigil to the moon. The infernal cry filled the cave, filled the mountains, the very earth with a sound of indescribable torment and, sobbing in each other's arms, both of us would die of fright.

'OoooooooooooaaaaaaaaraMooooooooooooaaaaaaaaaaaara,'

I had escaped before and would escape again. Freedom beckoned through a slice of dim light. Only one presence in the cave, mine, and consumed with fear, it cared for nothing but itself. Crouching in readiness to run, my fingers closed about a rope. What was a rope doing in my den? Then, something triggered in my fevered brain, and as the feral call trailed into the night, I pulled on the rope. Something was supposed to happen with the pulling of a rope. But nothing happened. With all my body weight behind it, I pulled again and all that happened was a rope, flaccid in my hands. Nothing happened.

But something terrible was happening outside and the cave was filled with roaring noise and I was bolting through that slice of dim light and teetering on the edge of a hole that I had never seen before then, I was sprinting to where I knew a path to be. Below, the mountain was shattering, dissolving, and behind, an inexplicable shrieking which I ignored in a frenzy of flight.

In mindless panic, I missed the entrance to the path, crashing like a bull through fern, nettle bramble and gorse until, quite by chance, I stumbled upon it. The lunatic had escaped the rock fall and I sensed him close behind me. As my head lurched crazily from side to side, my peripheral vision caught him first at one side, then the other, flapping like a giant bird. Guided only by instinct and propitious providence, I took the slippery path in crouched, insane sprints and giant leaps of faith and did not stop the crazed descent until I reached the sparse and level approaches to the tip. Here, with my heart pounding and breath heaving in huge gulps, I dared to look around about me and, seeing nothing in pursuit, stopped and remembered Poppy Boyle.

Immediately, my mind began to rationalise events; the unearthly cry, the rope, the rock fall, the girl still with me in the cave, that shriek and my own fearful flight. Poppy had fallen into the excavation at the entrance to the cave. Was she lying there helpless at the mercy of something unspeakable, exacting some terrible revenge? I started to absolve myself. Did I not tell her repeatedly to stay close behind me? How I warned her not to fall. How throughout that frightful descent, I was certain she was right behind me. Could I not hear her crashing through the brush? Would someone, who, that very day, had saved a girl from drowning, leave that same girl to the mercy of a lunatic and run away? Of course not.

Every fibre of my being urged me to run again and reach the safety of my home. No one knew the girl was with me and if she was found dead, then who could attach the blame to me? But guilt began to haunt me and I stayed where I was, peering back into the darkness, motionless, like a frightened rabbit in a beam of light. Then in the distance, a thrashing in the undergrowth and my body tensed itself to run. Who or what was coming from the dark?

Small and blue and muttering incoherently, a figure emerged into moonlight and my heart lurched with exaltation. Bounding towards her with arms outstretched, I cried out joyfully, 'Poppy, thank God you're safe! I swear, I thought you were right behind me.'

She did not respond and, in a mantle of skylight, I saw her eyes were glazed and unseeing. I caught up with her and as gently as I could, tried to slow her to a stop.

'Jennifer, I thought that you were right behind me all the way. What a shock I got when I realised that you were not with me. Soon as I realised that you were not behind me I turned back. Well, you saw me running back towards you, didn't you? Didn't you, Jennifer, see me running back for you?'

I had slowed her to a walk but she was still purposefully moving forward, her unseeing eyes, trance-like, fixed ahead. She did not answer me or look at me. Physically, I stopped her and forced her around to face me.

'Jennifer, you gotta listen. Say nothing to anybody about what has happened up there.' I was pleading, close to weeping. 'Jennifer, please understand, go to St Killian's, act normal, do something with that coat, it's in a state. We're in big trouble. We killed a man up there. Jennifer, you're not listening to me.'

Her eyes were blank and her face was so white I thought that she might faint in my arms. I shook her. 'Do you understand how serious this is? How much trouble we're in? No one saw us, no one need know anything. Your glove, Jesus, Jenny, I'll go back and get your glove. But you simply gotta realise...'

She was running again and I didn't catch her until we were past Calgary. 'Jennifer, for Christ's sake...' I was crying openly.

Her eyes met mine. There was no recrimination in them, no repulsion, only emptiness. 'You left me in that hole,' she said.

Chapter Twenty-nine

*O*f course I didn't leave her in the hole.

As she hurried, ashen-faced and rasping for breath, towards the hall, I kept pace with her. Things inside my head were tearing at my mind, the enormity of events causing involuntary spasms in my throat as I tried to convince her she had not been abandoned. I had blazed wildly through the brush, yes, but that was to make it easier for her to follow me.

'Poppy, how could you think that I would deliberately leave you?' I choked. 'I thought that you were right behind me, I didn't see you fall, I didn't hear you fall. Didn't I save your life, this very day? Yes, so would I run and leave you in a hole?'

She had slowed to a fast walk, her breathing short, sharp, sobs, her attitude blank and unresponsive and the forlorn searching of her hand for mine went unrewarded. I could deal with anger, petulance disgust even, what I could not deal with was a numbness, so out of character. Her coat was covered in mud, the stitching was torn, a hem was hanging loose and she had left a glove behind. She would need to hide her coat when she got home. I tried to gather my senses, choose words carefully. I suggested explanations which her mother might accept but her dormant expression remained the same; eyes glazed, she wasn't even listening.

With the hall in sight, I barred her way. 'Poppy, stop, we gotta talk, I don't think you realise how serious this is, how much trouble we're in. There's an old man up there and he's most certainly dead and if by some miracle he's not, then he must be very badly injured. I know we should tell somebody but we can't, we just can't. We're responsible.' I gripped her shoulders and tried to shake her from her torpor. 'Come morning, people will see that rock has gone. Christ, they will only have to open their curtains and look out of their window. People will talk about it. Some might go up there to have a look. The storm, people were always wondering when that rock would go, well, it has.' I was pleading, begging. 'No one need know, no one knows we were there. I didn't leave you in that hole, I swear I didn't.'

Still in shock, I tried to rationalise an outcome. Taking into account the topographical difficulty of the terrain and balancing likelihood against improbability, I concluded that all that would be found would be the scattered remnants of a rock-fall with no one likely to go the trouble of climbing up the slope to see what had caused it, everyone would know what had caused it, the earlier storm. What I dared not take into account was anything else. I tried again to hold her hands in a comforting, collaborating gesture of unity but they were pulled behind her back and held, as if tied together with twine.

'Poppy, no one must know that we were there.' I shook her again but to no avail, her trance-like state disturbing me. 'Jennifer, you're not listening to me.' I shook her hard. 'Jennifer, listen to me. I pulled that rope and saved our lives. That's twice today I've saved your life. You bloody owe me. You know what that lunatic does to children? He takes them to the mountains and buries them alive. Nugget Nolan, he'll tell you what he does. If it wasn't for me, pulling that rope, we'd both be dead, especially you. Say absolutely nothing to nobody and we'll get away with it. Do you hear me?' I was frantic, I was crying, 'Jennifer do you hear me?'

Straining at my hands, her blank eyes avoided mine and, swinging away from me, she began to walk again. A pace behind, I followed her. 'Know what could happen to us, don't you?' Without a reaction, I answered my own question, 'We could get hung for murder.' She was heading for the hall and I made no further effort to restrain her, but trailed behind her, beaten. We reached the main door to the sound of singing, a lively chorus of children's voices. Silently, she took off her coat and folded it over her arm and for the first time there was expression on her face as she composed herself to enter.

She was going to leave me on my own. I couldn't bear to be left on my own. In panic-stricken despair I begged, 'Don't leave me, Jennifer, and don't say anything to anybody, my life depends on it and so does yours,' my words underscored with a last, desperate passion.

She opened the door to a swelling of music and warmth and, as she closed the door in my face, she said acerbically, 'You left me in the hole.'

Of course I didn't leave her in the hole.

My mind in trauma, I waited by the porch a while, the sound of gaiety within serving only to engulf me further in a wave of black despair. I was mad, of course I was, my first hack at the ground at the base of that rock unpardonable, beyond forgiveness, beyond redemption. My miserable life was over. I thought to wait outside the hall until the concert was over, try with Poppy one last time, but what was the point when a miserable life is over? Close to her home was the quarry. It was where my father had got the clay to make his bricks and at the bottom of that quarry, they would find me in the morning.

A terrible blackness folded over me and I heard my sisters laughing and playing that game of theirs. They were playing 'You are your child's child', a game of trans-generation, so incomprehensible as to have a touch of genius. I hoped I would be missed, but consumed with unendurable self-loathing nothing mattered any more. My mother and father would be terribly upset but they would say I'd fallen, with no way of knowing otherwise.

I entered the quarry grounds through a gap in the fence and, blinking away thick tears, made my way along the perimeter to the highest point and the concrete raft, where by day the lorries stood. The moon shone brightly on the quarry just as it shone on pawns of circumstance, playthings of fate, on bunglers stumbling through the chaos of a life. How much hopelessness had it espied in its timeless lonely vigil of the sky? It shone brightly on the path that I was taking now because it knew me well as one of the many thousands it had seen before in its all-seeing but indifferent light. We're born we die who needs the cruel nonsense in between?

In the void below the raft, a long way down, there was no water, only rocks. It was where they would find me in the morning. Making one last apology to God, I gazed into the void below, as pitch black as was the dock, that black precursor of a year ago. All my dreams would end now, but so would my torment. I would boil and burn for eternity, but with the satisfaction of knowing I deserved it.

There was no way out and I teetered on the edge. No shock, no pain, only oblivion calling for me as the only way. I hesitated and suddenly my mind cleared; there was only one witness to the death of a man who would not be missed. I was not mad, I was thinking clearly and I knew what must be done. There would be a body at the bottom of the quarry in the morning, Poppy Boyle's. I went back to the road and waited by the gap in the fence.

I waited until the distant music stopped and the night stilled; waited until homeward stragglers crossed the bottom of the road. At least Poppy wouldn't boil and burn.

I waited until I knew she wasn't coming home that night.

Chapter Thirty

I had enough presence of mind before entering the kitchen to clean myself up in the water barrel. I was very late but I was very sick, so sickly that my father, who had been out looking for me, was silenced by his concern at how ill I looked. It had overtaken me so suddenly, the symptoms very similar to the cerebo-spinal condition which it seemed I hadn't fully recovered from. I had been playing with other boys at the rear of St Killians and had been unaware of the time until the concert finished. That was when I first got sick, yes, yes, I had almost drowned that day, which was the likely cause, but I felt too ill to talk about it. Pale and shaking with this suspected fever my mother placed a precautionary cold flannel across my forehead and full of remorse for my foolishness that day I was helped to bed by my father, whereon I immediately pretended to fall asleep.

Unbeknown to anyone, our antics on the rocks of Carraig Eden had been astutely observed by Sergeant O' Neill from a high window of the Police Barracks and related to my father some time later that day. I was to learn later that Sam, to her credit, had interceded on my behalf, nobly accepting complicity in the near-tragedy and I never heard any more about it. Understandable as my parents had more pressing matters on their mind, joy at my rapid recovery tempered in dismay that in spite of appeals, the landlord had insisted we vacate Calgary before Christmas.

Before retiring to bed, both parents visited me that night, satisfying themselves that I was not thrashing about with a fever and thankful that I appeared to be sleeping soundly.

Sleep? All the foregone trouble of my life, amassed, could not begin to weigh against the trouble I was in now. What was I thinking of, to do what I had done? To take vengeance as an ally is to choose the falsest friend of all. Sweating profusely, I tossed and turned, burying my face in the pillow to stifle nervous retching, my mind a riot of uncertainty and indecision, a vicious circle of anguished thought and sensation.

Where was Poppy? Had she told the police? I must get rid of the evidence. Where was Poppy had she told the police? If so, why weren't they knocking at my door? Incriminating evidence in the cave must be got rid of this very night, and, in the morning, Poppy reminded once again how imperative was silence. The first priority would require undreamed of courage and the second, a level of persuasion which had hitherto never surfaced in my life. To do nothing was the most welcome alternative, but to do nothing would be to give free range to vagaries of merciless fate already stacked against me. Something had to be done and be done tonight. A feeling of dread overwhelmed me and I began sobbing silently. Where was Poppy, why had she not come home?

A litany of pre-emptive excuses began to fashion in my brain, a childish prank gone wrong. A sheer accident, an unfortunate fall of rock following a high storm. Oh, how Jennifer Boyle and I had laughed and joked in that cave talking of nuns and priests and crash helmets and yes, we had toyed with the end of a rope, knowing it was attached to a prop which in turn supported a giant stack of rock, but no, we had no idea who could have done such a stupid thing. And in any case, how were we to know that a demented foreign nut-case would decide that directly beneath that rock was just the place to start howling at the moon?

By morning light, the fallen stack would be the talk of the town with, possibly, people tracking to the head for a closer look. How soon before headlines were reading, 'Feared Wanderer of the Wicklow Mountains Found Dead', 'Infamous Russian Count

Washed up on the Coast', 'Carnage on the Head, Suspicious Circumstances' 'Garda Investigate a Nearby Cave' or 'Unexplained Excavation Found' and later and inevitably, 'Twelve-Year Old English Boy Arrested On Suspicion of Murder'? And as these horrors ran rampant in my mind, all led to one inescapable conclusion; I had to return to the scene before daybreak and remove every piece of evidence that could link me to the scene.

It would be done tonight. But then my troubled mind was besieged by another awful thought. That rumble of rock could have been heard for miles, certainly in Greystones and, quite likely, Bray. It could even have been seen. Were the Garda and the Coastguard already mobilised to conduct a search? Was the old man, be he alive or dead, already found? Were suspicious men with searchlights already rooting in my den?

Restlessly, as I watched the pointers of my bedside clock nearing midnight, I heard the muffled sounds of my parents checking on me and then retiring to bed and I swooned at the horror in which I found myself. I was once a happy child, what had become of me in the twelve short months since I set foot in Ireland?

I got out of bed and went to the window. The night was clear and a full moon amid a halo of stars shone brightly on the sea and frosty ground. How much longer could that awful secret lie unlit beneath the mantle of this lovely night?

Fearfully, my eyes turned to the north to that giant whale of land so much the centre of my imaginative and adventurous youth, now a bleak and sinister place, slug-like in the sea, a reminder of terrible folly and the frightful measures I would have to take before sunrise. A hill, which had meant so much to me had turned on me, the image now, an old man abandoned to the same fate as his poor wife, immured in earth and stone in a grave designed for worthless boys. What had that man ever done but trail what was left of his world in wretched loneliness, crying out for someone who could not return, only for me to unleash on him the creature of my vengeance, capturing and burying children alive, indeed, only so much Nugget Nolan hogwash.

Two o'clock in the morning saw the frost sharpen in the air and thicken on the ground with the relentless hunter's moon, still looking down. I could not rid myself of the image of the old man. In the dim light of my room, frail hands were raised to fend a thousand tons of rock and, joining this spectre, a small, blue, frantic shape with glazed unseeing eyes who thought she had been abandoned. I left the window and returned to my bed, a dead man on my conscience and a girl's eyes blighted and burning in my soul. The pointers of the clock crept onward to that hour before dawn when I would have to dress and force myself back to that desolate site. Thought of the silent and lonely journey filled me with untold dread and I didn't know if I could do it. Super-human courage was required and if I was equal to it, then I might be safe. Would it be a noble thing or simply a desperate act of self-preservation? I tossed and turned and trembled in agitation. I would do it, for at the very least it would restore some self-esteem, make Poppy admire me again. She had told no one, because if she had, a rescue mission would have been undertaken long before now. But where was she, where was Poppy Boyle?

Dawn was still a long way off when I heard muted voices coming from the North Beach road. Throwing the bed covers aside, I bounded to the window to see clearly three figures making for the Head. Ghostly in the moonlight, I could hardly believe my eyes. Two were civilians and the third, unmistakeably in a uniform with glinting buttons, was Sergeant O'Neill, but what shocked me most was that one of the civilians was carrying what looked like a folded stretcher. If Poppy hadn't told, how did they know what had happened earlier that night and if she had told, why were they not knocking at my door? Even if the rock fall had been heard, how could they know that someone, something needed to be recovered? So many questions with no answers but how glad I was to see them; my heart sang to see those men. I would not now have to journey alone; unseen, unheard but not alone and what was more, I could get there first.

Dressing quickly, I crept to my mother's bedside and, mumbling sleepily, she awakened to the gentle shaking of her shoulder. Opening one eye, she grumbled something and, raising herself to her elbow, blinked uncertainly 'What time is it?' she complained.

'It's nearly light,' I lied. 'I'm feeling much better, I need some fresh air.'

She slumped off her elbow and was fast asleep again. My father groaned and turned over but did not awaken. My intention now legitimised, I stealthily left the room and crept silently down the stairs.

Within seconds, I was heading north in pursuit of the three men. The ground that had earlier been thick with mud was now hard and brittle with frost and the pools were filmed with cat-ice. Keeping to the verges, I lessened the sound of my running feet, my eyes straining forward for sight of the men. By Nolan's shack I was surprised not to have reached them but knew that I could catch them at will once I reached the low slopes of the mountain. There was no wind at all, the pre-dawn light burnishing a calm sea and moonlight carpeting brightly where it touched the land; only in the hollows of the mountain did black of night prevail. Now I must be careful where my feet would hit the ground, because I was close to the men. On the tip side, I leaped from one crisp, grass patch to another, marvelling that I made so little sound, tufts yielding gently to the impact of my feet. Then, surprisingly close, only slightly below me, keeping to flat land near the sea, three shadowy figures.

Staying well behind but with their misty figures still in view, I followed to the point where my route branched away from the trail, upwards to the entrance to my path. Within minutes, by parting the brush, high above them I could see that I had drawn abreast, with no way to be seen by them against the high, dark curtain of the mountain. From this vantage point and whenever I wanted, I could view them clearly in the moonlight, augmented from time to time by the beam of the Sergeant's flashlight as it awakened alien shadows which seemed to follow them like trailing veils. When they stopped, I stopped and once, when the two civilians shared a match to light cigarettes, I felt I knew their faces in the quick bloom of tactile light.

As they progressed onwards, I swiftly overtook them. My path was protected by undergrowth and virtually ice-free but sufficiently hardened by frost to make the going easy. What I had to be careful of was getting too far ahead, as the men, especially the Sergeant, must be kept in sight, within earshot, because I feared dreadfully what might yet await me, and I knew in my heart that without them I would have never dared to make this journey alone.

As I neared the sight of the fallen stack, I paused and listened intently half-expecting that awful howling to echo in the cliffs, but all was quiet except for the gentle rhythm of the sea. Slowly, silently, I ventured on to the open plain, my muscles coiled and tense, ready at any moment to turn and run. The men below me had disappeared behind a crag and I did not move again until they reappeared beneath me. They were approaching the rock-strewn fishing site, walking with a purpose as if they knew exactly where they were going. I looked for the stack, but it was not to be seen. Had it broken into pieces in the fall or had it fallen in the sea?

Now they had reached the fishing site and the stretcher was unfurled. Now would be laid what was dead or dying on the stretcher and, as they picked their way among the rocks and rays of moonlight, they might be cadavers from open graves in a troupe relentless to reclaim one of its own.

The beam from the Sergeant's torch was persistent and was focused on a large boulder close to the sea at the extreme north edge of the plateau and I had a sudden terror that they would disappear behind it to carry on, on a different venture altogether.

I moved to the edge of the excavation furthest from the cave and watched. Small rocks and boulders lay scattered on the scree and on the trail where they had come to rest, with the vegetation flattened where the stack had fallen. The excavation was wider and deeper than I imagined it to be and I thought of a young girl writhing in its depths; she should have taken notice when I told her not to fall. It yawned below me and the frozen talus surrounding it looked like snow. The high cliffs above reflected white in the moonlight, giving a kind of eerie daylight to the place. The cave where I must go, a jet-black maw, and I felt I saw something move inside.

I watched as the men stopped, seemingly concerned with something behind the boulder they had been aiming for and in the light of the Sergeant's torch, I could see the vapour of their breath. I found this greatly reassuring as they were still close enough to hear my call and in an extreme state of alert, my eyes flicked between them and the entrance to the cave.

It had to be done. Stopping short of the cave entrance, I cursed the haste which made me leave my torch behind. The torch I got for Christmas last, with a beam to cross the bay and reach the pier. It had stood at my bedside an arm's length away. Was there a limit to my stupidity?

Moving closer to the cave, I peered inside and could swear that I saw movement in its depths. Stepping back, I looked to the plateau below. The two civilians could not be seen but the Sergeant was clearly visible, directing some unknown business, out of sight behind the boulder. I peered, I listened; I scuffed my feet on the loose ground for what was in there must be made to pounce before I got too close to scream, to run.

Nothing and I edged a little closer. Still nothing and I boldly stepped inside. A moonbeam partially illuminated the floor of the cave and I could see Poppy's glove. Quickly, I moved my arm across the stone shelf and with huge relief grabbed the wrapper and the rubber mat then leaped outside. Surely those men below must hear the beating of my heart. Poppy's glove, where was it? I must have kicked it into the shadows in my haste. Returning on my knees, I swept the floor with my hands until I found it. Poppy's missing glove. By morning she might need to know the courage I had shown and be one with me again.

Calmly, I laid the recovered items from the cave at its entrance and looked about. The rope had whiplashed and lay some twenty feet below me on the slope where it was still fastened to the prop.

Mindful of the moonlight and a mini avalanche of scree, I slithered slowly, cautiously down the slope to the prop, wedged beneath a large rock and impossible to move. Luckily the rope untied easily and the second prop, I perceived, broken in two on the trail, I vowed to recover later.

Below, the two civilians had reappeared, and joining the Sergeant, they squatted on their hams over the stretcher, where unmistakeably lay a blanket-covered body. The men made no sound and for a little while, no movement, being engrossed with what was on the stretcher, the Sergeant's buttons glinting like tiny beacons against the black of his tunic. Winding the rope in a loop around my hand and elbow, I waited for the men to move. When it was safe, I scaled the incline to a small escarpment from where I could safely view the scene below. I watched as the men carefully began to carry the stretcher across the terrain, back the way that they had come.

The moon had paled and beneath waning stars the first film of morning light in a freshening breeze began its shift across the sea. Sea birds were awakening in the cliffs and calling to one another, with gulls spreading their wings and gliding out to intercept the dawn. And I was not frightened any more. I would wait now until the men had reached the trail, then, moving very fast, I would overtake them and wait for them at the wall at Calgary.

I was not frightened any more, but as I waited unanswerable questions jostled for attention in my mind and I was still sick with worry, sick at what I'd done. Was the old man on the stretcher dead or merely injured? If injured, what story would he tell? Would he be intelligible? Would he be believed? Better for me if he was dead.

The men began to move slowly upwards towards the trail and it was time that I was gone.

Disposing of the rope quickly, I waited until I had reached the tip before hiding the rubber mat and wrapper beneath debris, vowing that as soon as I could, I would return for the broken pieces of the prop. Poppy's glove was in my pocket, invaluable evidence of my courage.

As I neared Calgary, a tip of sunlight appeared on the horizon, touching the stones and grasses of the foreshore with an icy light. From Bray Head, a chorus of sea birds and to the south, behind Calgary, the breathy, indistinguishable sounds of a town waking up and yawning.

The windows of Calgary were in darkness, my family still asleep. I shook my mother awake and told her I was home again but in her sleepy state, she did not even know I had been gone. My father snored softly beside her. Returning to the garden, I stood behind the wall and waited.

It seemed an age before the men appeared in the distance. They approached slowly, the Sergeant leading, with the men carrying the stretcher a pace or two behind. As they closed on me, I could hear their footfalls crunching on the ice and anxiety like stab wounds centred in my stomach and I began to retch nervously.

Daylight and the sea in the early sunlight rose like a marble lake behind the men. Bray Head was greener and brighter with their every step and the tips of the Sugarloaves were white, as if snow had fallen in the night. The men grew bigger as they neared and were unsmiling and unspeaking, as if what they carried was a corpse. Sergeant O' Neill's face was sepulchral, like Brother Brady's when he entered class. The bearers each had a lighted cigarette clamped grimly in the corners of their mouths, smoke rising in twin columns to join their breath vapour in a canopy above the stretcher. Their march was slow and measured, funereal, the men looking to neither right nor left and I trembled as if my fever had returned.

As they drew abreast, I collected myself and, standing to my full height offered them a breezy good morning, to which the man at the front of the stretcher grunted and spat his cigarette butt to the ground. Yes, I knew these men from somewhere, but where? Maybe some gothic horror movie, I had seen.

Vaulting over the wall, I fell in behind the man at the back of the stretcher. 'Good morning. What's happened?' I asked pleasantly, an innocent curiosity disguising the tremor in my voice.

The man sniffed and did not reply but, with a grunt of dissatisfaction he adjusted his grip on the handles of the stretcher.

My gaze was transfixed on the form lying on the stretcher; no movement, a form completely covered in a blanket and as motionless as a bag of sand. 'Is he dead?' I asked but my question went unanswered. I shuddered, for I had never seen a dead man before. The dead that I knew had black Stetsons and smoking guns and paint and powdered death throes. Bizarrely fascinated, I wanted that blanket removed or disturbed, I must see the death mask of Ooara Moara, that spectre who had lived a year now in a scary prism of my mind.

'Is he dead?' I asked again. On the stretcher was not a big or heavy man, for his weight did not appear a burden on the arms of the men who carried him and I could tell by the purposeful and authoritative way the Sergeant strode ahead that his role was leader and that at no time had he offered to relieve them. I kept pace, trying not to appear too curious, but constantly glancing sidewards, wanting the blanket to slip from the face, wanting in ghoulish compulsion to view the face of that dead man, yet expecting, all the time, to be brusquely told to leave. 'Where are you taking him?' I asked.

Being ignored made me bolder and now I found myself walking so close to the stretcher that the back of my hand could brush it at will. The anxiety in my stomach was still there, but it was being soothed by adrenaline pouring through my system and I knew that I was going to tug that blanket low enough to see a face.

The bearer at the rear spluttered his cigarette to the ground and, as they reached the wide expanse of road in front of Dan's pub, the bearer at the front slipped on an ice patch, going down sharply on one knee. The stretcher lurched and tilted forward and I sprang sideways in alarm. An arm had fallen from beneath the blanket, almost touching me and as I stared at it searchingly, incredulously, a screaming started in my head.

Cursing loudly, the man who had slipped regained his feet and the stretcher levelled but the arm remained dangling, only inches from the road. The screaming in my head got louder. Something here was wrong. The Sergeant spoke to the man who had slipped, but I could not hear what was said for the screaming. Something here was wrong. The hand that protruded from a dark denim sleeve was not the gnarled, liver-spotted claw of a decrepit but was pale-skinned and soft with long slender fingers. It was a woman's hand, his wife's, and a girl's warning from a cave sounded like a siren in my brain, a siren sound amid that screaming.

'Who is it? Who is it?' I demanded, unable to take my eyes off the alabaster appendage jerking just above the ground.

The sergeant stopped and turned around. 'It's you, you bloody nuisance. Clear off.'

'But who is it?' my demand, louder, more earnest.

The sergeant took a menacing step towards me. 'CLEAR OFF YOU BLOODY NUISANCE.'

'Who is it under the blanket?' The voice could not be mine it was too high-pitched, too hysterical.

The men stopped and the leading stretcher bearer turned his head on me with a menace of his own and full-faced and I knew who he was, I knew who both men were and in an electrifying instant knew who was beneath that blanket, too. The sergeant took another threatening pace towards me, but before he could jerk me away by my collar, I leaned forward and tugged at the blanket. Deathly white and either dead or fast asleep was the face of Shonti Plunkett.

Chapter Thirty-one

*I*n severe shock and not having slept that night, I was running on raw nerve. My parents could not believe me when I told them I felt well enough to go to school. 'We're flitting tomorrow,' my father reminded me. 'We don't want you ill again. Last night you frightened us to death.'

I beat all the brothers to the school and waited by the outbuilding where they parked their bicycles. Brother Molloy was second to arrive.

'Brother,' I began.

He pretended to fall off his bicycle in shock. 'Dear God, you're after finding them, I knew you would I knew you had it in you. Don't forget our deal. Oh we're rich, we're rich.'

I laughed because I was supposed to, but had no inclination to banter. This was serious and with dry lips I managed, 'Brother, what do you know about Rasputin?'

The cleric looked mildly surprised, then his expression changed to concern and he remarked on my sickly face and the black rings around my eyes. He unhooked his bicycle clips. 'Ooara Moara, it used to be, yes, Rasputin nowadays. You look as though he's had you in his sack.'

'Brother, have you ever seen him or ever heard him wailing?'

For a moment, the cleric was caught off-guard. He smoothed his hair back where it had been ruffled by the wind and flexed his shoulders. 'Indeed I have, the once only,' he answered and nodded as if agreeing with himself. 'You know what happened to his wife, all those years ago?'

'I know what happened to his wife.'

Brother Molloy smiled ruefully. 'Ah sure, there's so many exaggerations and myths about the poor man that it's hard to know what is true and what isn't. Why is it important to you?'

'It isn't important, but if you've seen him, what's he like?'

He answered immediately, surprising me. 'About two years ago, I was with the hurling team after playing at Kilcoole. It was late and the bus broke down; we had to walk back along the Killincarrig road. We saw him on the Killincarrig road. It was early night, there was a moon and he was in black rags in a farm gateway wailing like an owl banshee. It was quite a scary sound for all of us, I can tell you and we all ran past him, even me. Why is it you ask?'

'It's nothing important, thought maybe he was a ghost, it's just something I need to know.'

Either I was going mad, or else I was already mad, as people said. That day passed without measure in an insubstantial world where nothing mattered except the all-consuming worry in my head and immediately after school I was hidden in laurel bushes in the grounds of the quarry waiting for Poppy Boyle.

She passed, but was with her sister Mary. I was expecting her to look different, like the last time I had seen her but, chattering amiably she appeared to have fully recovered. I must catch her on her own and I would be back again tomorrow and every day until I had some answers.

I had some. School the next day was buzzing with news of the fallen stack and Shonti's injuries. (So he wasn't dead.) Word from the Dublin hospital where he was confined was that he was upbeat about the whole thing, his quite significant injuries, including a fractured arm, were repairing well, but there were complications with a broken femur.

At school I talked about that fallen stack in the most indignant terms. How often had I warned of what a storm could do? Hadn't

I advocated its felling many times before some poor soul got hurt; all the time gathering what information I could on exactly what had happened that night until answers began falling into place like pieces of a jigsaw.

It was from Patsy holding court in the schoolyard that most of the information came. On the Saturday afternoon after I had got bored with my sinister vigil at the stack, he and Shonti had arrived and cast their fishing lines to be left overnight. Prevented by the storm from retrieving them on the Sunday morning, Shonti had waited until the late afternoon when the storm had calmed, before setting off alone to recover them, Patsy being with some mott at The Ormonde. He was on rocks, making up the lines, when, in his own words, 'half the friggin' mountain fell down on me'. In spite of an injured arm and leg, he had managed to crawl to safety, knowing that someone would come looking for him, and someone did, his father, who returned to town for assistance. It was Shonti's father and uncle whom I finally recognised as the stretcher-bearers.

Too simple. An explanation posing more questions than it answered and I worried with them as a terrier with a bone. Shonti would not be making up fishing lines alone after nightfall and who was with him, because someone certainly was? Poppy had thought she had seen a woman on the slope; what of Rasputin? – No mention of him. No mention of his fearful howling nor of children or voices or laughter from a cave and most important of all, what of Poppy Boyle that night? Seemed she hadn't talked and renewing contact with the girl became obsessive.

I was getting up on a morning, going to school, coming home, eating and drinking although nothing seemed to taste of anything anymore, pretending I was focused, happy, normal, pretending that I wasn't really mad. I withdrew into myself, a troubled mind, my sanctuary. So preoccupied with their own troubles, moving house and an ever worsening financial situation, my parents did not recognise my suspect behaviour.

Very early one morning I had returned to the mountain and

disposed of the broken pieces of prop, even managing to infill some of the excavation. Now that there was nothing left to link me to the site, I adopted a profile of indifference to everything, an act an ultimate pretence; truth was, my interest in everything relating to that night was paranoid.

For days afterwards, the town had talked of little else but the storm, the toppled landmark and how lucky Shonti Plunkett was to be alive, but no one, as far as I knew, had bothered to venture to the mountain to see the wonder for themselves, certainly none of the Garda force had felt it worth their while and behind my mask of sanity I probed for more information but without daring to ask a single pertinent question. Life was hell waiting for a body to be found, a knock on the door or a grim-faced summons from the classroom, or to feel Sergeant O' Neill's heavy hand of justice on my shoulder. I began to see accusation in every glance and, haunted by the absence of any tangible suspicion or investigative development, I began to suspect conspiracy. That very moment was a rock-fall being prepared for me? At school I constantly looked to Patsy and Christy for signs of censure but could find nothing other than their inherent, vacuous coarseness and, out of school, a glimpse of a uniform caused the ground to lurch beneath me. So depressed was I that if anyone called my name, my heart stopped beating and I could feel worms inside my head, eating at my reason.

Poppy had been with her sister the next day, too, and the day after that and although I kept myself busy helping my parents settle into our new home, I was crazed with worry and desperate for reassurance. I could not approach her with her sister present. Mary didn't like me and if she had learned anything new about me during the last few days I thought it most unlikely to have enhanced my reputation any.

A bitterly cold Sunday morning and once again hiding in the laurel bushes, I hoped to waylay her on her way home from Mass. Another hope was that she would be on her own. She was.

As she drew abreast I almost lost my nerve and shrunk back in the bushes, but my desperation for dialogue was stronger than my fear of rejection. Trying to look and sound casual, I stepped out of the bushes beside her. 'Poppy,' I said quietly.

She jumped sideways in alarm, but after one rapid, withering glance at me, she regained her composure and purposeful progress towards her home, saying 'You can piss off. I wondered how long it would be before you turned up again.'

I kept pace with her. 'Poppy you've got to stop and talk to me before I go insane.'

'It's Jennifer now an' you're already insane so I wouldn't worry.' Her voice was as frigid as the air. 'I'm Jennifer an' I've turned over a new leaf.'

'I'm desperate, Jennifer, sick with worry, can't sleep, can't eat, can't understand what happened that night. An old man is dead, he's in the sea. How long before his body is washed ashore? How long before I'm arrested? Jenny, do you know what the hell happened that night?'

Stopping abruptly, she faced me squarely, her small taut body pulsing with resentment, her lips tightening as she spoke. 'I don't know what happened that night an' I don't care. Know why? Cos I want to forget what happened. I couldn't give a shit what happened because I had nothing to do with it. If you want to know what happened, ask Shonti friggin' Plunkett.'

Her disregard surprised me. Somehow I had expected her to be as consumed with worry and guilt as I was. 'But we were in it together, so we ought to stick together,' I ventured hopefully.

'We're in nothing together,' she scorned. 'You dragged me up that bloody mountain to see somethin' wonderful, oh yes, I'll never forget how bloody wonderful it was. On'y thing I've done wrong is to keep quiet about you.'

Awash with relief, I tried to grasp her hand but she withdrew it quickly. 'So you haven't told anyone about me? Oh, Poppy, thank God for that. Where were you that night after the concert? You know I waited for you, right here where we are now I waited. I was so worried about you. You didn't come home and I was worried sick. I waited quite a long time.'

'I stayed with my cousin. Mammy rang from Dublin, her an' Mary had to stop the night with my Da. Mammy rang my Aunt Molly an' I stayed that night with Aunt Molly an' my cousin Rose.'

'Oh, Poppy thank God, you told nobody nothing.'

'Nothin', next mornin' at school I heard about Shonti, thought, Jennifer, you've done nothin', so say nothin'. Any talkin' to be done let the friggin' eejit that caused it do the talkin'.'

'But we're in it together, Poppy, you and me we'll stick together and we'll be ok.'

She started walking homeward again, fast. 'We're in nothin' together. How could you run away an' leave me in that bloody hole? I was lyin' there an' I was hurt an' I was terrified. I couldn't get out an' I was absolutely terrified. I was waitin' to be put in a sack an' buried alive. I couldn't get out.' Her lips were trembling as she relived the horror of the moment. "You see…' I couldn't – I couldn't…'

'But you saw me coming back for you,' I gambled.

The look she gave me stopped me in my tracks. Behind the look was loathing.

I didn't go back to the house in Kimberley Road. I went to the beach and sat on the stones outside Calgary. I watched the breakers rolling in; they were like rows of great white teeth ravenously devouring the coastline. I couldn't bear what was going on inside my head and tomorrow I would try to see her again.

'Poppy.' This time I didn't make her jump, but met her face to face as she was leaving Riley's shop. It was early evening, overcast and colder than ever and I was armed with her lost glove and different tactics. Contrition. I didn't know that she had fallen in the hole, but unquestionably I should have been more protective of her. 'Last time you didn't give me chance to explain things,' I complained. 'That same night I went back to the cave and got your glove. That was brave, Poppy, you got to admit it. Saw the rescue but thought it was the old man. I was very brave that night.' I did not sound boastful, my voice was plaintive; my expression of deep unhappiness surely must reach the understanding and forgiveness in her heart. 'You know I was going back for you, but I should have let you out of the cave first, that way I could have kept my eye on you. You must know how much I thought about you. After the concert I waited for you by the entrance to the quarry and was worried sick when you didn't come home.' I handed her the glove, but she did not take it, only looked at it disdainfully.

A mongrel dog chased a cat along the road beside us. The cat skipped sharply sideward, and the dog, in trying to brake, skidded on a patch of ice and collided heavily with the kerb. Whimpering in pain, it limped off. The cat, now sitting on a wall, observed it bemusedly.

She had not spoken a word to me but could not ignore me. Keeping pace with her, I continued determinedly, 'We've moved from Calgary. We live in Kimberley Road now. I'll have a word with my mother see if you can visit us. She'll be pleased you've turned over a new leaf and my sisters want you back. There's a piano in the drawing room, you can have a go on it.'

For the first time she spoke. She did not look at me, neither did she slow down; her words falling on my ears were heavy with sarcasm. 'A piano in the drawing room, my, my.' Then, walking on, she refused to say another word. The injured dog limped past, looking up at me with limpid self-pitying eyes. The cat watched it go, yawned and began washing behind its ear with a paw.

Getting nowhere, I was waiting by the quarry again with a fury overtaking me. I had got rid of the evidence and she must now know she had no hold on me. Her word against mine; this was criminality; she wouldn't be able to rely on Father Fallon coming to her defence. My maturity and command of language would surely win the day and, Poppy well strings of expletives wouldn't help her case. I waited until she was passing then grabbed her roughly by the arm. 'Listen, I've come here to be friends. I saved your bloody miserable life twice that day and when I realised you wasn't behind me I was coming back for you and I waited for you after the concert until it was really late and I went back for your glove that night so's you wouldn't be blamed. I was thinking of you all the time. I want us to be friends. I won't have you ignore me.'

I walked beside her until we reached her gate, where I prevented her from opening it. She tried to pull my fingers from the latch. Our heads were close, our breath buffeting uneasily in the frigid air. The atmosphere between us was now freighted with deep resentment. Her co-operation and friendship didn't matter any longer. 'I should o' let you drowned or die of fright in that cave. You'd of been the centre of attention then, wouldn't you, dead?'

She then turned the tables on me so effectively I was stunned. She said calmly, 'I was ready to be friends again but needed to see if you would do something, but you haven't and you've ruined your chances now.' She eased my fingers from the gate latch and began walking down the path to her house.

Blighted by another failure, my voice cracked. 'What is it you want me to do, Poppy? What's the way we can be friends again?'

She stopped at the door. 'You're not up to it.' She closed the door quite gently and I was a long time at the gate, still stunned.

What did she want me to do? Did she want me to confess? I would confess, I was mortally sick of the life that I was leading, sick of the worms in my head fattening on reason.

To whom does a troubled Catholic turn to but the comforting bosom of Mother Church, and I confessed to Father McCartney on a Saturday morning a veritable catalogue of sin, every sin I had ever committed, with fitting snugly among them, my contribution to the death of one and the near-death of another, but as I knelt awaiting judgement and the quietude of closure, all he had to say, was, 'Tell me child, when you had these impure thoughts, words and deeds, were you on your own or with another?'

Frustrated and disgruntled, I marched straight to the Garda station and knocked boldly on the great hardwood door. A young man in civilian clothes answered and, shifting his weight from foot to foot, eyed me curiously as I demanded to speak with Sergeant

O' Neill. Then following low voices from inside and approaching footsteps, the Sergeant was squinting at me from above a pair of horn-rimmed reading glasses.

'You,' he said.

'I have to tell you something, Sergeant,' I said.

'You,' he said again, this time with real meaning.

'Shonti Plunkett, Sergeant, it was me. That night, well, it was me.'

His face hardened and for a moment he appeared lost for words.

'I need you to understand something, Sergeant. You see that night ...'

Sergeant O' Neill understood everything and threatened to throw me down the steps if I ever bothered him again. 'FECK OFF BEFORE I BREAK YOUR BLOODY NECK,' I heard him yell, as I bolted up Marine Drive.

I must unburden myself or else explode. My mind unable to withstand much longer the turmoil it was in, anxiety that must stop feeding on itself. Who had I left, but Mr Malone? A man I knew would listen. And after two evenings seeking him about the town, I set off, late Saturday afternoon, to his house but was surprised to find him sitting on a bench overlooking the south beach. There was so much black smoke hanging above him that I thought his hat must be on fire.

He watched me coming and, taking his pipe from his mouth, gestured with the stem for me to sit beside him. Holding myself in check, I began by talking in general terms about the weather and the likelihood of snow but when I started talking in earnest, my theme was once again rhetorical patriotism, hinting strongly at my knowledge of his involvement. Again I evoked the images of 'Kathleen Ni Houlihan', 'Dark Rosaleen' and ancient freedom, affirming that in their honour, he may well, himself, be guilty of the very act that weighed so heavy on my soul.

'I tried to kill someone,' I blurted. 'And, Mr Malone I have, killed someone.'

A seagull alighted a few feet away, a magnificent, snow-white bird, surveying us with one distrustful eye, then, in a show of splendour, it flexed its wings and called its timeless cry. Perhaps, instinctively sensing my propensity for sustaining chickens and others of its kind, it hopped so close to me that I could touch it, but as the old man hoisted the collar of his coat, it fluttered sideways in alarm, lifted its wings and glided effortlessly over the shingle beach to join its fellows in shallows of the sea.

Billows of smoke escaped from within the folds of the old man's collar as he relit his pipe and from the depths of his coat a coughing, spluttering face emerged, livered with tremor, appearing slowly, like an inquisitive turtle from its shell. Through the smoke, pale, moist eyes squinted accusingly at the pipe. 'Dear God, this thing is killin' me,' he wheezed.

I thought my unheralded admission would shock the man into some reaction, but he didn't even change expression. But then death to this old warrior was in the context of noble ideals and liberation. Had he somehow sensed the tenets of my disclosure, jealousy, vengeance and spite and that at once I felt shabby and ashamed?

The great bird returned, surely a symbol of simplicity and the reality that was about to purge my soul. It set down in the same place as before and the old man smiled first at the bird and then at me and a nodding of his head in coalescence was the spur I needed to outpour truth upon them both. Hopping closer to me still, the seagull appeared to listen intently.

'Kids from school ganging up on me, if only you knew how sick I am of kids ganging up on me, but it was these brothers, older than me, bigger, who made me feel really bad, they made me feel a fool, like the lowest of the low. I was called the lowest of the low once by someone high up and important and I don't think I'll ever really get over it in all my life. Mr Malone, you might think this is kid's stuff, hurt feelings and all but I'm only twelve and not in my own country and if I don't find some way to fight back then I'm finished and I really am the lowest of the low. They say a worm can turn, but it can't. Once people turn you into a worm, the lowest of the low, then that is how you're gonna stay. Mr Malone, I know more about you than you think the stuff that you've done in your life but I need someone to understand me and the things I sometimes do, really stupid things, crazy things. Three brothers and an adult man, my best friend, ganged up on me and I should have jumped them like I do at school, gone in swinging but I didn't, I just slunk away. There were six of them and they were laughing at me, and one of them I thought an awful lot about, not the friend, another, she was laughing. Truth is, Mr Malone, I didn't slink away, I ran, ran straight up Bray Head and if Bray Head had been the edge of the world then I would have run straight over the edge.'

Head cocked to one side the seagull moved closer. Never had I had a seabird so close to me. Maybe I had fed this bird before, for I often fed sea-birds as well as chickens. I think it may have recognised me as a friend.

'I planned to kill all three brothers and the adult if I could. And I wasn't kidding, I really meant to do it, bet you think I'm exaggerating but I'm not, maybe you don't believe me, but I'm telling you the truth. I killed one and almost killed another, but then everything got all mixed up.'

Buried within the wrappings of his coat and hat, the old man was silent, listening intently as usual without comment; his pipe, cold and neglected lay on the bench between us. The seagull, having never taken its eye off me, moved even closer, its keen head nodding as if in sympathetic understanding.

'I set a trap for them, not some kid's trap, not some hole in the ground with twigs and grasses over. Oh no, boy, you should o' seen this trap, it cudda killed an army.'

Behind us, the rumble of Kilbain's refuse cart, its stench preceding its approach. 'Gerupouadath,' Kilbain shouted at his horse above the noise of the cartwheels crunching on the gravel. I turned and waved for Oliver Kilbain often let me sit proudly beside him on his cart. He tipped his whip at me and shouted, 'Gerupouadath.' The seagull squawked in protest at the noise and interference and flew so low and close in front of us that I could feel the draught of its wings. To the south, earlier drapes of cloud had parted, forming a frame of bright, blue sky, telling of snow that night and fields of snow by morning. The wind had picked up, causing small wavelets, like scales on the shallow shore-line and beard grass stirred and bristled at our feet. The sun had lowered swiftly in the sky, making yellow the late afternoon light and the beach, cold and yellow with small white patches where the sea-birds were.

Characteristically, Mr Malone had remained silent throughout my effusion. Once he had grunted and another time I thought I had heard him chuckle, or maybe he was just clearing his throat. I would not disturb him or even look at him too closely for only my words must have the impact I was seeking.

Elbows on my knees and chin cupped in my hands, staring out sea, I continued sadly, 'Yet when it happened, I didn't want it to, I had kind of forgiven everybody. Mr Malone, you probably know who I'm talking about. The whole town was talking about it. The storm didn't bring that rock down, I did, down on top of Shonti Plunkett. I killed old Rasputin by mistake and almost killed Shonti Plunkett. He's in hospital now, maybe crippled for life and old Rasputin's dead out there and I can't sleep for thinking about it all the time.' I was close to tears. 'It was a crazy thing to do and I shouldn't get away with it. And I ran away and I feel guilty about that, too. I had to tell somebody, I'm telling you cos I know you listen. Sometimes people don't listen to me, but you always do.'

I blinked at my stinging eyes as the old man shifted his weight. High above, the shriek of a herring gull, dusk was beginning to settle on the sea and the bright sky was beginning to fill with snow. A wind whistled in the grass.

Overcome with the drama of my confession, I now wept openly, but even though long accustomed to Mr Malone's taciturnity, I was unsettled when he did not even react to my choking tears. This time I had bared my soul to him, laid my future in his hands, my trust in him a wondrous thing of which he should be proud.

Oh, he might well think what I had done, an accident and trivial by comparison to his own exploits, but a murderous schoolboy should never be ignored. I was sorry and I had confessed and I needed him to lift my guilt and so face Poppy Boyle again. Angry at his lack of response, I stood up and faced him squarely. Tilting the brim of his hat, I found him fast asleep.

Chapter Thirty-two

Wrapped up against the cold, I sat on the dock wall, think-ing, and watching fishermen tend their boats. The snow of days ago had been held in place by hard night frosts and the ice-cold sunlit days that followed. Faded drapes of cloud hung above the promontories of Dublin and Dun Laoghaire, dissipating south-wards until only wispy mouse-tails laced the coast of Wicklow. Behind me the cheerful sound of adolescents gathering at the Milk Bar.

I had learned a lot about myself this year in Ireland and al-though I hated to admit it, most of it I didn't like. Although in fairness to myself I had had a lot to put up with; girls ignoring me, boys ganging up and a clergy conspiring to bring me down. And so much for my so-called friends, Nugget Nolan beneath contempt and what a disappointment Mr Malone had turned out to be, a hero figure in my mind, not even managing to stay awake while I emptied out my heart and soul. Anyway, I still had Frank, although what Poppy Boyle had had to say yesterday about Frank worried me.

I had been treated badly, yes. I mean, looking up 'egg' in a dictionary, how bad was that? Thrashed for trying to defend myself against overwhelming odds, hounded for being born at the other side of a narrow strip of water and publicly humiliated by clergy over some confuted pencil drawings, yet, trying to confess to murder and no one in the country gave a shit. Maybe I shouldn't feel so bad about myself, yet I did. That derelict still squatted in my core.

Poppy had been going to great lengths to avoid me and although I was still deeply depressed, at least I was losing some burden of anxiety. Many days had passed and still no body had been washed ashore and although I still cared deeply about what I had been responsible for, I was coming to terms with my confession being of no consequence. Surely, Shonti's well-being was as vital to him as mine was to me, but it didn't seem to be of much concern to anybody else. Really I should put it out of my mind as Poppy had done, but how could I with so many questions still unanswered? Anyway, hope of renewing friendship with her was well and truly over after the blazing row of yesterday, all her fault.

'You have a good name, you have, Boyle. Them blotches on your face don't look like little sweet poppies like your dead uncle said, they look like boils. You should have your head squeezed, that's what's done with boils, especially when they're full of shit.' I had caught her early in the morning on her way to school. Once again I had wanted to make friends and had begun equably, refuting any suggestion that I might have left her purposely that night and telling her of my attempts at confessing what I had been responsible for, but once again she had rudely rebuffed me and I wasn't taking that from an eleven-year-old girl. 'Boil head,' I called her.

'No wonder you haven't any friends,' she said.

'I've got plenty of friends.'

'Course you have, like Nugget Nolan.' I ignored her but couldn't ignore what she said next. 'Like Frank Moore.' Frank was a true friend and should not be mentioned in the same breath as the traitor Nolan and I spluttered to find an answer.

'Poor Frank havin' to lock the cinema doors the minit he sees you comin'.'

'Of course he locks doors he doesn't want a hundred kids barging in on him.'

'Well, no, not if you're among 'em.' Her voice left little puffs of barbed vapour in the frosty air. 'An' of course your great friend 'Dodger' an' the way he does be listenin' to your every word.' She was wearing a woollen shawl about her school uniform, a woollen hat and mittens, a little woollen ball of ridicule. 'Dodger' Malone the bold Fenian man, oh Jesus, have you not seen the statue of him beside Parnell in O' Connell Street, wanted both sides o' the border an' for what I wonder? Let me tell you now, what my Da tol' me about 'Dodger'. Mr Malone was over forty years at the 'Lectric Board in Dublin, in the power plant he was. It was workin' in the power plant what left him stone deaf.'

'Stone deaf?'

'Yeah, somethin' you wouldn't o' noticed with you blatherin an' thinkin' he's hangin' on your every word when in fac' he cannot hear a word cos he's bloody stone deaf after years in the power plant, so bloody wrapped up in yerself, so full o' high follutin' shite an' tryin' to impress that you couldn't notice that the poor owl fella couldn't hear you.'

Talking absolute nonsense, she was trying to score points. 'Boys as school say that your Mary is a whore,' I said simply.

She flinched, the posture of her body altered; head forward, shoulders back, mittened fists clenched tightly her freckles bright orange in little spots of outrage. She didn't know what a whore was, and neither did I, but we both knew that it was a hurtful word and I braced myself for what was coming next. Nothing came, well nothing that I expected. There was sudden candour in her posture and kinder eyes met mine. 'Remember you once asked me to do somethin' for you?'

My heart flooded with hope; was this reconciliation?

'In the cave that day you asked me to listen out for Cora Casey, you know, if she had anything to say about you.'

I snorted dismissively: 'Oh that, huh, you can forget that.'

'Ok, I will.' She turned and walked away.

I ran to catch her. 'Wait, with all what's happened I'd forgotten about Cora, but seeing as I'm here you might as well tell me.'

She said sweetly, 'Well I heard Cora talkin' about a lot o' boys, but you weren't one of 'em.'

I jumped down off the dock wall. Poppy could go to hell, but what she had said yesterday about Mr Malone and Frank worried me as if I didn't have enough to worry about, but there was only one way to find out, go and see them both and find out for myself. She couldn't possibly be right, but if she was at least it would explain things about old Malone. I went straight to his house and yes, she was right, incredibly the man was stone deaf; God only knows how I hadn't noticed. She was wrong about Frank, though. After leaving Mr Malone I went to The Ormonde and, catching him dusting ledges in the foyer, I came straight out with it. 'Frank, when you see me coming, do you lock the doors?'

'Of course not,' he assured me.

'And are you my friend, Frank?'

'Of course I am,' he assured me and we would have been chattering for ages if it hadn't been for Mr McGrath, who, Frank said, was expected at any moment. Bidding him a cheerful goodbye and promising to call and see him again soon, I returned to the dock wall, kicking solid wedges of snow on the way then, still deep in thought, I slowly made my way home to what turned out to be a truly great day, the first for a very long time.

I had never known anyone to get a major present just weeks before Christmas. But in my bedroom I was blinking in disbelief. What were two pairs of grey long legged trousers, one light and one dark, doing at the end of my bed? Was this why my mother some days earlier had accosted my inner thighs with a linen tapemeasure?

Stiff-legged and self-conscious, I strode into the kitchen to find my mother and Grandma Plunkett poring over a world atlas. 'No, Mary, it's Aberdare, not Aberdeen and look how far away it is,' my mother pacified, poking a finger somewhere into the innards of equatorial Africa. 'And they don't attack with pandas, it's "pangas" a kind of African sword.'

But the old lady could not be mollified. According to the BBC

World Service, the devil worshipers were congregating in the Aberdeen Mountains, armed to the teeth and were preparing to strike at any moment. Patiently, my mother corrected her, but Grandma Plunkett was not convinced until finally conceding that the distance involved was far greater than she had at first thought but in geographical terms the Mau Mau were still a lot closer to the shores of Catholic Ireland than either the Chinese or the Korearionians.

I waited for them to acknowledge how grown-up and how smart I looked before presenting myself before the full-length mirror in my parents' bedroom. With long trousers things would change. I was yet to lay to rest the disquieting, disturbing and worrying event of recent weeks but because of them I was becoming more self-aware, more self-critical.

Having got off to a good start in Brother McBride's office, things had spiralled downwards ever since. As an erstwhile emissary of colonial occupation, as I had kind of fancied myself at first, I had been a let-down. And an orator, hardly, Mr Malone being not so much unresponsive to my eloquence, as deaf to it and as a wave dodging, hand-walking young Burt Lancaster, I should be admired, not ridiculed. And success with girls, well, it just had to be faced, I didn't even register on the barometric scale of magnetism, my allure about on a par with incontinence and bad breath. But with long trousers, things would change and I would start by toughening up my image. How could I have ever hoped to fill the boots of Lemuel H Caution wearing short ones? Absolutely impossible to swagger in short trousers, but now I could act and talk like Lemmy and I began practising in front of the mirror.

Was I finished with that Nolan punk, or was I? I was through with them crummy crown jewels and I don't mean maybe and those goddam Plunkett Palookas, them wise guys, what the hell. And girls were not motts any more, not babes, broads or even dames, they were 'frails'. Does that frail Cora Casey look good in a school uniform? I'll say she does. And so for a good hour I preened myself, deciding that a swagger and a lop-sided smile went well with long trousers and maybe, really, I must start smoking.

But forget leadership, it wasn't to be. Let others lead, they had it, I didn't; I had tried, and how but I couldn't get a single foot-soldier on my side not even my two, less than combatant younger sisters. Incomprehensible, born under Leo, the zodiac sign exemplifying leadership, yes, slap bang in the middle of that astrological dominion and reduced to evangelising birds and leading phantom armies across the Head. Forget leadership, I was not a leader of men, it had to be accepted, I was more a leader of chickens.

Grandma Plunkett's toffee was special. Always made in the same pan, it always came out the same size, about thirteen inches in diameter, a disc-shaped slab about half-an-inch thick. When it was set as hard as golden marble, the old lady would whack it with a spoon, breaking it into a couple of dozen wedges, some so sharp you could easily impale your tongue on them. It was like sucking a shard of glass, until, within seconds, a reaction would take place, turning the wedge into a glutinous mass, the forerunner of what later became known as 'superglue'.

Adults and worldly-wise children knowing the properties of this jaw-locking melange would never dare to chew on more than one piece at a time, but I, with my tendency for indulgence would often cram three or four pieces into my mouth at the same time, and this is what I did following my self-analysis in the mirror.

'Such a pig,' my mother admonished after Grandma had offered me the tin and Grandma, unknowingly, would exact some revenge for what had been done to her grandson and the irony would not escape me.

There was a knock on the front door and, unthinking, I went to answer it with my jaw glued shut, the four wedges of toffee having undergone an immediate catalytic conversion. The mirror had lied. What had looked and sounded great in the self-delusionary seclusion of a private bedroom was confounded when on your own doorstep appears the one thing capable of turning underpins to par-set jelly whether clad in flannel blades or not. What use image and dialogue as sharp and pithy as permanent creases if your gob is full of quick-setting, honey-coloured goo?

I couldn't speak, I couldn't even smile for fear of trickling down my chin so I managed 'glarp' as I convulsed in swallowing, but the girl's smile was genuine and still broadening and as friendly as her greeting.

'Hello, Christian, Mother Superior has sent me to give this to your mammy. It is an invitation to the Christmas Fayre at St Jude's, the day after St Stephen's day,' Cora said, as she handed me an envelope.

Cora Casey knew we had moved house, knew where we lived and was going through our gate as my innards dissolved.

This day wasn't over. My father beckoned me to join him in the drawing room. Kimberley Road had heralded a change in fortune. Two days earlier a letter from the bank had arrived, his application for a loan had finally been granted and he sat me down and told me of his plans. He would buy a plot of land, he knew of one available in Blacklion. He would build a bungalow, sell it, pay off the bank loan and get back to Cravenvale. He had relatives, friends and business associates in Cravenvale whom he hoped would help him get back on his feet. But he didn't appear overjoyed or anything at the prospect, because I knew just how he was gagging at the thought of how much pride he would have to swallow.

His plans also involved me. August of next year, I would be thirteen, old enough to leave school and help him build the bungalow. Money was going to be very tight and I could only expect a very low wage. Well, I was happy enough with these proposals but when I chipped in with the suggestion that he stopped paying for my three sisters to go to private school, he looked at me as if I should be confined somewhere and forgotten.

Chapter Thirty-three

*I*n spite of a new vitality at home, glad expectation at leaving school next summer and above all the thrill of hearing my name on Cora's lips, I could not rid my head of demons. I had given up on the chickens and hadn't been back to my cave since retrieving Poppy's glove. Instead, I had taken to trawling the north beach every spare hour that I had looking for the body of Rasputin and forever seeing it swirling in tide-wracked shallows. Here among these grey stones and in the rocks of the Head above me there was a sinister aura of the unexplained.

But in the days left at school before the Christmas break, there was one question I was determined to get an answer to; what did Brother Brady mean in calling me Otello?

Brother Mulligan was chalking long division sums on the blackboard, the irritating scratching of chalk in perfect sync with my enthusiasm for the subject. A useless point with endless worthless numbers strung along behind it was a waste of time in tandem with another that the brothers were so predisposed to waste, to whit the force-feeding of a language, long since abandoned by forbears, in favour of another, distinguished in use by most of the world's greatest speakers and writers for over four hundred years, ironically many of them Irish.

'Your mammy is in with Brother Brady,' Rogan's plump face making no effort to hide its glee as he returned from a visit to the lavatory.

I had misheard him, surely. 'What?'

This could not be. Such an event was unheard of. Other than the induction of a pupil, never in the history of the school had a parent ever been called for and the idea of a parent calling of his or her own volition was too inconceivable even to contemplate. But news of the unparalleled event was being whispered around the classroom and eyes were seeking mine for explanation. I didn't have one and I was shrugging and shaking my head in a manifestation of ignorance. All academic, disciplinary and behavioural issues were dealt with exclusively by clerics without recourse to parental interference of any kind. Children who wanted to get taught, got taught and those who didn't got strapped and those who wanted to get taught got strapped too, a system of education tried and tested over many years and so simple and efficient in management that there was never any need for influence from a single idealistic mind. Reformers were a rare breed indeed in Irish Catholic schools, circa 1951.

Rogan was mistaken, but, if he wasn't, there could be only one reason for the summoning of my mother and it was in hospital with a complicated fracture of the femur. Paranoia returned with a vengeance. What was my mother doing in the office with Brother Brady? Why not Brother McBride or Brother Mulligan? And why my mother? Ireland was a patriarchal society, surely it should be my father called to deal with something as serious as the murder of an old man and the attempted murder of a fellow pupil and I half-expected to see Sergeant O' Neill coming through the door with an arrest warrant. Then it dawned on me, she was in the office with Brother Brady over what had happened yesterday

Time to throw caution to the winds: 'Excuse me, Brother,' I had ventured meekly, 'you know you are always calling me Otello. What does it mean? What is an Otello?'

I had feared a tongue-lashing but what I got was far more extreme. He reared, snorting like a skittish horse, his nose hair quivering in outrage. 'Don't be clever with me, you insolent young pup,' and, gripping my right ear, he twisted it so hard that I fell to my knees in pain, 'you pretentious, posing, presumptuous young pup.'

'Oh Brother…I didn't…oooooooooo,' I squealed, down on one knee to the concrete yard.

'Be clever with me, would you? Tinkin' we can't see trew you, how dare you mimic me?'

'I'm sorry, I'm sorry.' My ear was on fire yet he still held on to it, still twisting it, surely it must come off in his hand. 'Please, Brother, mimic who, mimic what?'

'Otello, is it?' he snorted and with a final twist he released me. Pain-wracked I fell in a heap as he marched off towards the school house, nose in the air, nostrils gaping like hairy windsocks. My ear felt as if a burning mouse had crawled inside and was clawing its way out. Crying with pain and rage, I jumped up to follow him. Come what may I would call him to account for this harsh and unjustified treatment. I was not a small child to be bullied unmercifully I was grown up and wearing long trousers now. I had asked a polite question and did not deserve to be called names and I did not deserve this terrible burning in my ear.

Brother Mulligan caught me in the corridor and, seeing my distress, ushered me into my own empty classroom where he sat me at my desk and slid along beside me. 'You are very upset I see,' he observed kindly.

'Brother Brady has hurt my ear,' I blubbed, tears unrestrained. 'He called me names and accused me of mimicking him. All I did was to ask a question and he hurt my ear, bad.'

'What question did you ask?'

'I asked him what Otello was.'

'And what names did he call you?' The cleric's voice was soft and looking at him through misty eyes, I could see that he was concerned and caring, not liking what had been done to me.

'I can't remember, but one of them was pretentious and another one was pup. He said that I was mimicking him and I wasn't. What did he mean, mimic?'

The brother turned in his seat and was facing me, 'He thought you were. It's Othello really.'

'But what does it mean? I thought it might be Gaelic, but it isn't.'

The cleric scratched his nose. 'It certainly isn't Gaelic,' he said meditatively, then, taking a clean, yellow duster from his pocket he began folding it into squares until it could not be made any smaller. 'I think I know what has happened, there has been a misunderstanding.'

This man was on my side and I pressed home my advantage. 'Honest to God, I wasn't cheeky. I thought he might get angry with me, so I was careful what I said, but he got real angry and twisted my ear and it hurts.' I held my hand over my ear in an attempt to relieve the pain.

He looked at me judiciously. 'You genuinely don't know who Othello is, do you?'

'Otello,' I corrected.

'Othello, Otello,' he smiled. He was speaking to himself as if satisfying some question in his mind and at the same time opening the squares of cloth as if looking for corroboration. Presently he said, 'Gilla Christe, do you ever consider that sometimes you might give people the wrong impression, perhaps not the one you want to give?' His expression was grave and I feared that he might start talking in riddles again.

'The wrong impression,' I queried.

The cleric lowered his head and sighed. 'It is fair to say that you are not like the other boys in your class, indeed in the school, alike in some ways yes, as all boys are, but in many other ways, no. Although you might not think it, we teachers watch all of you closely and we notice things. We know that it has not been easy for you this last year and that you have had a troublesome time with some of the boys.' He smiled and glanced sideways at me quickly before returning his gaze to the duster. 'But I think it is fair to say that some of the trouble you have experienced you might have brought upon yourself. You do not mix well with boys your own age. You do not seem to try, spending far too much time with the likes of Nugget Nolan.'

'I'm finished with Nugget Nolan,' I cut in quickly.

'Come the new-year, the new term, I want you to try and make friends with the other boys and you might be surprised how readily they will respond. Perhaps they think you try to talk down to them, put on airs and graces. Boys don't like that you know. And you spend an inordinate amount of time on Bray Head, too much for your own good.' He gave a little mirthless laugh. "Tis a wonder to all of us, what on earth it is you find to do up there.'

He was not talking in riddles; I understood everything he was saying, he was echoing my own reservations and although I was still in pain, I found his forthright manner comforting.

'Now Brother Brady called you pretentious, do you know what he meant by that?'

'I'm not sure, Brother.'

He paused before continuing. 'Pretention is someone or something trying to appear more important than they are. An example might be someone trying to appear wealthier than they really are. Or it might be someone using words and phrases beyond their understanding or their years and likely not be understood by others. This is affectation, a kind of dishonesty and very irritating to others.' His long pale face seemed to grow longer and paler as he spoke until it was close to looking baleful and so intense was his expression that he appeared to suddenly become aware of it himself, for he straightened his back and his voice became instantly lighter and more sanguine in tone. 'Gilla Christe, can you think of anyone to whom this might apply?'

'You mean me, Brother.'

I detected the hint of a smile playing at the corners of his mouth. 'It is your pretentious and precocious Shakespearian quotations that caused Brother Brady to christen you Othello.'

Now he was talking in riddles.

'Otello is just the way the good brother says it. Like most Irish, myself included, he has difficulty with the 'th' in words, but with

Brother Brady it is more pronounced, as well you know. And when you asked him about Otello, instead of Othello, he thought you mimicked him.' Elbows on the desk, he supported his chin with his thumbs and spoke to his fingernails. 'Othello, the Moor of Venice, a character from Shakespeare, one of his most famous, a poor man driven insane with jealousy, but considering how familiar you are with Shakespeare, I'm amazed that you had to ask who Othello was.'

'Who's Shakespeare, Brother?'

Now the cleric was shaking his head and chuckling quietly to himself. 'This misunderstanding might well be bigger than I thought.' The sound of the school whistle interrupted him. He sat back and clapped his hands. We will have further words about this matter. The pain in your ear will go the minute you forget about it and I can assure you that Brother Brady will not have meant to hurt you, a big man, so he is, and sometimes he doesn't know his own strength.'

The classroom door flung open and boys began teeming into class.

But that was yesterday and now my mother was in the office with Brother Brady and if the meeting wasn't to do with Shonti Plunkett, then it was to do with a twisted ear and I fervently hoped that I was wrong on both accounts. Brother Mulligan finished a sum on the blackboard and turned to find my hand aloft. He raised an eyebrow: 'Yes?'

'May I be excused?' He nodded and I left the classroom hurriedly.

The corridor was empty and as I held by ear to the office door I could hear a murmur of voices, one unmistakeably that of Brother Brady, the second too low-pitched to be certain. Then I heard a throaty purr of amusement which was my mother's and I was pleased that things were amicable between them. A little more muffled conversation and then I heard something that chilled my blood and made me jump back from the door as if I had suddenly seen an eye at the keyhole. A shrill, discordant caterwaul that had me thinking for a terrible moment that they had Rasputin in there with them. I tried to think where I might have heard such a sound before; a fairground laughing policeman with the mirth removed; a farmyard and the squealing death throes of a stricken pig. Or was it something never heard in the school before, the laugh of Brother Brady?

Reeling back into my classroom, I was conscious of Brother Mulligan eyeing me worriedly. 'Are you not feeling well?' I heard him ask as I slumped down in my seat.

'You're as white as a sheet,' Coyle whispered.

The brother beckoned for me to join him at his desk. 'It's not your ear, is it? Maybe you have not fully recovered from your recent illness. You have not looked well for some time.'

'I'm ok, Brother, my ear still hurts, but I'm fine.'

'You know I spoke with Brother Brady as I told you I would and we agreed there had been a misunderstanding and he quite regretted giving your ear a tweak. Yesterday when you got home from school did you happen to report the "ear" incident to your parents, your mother maybe?'

With this question my dreaded suspicions were confirmed. A mother was in the school office talking about a son's twisted ear. My mother, oh she might have laughed in there, but how could she humiliate me so? I would never live this down. Was I not Oliver Cromwell, the English dog? A monster who in spite of my protestations to the contrary, afforded me a little pride, did I not epitomise colonialism and British brutality? English dog, a nomenclature evoking menace and challenge, even grudging respect downgraded to an English puppy with a twisted ear, a song and dance about something so trivial as to need a mammy's intervention and protection, unheard of in the annals of Irish Christian Brother dissemination. I looked up into Brother Mulligan's troubled face and nodded feeble affirmation of his query, together with a few gauche words of apology for being the root cause of so much fuss.

'Ah sure there's no need to apologise, quite unnecessary,' he said, patting me on the shoulder.

'But, Brother, I didn't "report" it. I just mentioned it. No more than if I told my mother about getting a sum wrong or getting the strap. I didn't "report" it I wouldn't do such a thing.'

'Ah sure, I know you wouldn't and Brother Brady knows it, too, and by now your mother will also, for she's away now,' he said, looking out of the window. 'A misunderstanding, the good Brother thought you mimicked him and gave your ear a playful tug, nothing else, a playful tug.'

'That's what it was, yes, a playful tug,' I concurred eagerly.

The cleric appeared relieved and I was, too. 'Well you're looking a little better now colour has returned to your cheeks, so it has. You know you have not looked well since your illness.'

Familiar mincing footsteps outside the door and as always the class fell silent. I didn't want to be found by Brother Brady, exposed at the head of the class so I made a move to return to my seat but was restrained by Brother Mulligan's light clasp to my shoulder.

The deputy entered, erect and self-assured and had my own teacher not been present, he would have immediately asserted his authority (as if he needed to) by picking fault with a boy, any boy, but more likely me because I was exposed in front of him. Looking to neither right nor left, he strode across the room and addressed his colleague directly. *'Factum est, Brother, factum est.'* Towering above me, he was always bigger, fiercer and more intimidating than the time before, his presence imbued with a capacity to degrade vitality and subdue spirit, one look, one word from Brother Brady and you had failed before you started. He did not look at me or speak to me but I felt his dreaded hand upon my shoulder. *'E pluribus unum,* Brother. *E pluribus unum.'*

His colleague answered in Latin and smiled weakly and now, with each of the cleric's hands upon my shoulders and profoundly suspicious of their Latin exchanges I wondered which of them would be the first to reach for his belt. Brother Mulligan I hoped, but surprisingly, no talk of a visiting mother, pretentiousness or twisted ears but a religious programme on the wireless with which they both profoundly disagreed. Brother Mulligan let his hand drop from my shoulder to my elbow but disconcertingly the deputy tightened his grip, a finger drumming on my clavicle as he emphasised a point. Trapped between the two of them, I had no idea as to how I should conduct myself, so I remained as impassive and inconsequential as a post on which they might be leaning. After a while, with their discussion losing no momentum and not wanting to appear dumb, I started switching my eyes from one to the other as they spoke, nodding agreement to each in turn; surely they must allow a totally agreeable and compliant boy to return to his seat unmolested.

There was no doubt now in my mind that my mother had called on the deputy to remonstrate with him about the brutal twisting of my ear, an interference for which she would get no thanks from me, but the office meeting which I thought would be uppermost in their minds was receiving no attention whatsoever. Brother Brady appeared to have won her over and I was eternally thankful to be out of it, but suddenly he appeared to notice for the first time what was propping him up, me, his black eyes disliking what he saw. 'Dear me, Brother, here we are chattering fifty to the dozen when there's a young scholar here raring to give us one his famous Shakespearian quotations. Our apologies for being so rude, boy, but you should have butted in.'

'Ah, but did I not tell you yesterday, that he had never heard of Shakespeare,' Brother Mulligan countered kindly, diffusing.

'Oh, I now know a lot more about this boy than you might tink, Brother.'

Brother Mulligan was trying to smile but his eyes were stressed, an unsure smile, indicative of appeasement and for the first time, I realised that he, too, was frightened of the deputy. 'Nonetheless, I have a strong belief that the boy was telling me the truth.'

Stretching himself to his full expanse, Brother Brady was in his element, for although he never smiled or laughed and his eyes never radiated humour, he often enjoyed himself, evident in the way he raised his great head, puffed his chest out and spoke as from a pulpit to a congregation. He now addressed the class, his eyes measuring archly the rows of boys in front of him, his voice pitch heightened, its timbre scratching at the ceiling. 'Truth is, boys, this last year we have had a sneak sitting in the front row of the class each day.' He now focussed on me, looping over me so that his face was almost upside down, gaping hairy nostrils only inches from my eyes. 'What do you know, boy, of an exercise book your mammy keeps locked up in her bedroom?' He straightened up, facing the class. 'Oh yes, boys it has all come out, so it has, in discussion with a certain lady. We now know of a private exercise book kept with other books and literature which were not intended for the eyes of sneaky children. What do we tink of a boy sneaking into his mammy's bedroom so as to go trew her private tings. What sort of a boy would stoop to a ting like that?'

I looked to Brother Mulligan but shame-faced could not meet his eyes. My mother now knew that I had access to her private library and I was worried at facing her.

Brother Brady continued, still expanding, outwards and upwards, 'The good lady's intention was to jot down in an exercise book all of a playwright's most famous quotations, a lady interested in crosswords, quiz words and literature in general, a fine endeavour from a lady, well-spoken and well-read and a pleasure to have a parley with, but with no idea that someone unexpected was sneaking into her room. Oh, yes, a boy with no time for lessons in Gaelic but plenty of time for memorising stuff so as to bore into a coma, anyone having the misfortune to wander into earshot. That's the kind of boy we have had with us this year gone.'

I admitted as much with glances of contrition and humility and a further sagging of my shoulders. Behind me the class was silent and expectant, knowing something must come to climax but not knowing what, knowing that this was another of Brady's games but this time using a colleague as an unwitting accomplice.

Standing without moving was making me uncomfortable and feeble and I kept shifting my weight from leg to leg. Twice, Brother

Mulligan tried to steer me towards my desk but each time, relishing my discomfort, Brother Brady resisted him by tightening his grip on my shoulder; my self-reproach and subservience being not enough, he wanted more. Yes, it was wrong of me to take credit for quotations knowing that they were not of my own making, but surely now that truth was out, recriminations should be of no concern to anyone but my mother, whom I thought had written them. Was what I had done any different from quoting lines from a book or a poem? I was quoting lines from my mother.

Indignation in proportion to his mass, the deputy now spoke exclusively to his colleague knowing well that I was listening intently to his every word. 'Disgraceful behaviour and I told his mammy that her son deserved a good hiding for himself. The poor lady was surprised to find that she had a snoop beneath her roof, but I declare to God didn't she find the whole ting amusing when I told her that her son had been spouting Shakespeare to the annoyance of the entire town but didn't I laugh myself at the presumption of it all. I told the lady straight, that should I have done such a ting at his age then I would of got a right whipping from my daddy, a right whipping for myself, a right whipping and well-deserved too.'

The image of Brother Brady's daddy invaded my mind like a gate crasher. I saw a huge bull-like man with his sleeves rolled up, beating on his children, especially a joyless one who would one day take his place.

I was now acutely aware that Brother Mulligan was almost as desperate as I was for the curtain to close on this fatuous floor show and, clasping my arms, he broke the deputy's grip on me by physically swinging me towards my desk and, as a small child might be admonished for bad behaviour, his voice was both patronising and disarming. 'And now, Gilla Christe, sit down. You know now why Brother Brady christened you Othello, there was no harm meant and no harm done and a very good thing your mammy called because now we're all in the picture so we are. Enough is enough so...'

'Wait now, Brother we're not finished yet with this snoop,' the deputy cut in brusquely, dismayed at his colleague's sudden action and determined to resist any effort to release me and, looping his heavy fingers inside the collar of my shirt, he hauled me back, calling to the class, 'We all deserve one last great performance and I have my heart set on Hamlet's soliloquy.'

I gulped and tried to speak, but my heart was beating in my breast, my temple, neck, wrists and groin, a huge thumping heart on legs too feeble to support it. The deputy still held on to the collar of my shirt and if he had not I'm sure my legs would have given way beneath me. With the other hand he smacked his thigh, summoning attention. His voice deliberately sober but still heavy with sarcasm, he said, 'A Shakespearian scholar, the only one we've ever had at St Luke's, a boy who loves bein' in the tick o' tings. A Shakespearian scholar who's never heard of Otello, yesterday he had the cheek to ask me who Otello was. Does he take me for a fool, does he take all of us for fools or is it himself, the only fool among us? Now I…'

A voice suddenly interrupted him. Astonishingly it was mine. How I hated this slab of black-eyed lard. A voice was shouting and that was mine, too, and it was shocking him for his hand had fallen from the collar of my shirt. 'I have never heard of Shakespeare, never heard of him. An exercise book with my mother's writing it, I thought my mother wrote that stuff.'

'You thought your mother wrote it?' His mouth had fallen open.

I would get a beating but I did not care. 'And there's one in there for you Brother, *Yet I do fear thy nature, it is too full of the milk of human kindness.*'

Something was happening, lines and fleshy fissures were expanding, opening sickly white from being denied the sun, large creases of skin were folding back on themselves and opening to air; incredibly what we were witnessing was a Brother Brady smile. A dumbstruck class was viewing the bombshell of the deputy head clutching Brother Mulligan as if to support himself and gasping ebulliently, 'Dear God, Brother, did yous hear that? He tought his mother wrote the stuff. She's after telling me today that being so busy she's only being able to manage tree, *Julius Caesar*, *Hamlet* and *MacBeth*. Oh, Brother Mulligan, tanks be to God it was only tree.' Letting go of his startled colleague, he smacked the desk in front of him with the palm of his hand and was laughing. Yes, Brother Brady was laughing, his great jelly face quivering, that same porcine squeal that had earlier froze my blood. 'Oh, Brother,' he crowed, smacking the desk again, 'can you imagine what we'd o' had to put up with if the woman had done the lot?' And still laughing he was gone, the door closing behind him and not a sound from the stricken class.

I couldn't eat any lunch that day, no one would let me. I was surrounded, my hand was shaken, my back slapped and my solar plexus gently punched with pulled punches. By the playing-field where I had been forced to retreat, I was mobbed by boys demanding to know exactly what I had said to make Brady laugh, questions coming so thick and fast it was impossible to field them. But I had had time to think and had been thinking from the moment he had shut the door behind him. I had made him laugh, I didn't quite know how but I was certainly getting the credit so no explanation was necessary. I was now the stuff of legend; let mythology take care of itself.

Chapter Thirty-four

*B*y late December, winter had taken a stranglehold on the country and one morning, those awakening on the east coast found that shallow arms of the sea had frozen over. It was on such a morning that Sean Thomas Plunkett was discharged from hospital to negotiate the icy ground on crutches. Supported by his parents, he arrived by train to be greeted by a small but vociferous group of supporters to whom he announced that he was pleased to be home for Christmas and although his arm was ok now, his leg would take a lot longer due to complications. Around town, he resurrected his mishap basking in the glory of his 'near miss' and the more he told his story, the bigger became the catastrophe, until the rock fall at Bray Head was vying with Vesuvius and Krakatoa for prominence and the complications with his broken femur were testing the highest medics in the land. How he loved the word 'complications', no doubt the biggest word he knew the meaning of, because he overused it at every opportunity.

Taking advantage of his volubility on the subject of his 'mishap', I joined a group of admirers surrounding him and bowled some enquiries of my own which I digested and analysed to the extent which would have the boy astonished, had he known the pertinence of the questions.

The fishing lines could be left until the following morning. Kids' voices and laughter from above, so unnerving, he thought the place was haunted. A flicker of candlelight from a cave, kids in a cave, how the hell had they got up there? What a gas to scare the shit out of those kids if only he could climb the slope. Never told anybody about climbing up that slope to scare kids as people would say that what he got had served him right.

'Shunt o' bin there on yer own,' Keogh admonished. 'Shonti, yer shunt.'

Shonti looked approvingly at Keogh, enjoying the reprimand for his bravery. 'Patsy wouldn't come,' he grumbled, 'courtin' motts more important to Patsy than shootin' lines, more important than gatherin' lines, motts, most important thing in Patsy's life is motts.'

'Yeah, but yer shunt, Shonti yer shunt,' Keogh said.

'Thought I'd wait 'til it got dark an' really scare 'em nearly got to the top,' he continued, 'right under that bloody stick o' rock an' then it happened.'

So the woman that Poppy had seen was a boy. No Rasputin, only Shonti Plunkett, making my panicked flight even harder to bear. Now there was only one question I needed an answer to.

'When you landed was you in much pain?' Rogan asked, viewing concernedly the boy's pot leg and wincing.

Pain apparently was another topic Shonti loved to waffle on about. 'Pain,' he echoed. 'Jesus Christ, I never knew what pain was 'til then. None of the big rocks hit me, on'y small ones, but pain, Jesus. It was draggin' meself away that caused the complications.'

Keogh moaned sympathetically: 'What if you'd gone in the sea with a broken leg?'

'An' arm,' Shonti reminded him, 'broken arm as well.'

'An' arm,' Keogh agreed, shaking his head slowly at the sheer incorrigibility of the boy. 'Shunt o' bin there on yer own though, Shonty, you shunt.'

'Knew me da would come for me, but honest to God, I thought he'd fin' me dead. I lay behind a big rock in awful pain but I was thinkin' about them kids. I knew nothin' could o' happened to 'em cos they was above the rock when it fell, but I was wonderin' who the hell they were an' how the hell they got there.'

'That when you passed out?' Sullivan asked sombrely.

'Must o' done. Nex' thing I knows is me da wrappin' me up in his coat an' goin' back to town for the Sergeant. Nex' thing I knows he's shakin' me again an' tryin' to get me on a stretcher. Remember thinkin', Jesus I'm still here an' so is the world. Never knew nothin' then until I woke up in the Garda Station. Next thing I knows, I'm in hospital.'

'Arm ok now, though,' Salmon remarked caringly, gently squeezing the bicep.

'Arm better now,' Shonti declared solemnly, shaking it about to reassure everyone, none more so than himself, 'but serious complications with the leg.' And balancing his sound leg with a crutch and with his face contorted, he swung the potted limb backwards and forwards, groaning in time to the rhythm. 'Doctor says the complications is caused by damaged nerves. Said when I landed I should o' laid still. Laid still, says I to him, Christ, I was expectin' another avalanche.'

'When'd you get the pot off?' Murphy enquired, proudly tracing his fingers along his name which was scrawled with others just above the knee.

Looking gravely at the pot, Shonti shook his head heavily like a cow shifting flies, and said, 'Don't know. All depends on the friggin' complications. Can't be soon enough, itches like crazy underneath. Maybe before the new year,' he finished gloomily.

My turn had come. 'What happened just before the stack came down on you?' I asked shakily. 'You know, like just before?'

The boy's face tightened. The dislike between us was mutual and it looked as if no one had told him yet that I was famous; answers to my questions had to be earned. From me he demanded subservience and I was prepared to give him all he wanted. 'Wha' do you mean?'

In a manner most cringing, I said, 'Well, there's you all alone on that mountain and ghostly voices and all, well me, I think would have run away, but not you, Shonti, you climbing up that slope in the dark and all you're thinking about is scaring the shit out of them kids. But did you see or hear anything just before that stack came down?'

He shrugged self-deprecatingly and I knew I had earned my answer: 'Jus' a creakin' kind o' noise an, then the bloody mountain comin' down.'

'Yeah, but just before it happened, you must have seen or heard something?' I urged.

'Nothin'.'

I had to stop myself from contradicting him. Why was he lying?

Duggan laughed. 'Word's got 'round. Tell him what you tol' us, what you did jus' before the rock came down.'

Shonti began chuckling softly to himself: 'Did a Rasputin, wanted to see them kids shiftin' out o' that cave.' His chuckle became a wicked giggle. 'I started howlin' like bejaysus an' that's when it happened. Nearly shit meself, thought I'd caused it, thought I'd caused the landslide.'

'Do it again for us,' Murphy laughingly encouraged.

Awestruck, I stepped back as eerily and unerringly Shonti Plunkett replicated my madman's unearthly wail to the lowest and highest decibels of simulation before basking in roars of approval from those around him. 'No one can do Rasputin like Shonti Plunkett,' Connelly attested. 'Better than the old boy himself, Shonti Plunkett is.'

Doyle got hold of my attention. 'We was playin hurlin' in Kilcoole a couple o' years back. The bus broke down an' we had to walk home along the Killincarrig road, it was night an...'

Salmon interrupted. 'We was with Brother Molloy. We saw Rasputin standin' in a gateway. He never saw us, we passed right by him an' he never even looked at us. He was like a ghos' in the gateway an' Jesus he started friggin' wailin', like a ghos', like a banshee he was, lookin' up at the moon an' wailin' for his wife.'

This was Connelly's tale and he cut back in. 'I tell you, even Brother Molloy was scared. Shonti was with us that night. We started runnin' to get past him, even Brother Molloy was runnin'.

An' Shonti, he could do Rasputin ever since that night. Jesus, he sends shivers down me spine when he does it, so he does.'

I took another step backwards and I was outside the circle of boys. Shonti had struck a chord, no, he had struck a full-scale orchestra. The last piece of a macabre and enigmatic jigsaw had just fallen into place. I felt light-headed, but at least it was all over, no more surprises left, no more searching for the body of Rasputin. The bloody Plunketts had asked for everything they got. Drizzly little Christy sticking his nose in with my sister, Pollack Gob picking a fight with me at the school gates and coming worse off. And now, cow-faced Shonti, not satisfied with betraying a 'sacred thrust', and humiliating me in front of Cora Casey, he scares me half to death, and loses me Poppy Boyle. Well, Shonti Plunkett could hobble about on crutches and drone on about complications for the rest of his bloody life for all I cared. I couldn't help myself. My eyes swung to the north to the great scarp. Could I find another stack?

Still holding centre stage, Shonti was doing all the talking, sweeping the circle of faces with his keen eyes, giving boys, in turn just enough attention to hold their interest. One arm, he cradled about a crutch; the second crutch, which he didn't really need, he wagged about, giving emphasis to his words, his potted leg swinging to and fro as he spoke. Boys blew into cupped hands to warm them and stamped their feet, no one spoke except to accord with Shonti. I was not listening, still trying to come to terms with answers to questions which had almost driven me crazy.

Flanagan joined us, grinning and bony and awkward, his heavy woollen sweater ragged and for a change, far too big: 'Hey Shonti, any room on yer pot?'

Shonti raised an eyebrow: 'What for?'

'Me name.'

'Jesus Flan, how long have you bin able to write?'

Flanagan grinned toothily: 'I can write FLAN.'

Shonti looked down jealously at his stiff, grubby appendage covered in scrawl; his sponsorship was something not to be taken lightly. Why, a boy's name on Shonti's pot had almost the same prestige as a ride in Kilbain's muck cart. 'Jus' Flan then,' he agreed reluctantly.

Tongue between his teeth, Flanagan squatted and added three capital letters, boldly on a rare space above the grimy shin.

At the other side of the road, a man in a cap was passing, another exponent of the gimp, but nowhere near as practiced as Nugget Nolan. He shouted, 'Hey there, Shonti, give it tump. Do yous hear me now, give it tump. That leg o' yours, give it tump.'

Shonti waved his crutch. 'Give it tump yerself Mick. Whip yourself.'

Amid a hum of conversation, only one voice could be heard clearly, Shonti's, with words that started a pulsing in my temple. 'Yeah las' time I did somethin' the likes o' that was 'bout a year ago in the dock.'

Moving closer to him, I became part of the circle again.

'I was a top o' the pier castin'. It was a pitch-black night, but in lamp-light, I was able to see this kid leanin' over the dock wall. Jesus, that night you couldn't see a han' in front of you, but didn't I see this kid start to go down the steps into the dock. Says I to mesel', what's that kid doin' goin' down into the dock at this time o' night? Didn't know who he was, still don't know who it was cos it was so friggin dark.'

Colour was draining from my face and my legs felt unsteady. I steadied myself against the boy beside me.

'So I set me line, an' I folleyed this kid. It was blacker than a witch's crotch down in that dock an' I couldn't see him but I knew he was hidin an' I knew he was scared. Thought to mesel', I'll move the little bugger an' I stood there in the middle o' the dock in the pitch dark an' did me Rasputin, an' bejaysus did that shift the little bugger, blutherin' for his mam, so he was.' Shonti started laughing and, slapping his pot with the palm of his hand, continued, 'Shot past me like a friggin' bullet an' up them steps, lost a shoe on the steps, nearly tripped over it so I slung it in the sea.' His pale, blank face flushed at the recollection and he tried to scratch his knee through his pot. 'Jesus, I got an itch what's drivin' me friggin' mad.' In a gap between ears tinged blue with cold, our eyes met. His laughter faded. 'Wasn't you, was it?'

'Wasn't me what?'

'Las' year in the dock, was you the kid?'

'What kid?'

'The kid in the dock.'

'What dock?'

'Sergeant O' Neill got knocked off of his bike that night. Heard it was you what knocked him off of his bike. Was it you runnin' from the dock'

'What dock?'

'Jesus Christ, there's on'y one friggin' dock.'

'I don't know what you're talking about, Shonti,' I croaked.

Chapter Thirty-five

*I*t was divine retribution for missing mass and going fishing, Grandma Plunkett concluded on evaluation of her grandson's flirtation with death and, after spending most of the last evening with her ear glued to the wireless, was full of doom and gloom. The world was in a sorry state, so it was, children missing mass, harlots in the house of God, and a planet heading for destruction full of foreigners and French. Oh, Mary Plunkett knew her bible right enough; was in awe of the revelations of St John the Divine, its prophecies, the anti-Christ, the prospect of Armageddon and the coming of the four horsemen of the apothecaries. Our house in Kimberley Road was nice enough and as long as she was welcome she would continue to visit us but hoped and prayed that she would never bump into the whore of Babylon who was living only doors away.

I was gloomy, too. A new year was upon us; joy in my heart at my new-found popularity was beginning to wane and the dark cloud that had never left me was getting darker and if I didn't do something about it, it would be with me all my life. I knew the truth now would deliver both of us. Surely Poppy Boyle must want to know the truth.

My father needed a box of screws from Ally Evans Builder's Merchants, but as I set off on the errand, I had a much greater mission in mind. Poppy had knocked on the door of Calgary, knowing well she wasn't welcome; was I brave enough to knock on hers? A last chance to draw a line under 1951 and start a new year cloudless and afresh.

Through Evans' shop window Shonti Plunkett was passing. His cast was off and he was walking normally but, spying me through the glass, he immediately started limping. Ok he could scratch himself now but I wondered who was the more disappointed at his recovery, me or him?

After picking up the screws, I turned into the Turn Pike and bearing down on me was Reardon and Donoghue. There would be no scoring points today, no skirmishes or fights. We were greeting each other cordially, we were equals; three of us wearing long trousers and long smiles.

Within seconds they were talking about motts, for each of them had a new one to celebrate the new year with and were excited at the prospect. I didn't have one, I admitted, but then I didn't want one, so instead I started telling them why I now called motts 'frails' and all about Lemmy Caution and the tough way he spoke, but I could tell that they were not really interested.

'You had a snog yet?' Reardon asked, a little condescendingly, I thought.

'What's a snog?'

Reardon raised his eyes to his friend as if to ask 'What's this gobshite doin' in long trousers if he doesn't know what a snog is. 'It's serious kissin' is snoggin'. French kissin'.'

'Why French?'

Reardon's eyeballs all but disappeared. Cos it's how they kiss in France, tongues in each other's mouths, wrigglin' about.'

'No they don't,' I argued, 'I've seen lots of French people kissing. All them war films set in France. All French people I've ever seen kiss each other on both cheeks. Not one cheek, both.'

Reardon was lost for words, Donoghue took over. 'We're not talkin' about every time a Frenchie meets a mott. They're not putting tongues in each other's gobs if they happen to meet at the bus stop.'

'You told me tongues in ears turned 'em on,' I countered.

Both looked skyward again. It seemed I was already getting on their nerves.

'Things move on,' Donoghue attested. "French kissin' is all the rage in Ireland now. For Christ's sake this is nearly 1952. You tell an Irish mott nowadays that she's in for a spot of French kissin', then kiss her on both cheeks, she'll think you're queer an' run a mile.'

Reardon cut in. 'But stick your tongue down her throat an' she'll thing you're the man.'

Tongues in ears, tongues down throats, my senses reeled, I hadn't tickled a palm yet. But I had to admit, the thought intrigued me. Maybe if I scooped a hole in a soft apple, I could practise until I was ready for the real thing.

I was conscious that my knowledge of all things earthy was wanting and I was a little disgusted with myself and from the expressions on the faces of the chief donors to my insight, it was obvious that they were, even more so, but then, wasn't I the boy who had just made Brother Brady laugh, and I could live on that alone for some time yet. And so we parted on good terms, our long smiles intact, they to meet their new motts and me to try and sort things out once and for all with Poppy Boyle.

I was terribly apprehensive walking down her path, my mind tumbling with the things I wanted to say to her, hoping that it would be she who came to the door, but preparing different things to say to whoever did. I hoped it wasn't Mary.

I knocked, it was Mary. 'What do you want?' she asked coldly.

'Could I speak to Poppy, please?'

'I'm afraid Jennifer is out,' she answered coldly. She wasn't out, because the girl appeared beside her older sister in the hallway. It seemed an age since I had seen her, spoken to her, yet it was only a couple of weeks and for the first time I appreciated what a lovely-looking girl she was. She wasn't smiling but she looked really lovely standing in the shadows of the hallway. After all the snow and frost the day was sunny and unseasonably warm and

I longed for her to come out of the shadows and join me in the sunlight.

'It's ok, Mary,' Poppy said. Her sister grunted and disappeared back inside the house.

I had rehearsed, over and over, what I was going to say to her. I would start with Shonti's bombshells, but my defences, appeals and emotional entreaties so serried for maximum impact were now tumbling about in my mind haphazardly, muddled but still desperate to express themselves. 'Poppy, I know the truth, it's so important to know the truth. It was Shonti Plunkett outside the cave that night, no Rasputin, no dead wife. He climbed the slope to scare kids in a cave. We ran away from Shonti Plunkett. Him that was howling, told me so himself.'

The girl looked at me a while in silence before saying flatly, 'Well, that surprises me. I'm shocked. Serves him right then, brought everything on himself. Yes, it really serves him right.'

'Exactly, I was shocked, too. Yes he brought it on himself.' I didn't tell her that it was also Shonti a year earlier in the dock, I was too ashamed.

'Kind of obvious now when you think of it,' she mused. Her voice and manner were not friendly but not unfriendly, an ambivalence suggesting that we might yet be friends again but still leaving me to find out how.

Calmer now and remembering rehearsals, I could begin my stratagem. 'No one knows that it was us in that cave. Better keep it that way.' And before she could disagree, 'See Poppy, how important the truth is. It was Shonti and we ran away from him and I'm ashamed of it. And I confessed what I'd done, well, I told you, but I don't think you were listening, I even confessed to Sergeant O' Neill but no one would take me seriously.' Try friendship. 'Think of the laughs we've had, remember that day on the north beach and my mother's face when you told us the stones were crucifying your arse.' Indebtedness. 'Dodging waves and me saving…'

She was closing the door on me.

'No, wait, wait.' I pushed it open. 'All that stuff, *"by the pricking of my thumbs' 'methinks the lady doth protest too much"*, that stuff, I didn't make it up, I thought my mother had made it up but she hadn't, it was someone I'd never heard of. I was being pretentious, finished being soppy and pretentious, going to talk like Lemmy Caution from now on.'

She closed the door. 'Poppy, I DID leave you in that hole,' I yelled. The door opened again and she stepped out into the sunlight. 'I did, I did leave you in that hole and you don't know how ashamed I am.' This wasn't rehearsed at all, this was spontaneous and unthinkable and I was pouring my heart out to her, just as I done with Mr Malone not so long ago, but this time I was listened to.' I'm not brave, I try to kid people that I am, walking the pier wall on my hands, dodging giant waves and people thinking what an eejit. How can I be brave when I can run away and leave you in the bottom of a hole? I heard you fall and in all that terrible noise, oh, I even heard you cry out, yet still I ran for my life. Oh please forgive me, Poppy, I'd give anything for us to be friends again. I'll make it up to you I'll do something really brave for you.'

'You just have,' she said quietly. 'It's what I've been waitin' for.'

We were walking slowly down the path towards the gate. She was wearing a sleeveless dress and the sun was targeting the bright white skin behind the freckles of her face and arms; she looked a little melancholy. But there was something more for which I sought forgiveness, so monstrous, it lived and festered in my mind. 'Poppy, there's something else about that night that's eating me alive.' We reached the gate and because I could not look her in the eye I spread my elbows along the rail and rested my head on my hands. I must confess or else I could not live. 'I was full of fear that night, full of misery and guilt at what I'd caused to happen. I went to the quarry edge, you know, that place where the lorry's stand and I swear I was about to jump I was going to end my life. But I didn't, instead I went back to the road to wait for you to come home from the concert.'

'Oh waiting for me again,' she sighed. 'Why do you keep harping on about waiting for me that night?'

'It was "why" I was waiting.'

She answered then, simple, matter-of-fact words without knowledge of their effect, their miraculous liberation. 'Well, all I can say is thanks be to God I didn't meet up with you by the quarry, know why? Cos you were goin' in.' And with laughter in her merry eyes she continued, 'That night as I lay in bed with Rose I planned to lure you to that quarry. Oh, how I hated you for what you had done to me. You had left me in a hole, but I would leave you in the bottom of a bigger one.'

And instantly an intolerable load was lifted. My thoughts that night were monstrous, but so were hers, but they were only thoughts. Running rampant through our minds, thoughts are as involuntary as the breaths we take, the beating of our hearts. Words, deeds, yes, but had I got it wrong, had Brother Mulligan got it wrong? Surely we will not be damned for eternity for our wicked thoughts or we could not now with bursts of humour, be laughing at the gate at the idea of bumping each other off. We have as much control over a thought as we do a shooting star.

Coming along the road towards us was the oldest man I had ever seen. So old and wizened and ragged he was more a spectre than a man. Bent almost double and mumbling to himself, he struggled by, so slowly and so close to us we could have touched him. We did not speak or even look at each other, for we both knew who he was. We watched him as he became small in the distance to then disappear. I wondered if she would let me hold her hand but thought better of it, maybe tomorrow.

THE END